An Easy Course in
Using the HP 19BII

by Chris Coffin
and Dan Coffin
Illustrations by Robert L. Bloch

Grapevine Publications, Inc.
P.O. Box 2449
Corvallis, Oregon   97339-2449

Acknowledgments

We extend our thanks once again to Hewlett-Packard for their top-quality products and documentation.

Printed in the United States of America
ISBN 0-931011-19-1

First Printing – July, 1991

CONTENTS

0. TO BEGIN 8

Read This First! 9

1. LOOKING UNDER THE HOOD 10

What's In This Machine? 11
What's In This Book? 12

2. IN THE DRIVER'S SEAT 14

Turning the Key 15
The Display 17
The Keyboards 19
Pop Quiz 21
Pop Answers 22

3. LEARNING TO DRIVE 24

Warming Up the Arithmetic Engine 25
Simple Arithmetic: A Matter of Choice 32

Arithmetic with the ⊟ Key (ALGebraic Mode)............................34

Arithmetic with the ENTER Key (RPN Mode)...............................40

More Math If You Want It 46

A Rest Stop 53

Arithmetic Quiz 54

Arithmetic Quiz Solutions 56

4. YOUR FIRST BUSINESS TRIP...60

Road Signs: Menus and Their Keys 61

Playing "What-If?" with Menu Keys 67

Review 73

Menu Quiz 74

Menu Quiz Answers 76

Choose Your Course..78

The Bread Value of Money: CURRency EXchanges 80

Loaves and Fishes: Getting Your UNITS Right 86

Conversion Quiz 87

Conversion Quiz Solutions...88

Checking the Map Again..92

5. THE TIME VALUE OF MONEY: TVM......................................94

Problem Understanding = Problem Solving 95

What Is TVM? 96

How Does Interest Behave?...97

Getting the Picture Right 104
Discounting Cash-Flows 109
Drawing the Picture for Your Calculator 113
A Typical Mortgage Problem 120
Variations on a Theme 128
AMoRTization Schedules 144
Other Side Calculations 150
TVM Quiz 160
TVM Quiz Solutions 169

6. ROUGHER ROADS: THE CFLO MENU 202

Problems with Uneven Payments 203
What Is NPV? 209
What Is IRR%? 216
CFLO Quiz 222
CFLO Quiz Solutions 228
Rest Area 256
Next Destination? 256

7. THE DATA YOU COLLECT: SUM LISTS 258

Saving Numbers 259
The Numbered Registers 260
Lists of Numbers 261
Editing Your List 265
Analyzing Your List 267

Naming Your List 268
FoReCaSTing with Your List 269
Quiz 273
Quiz Solutions 274
Which Way Now? 278

8. TIME TRAVELLING 280

Using the Clock 281
CALCulating with Dates 284
Making APPoinTments 286
Quiz TIME 289
Answers TIME 290
Whither Now? 293

9. BUILDING YOUR OWN ROADS: THE SOLVE MENU 294

Memory Space: The Final Frontier 295
Creating Formulas 299
Combining Formulas 309
Naming Formulas 316
Optimizing Formulas 318
SOLVE Review 332
SOLVE Problems 334
SOLVE Solutions 342
Where To Now? 406

10. THE NOTES YOU MAKE: TEXT LISTS 408

Saving TEXT 409
Multiple-Entry Records 412
Sorting TEXT Lists 415
Editing a Record 416
Finding an Entry 417
TEXT Quiz 419
TEXT Quiz Solutions 420
What's Next? 422

A. APPENDIX 424

Canadian Mortgage Interest Conversions 425
Canadian TVM 428
Index 434
"The Book Stops Here" 444
Other Books and Information 445

0. TO BEGIN

Read This First!

Time is an investment. If you spend it wisely, it will give you
ENORMOUS returns.

Invest your time in this book.

It covers exactly what you need to know to use your HP 19BII effectively
—and quickly. If you have time to *use* this machine, you have time to
learn it first (it doesn't take that long). And you've already finished the
toughest part of this Course (getting started), so just keep going.

In this book, you'll see many applications in financial analysis. But as
you read, keep in mind that the goal here is not just to memorize a set
of keystrokes and formulas. You're also going to get an understanding
of the fundamental *principles,* so that whenever you encounter a new
problem, you'll be able to analyze it and solve it confidently. That skill
is the most valuable asset of all.

1. LOOKING UNDER THE HOOD

What's In This Machine?

Your HP 19Bıı is a loyal and friendly calculator engine—congratulations on a great choice! It represents a new generation of calculators, with more power and flexibility than ever before. It can do all sorts of things for you, from analyzing investments to remembering appointments to customizing formulas.

You simply need to tell it what to do…. And that brings up the next question….

What's Not In This Machine?

As sophisticated as technology is nowadays, it still hasn't progressed to the point where the machine can speak to you in your own language. For now, you must "speak" *its* "language," translating your everyday calculation problems into forms it can understand.

Of course, this means that you must define each problem correctly for *yourself* first. And often this is the hardest part, so don't overlook this very important step.

But once you've done that—set a problem up so that *you* understand it clearly—it's quite simple to translate it for your HP 19Bıı. In fact, learning to operate it is a lot like learning to drive a car: It all seems strange at first, but after some training and practice, you'll be doing things quite automatically—without even thinking much about them.

That training and practice is what this book is going to give you.

What's In This Book?

This book is indeed your Drivers' School for the HP-19BII. After learning about your machine's controls and buttons, you'll take it through the Course for extensive "road training." There you'll encounter lots of explanations, diagrams, quizzes and answers. Once you complete those, you'll be ready to drive anywhere your vehicle can go (and that's a lot of places).

What makes the Course is Easy is the fact that you're allowed to choose your own speed and route. So don't worry about how fast you're moving. It's not a race; you can go over the same stretch of road again and again until you're comfortable with it. You'll get some rest areas, to stop and review where you've been, and some alternate "routes," in case you already know certain things and don't need to practice them.

*What's **Not** In This Book?*

You won't find equal time given to everything, because some things just don't need as much explanation. Anyway, if you want a complete description of everything, you already have it right there in your Owner's Manual. That's what it's there for—as a reference manual to let you conveniently look up keys, functions, and quick examples.

But this book is *not* a reference manual. It's an entirely different approach, a tutorial approach meant to be taken as presented. So start here and "stay on the road!" Then, when you finish, a good reference source like the Owner's Manual will be much clearer and more useful to you.

A Few Words about the Example Problems

You may be more interested in, say, real estate lending than in leasing, or in securities rather than personal finance. Well, there are example problems in each of these areas in this Course. But do yourself a favor: Don't skip over the ones that aren't in your favorite area!

"Why not?"

Because you're going to find that most financial problem-solving boils down to the same basic concepts—just expressed in different words. There are often far more differences in the *terminology* of the various financial disciplines than in their underlying calculations.

So don't skip over the problems that don't seem exactly fitted to your most immediate everyday work. That would be cheating yourself out of part of your investment. Every financial problem has something to teach you about the Time Value of Money, and the more practice you get with it, the more fluent you'll become in its language, and the more skilled you'll soon be in every area of financial problem-solving.

2. IN THE DRIVER'S SEAT

Turning the Key

Opening up your HP 19Bɪɪ, the sheer number of keys—on *two* keyboards—may be a bit daunting. Is it that complicated to use?

Not at all.

The ⟨ON⟩ Button

Turn the machine on. The ⟨ON⟩ button is at the lower left of the right-hand keyboard.

The ⟨OFF⟩ Button

Now turn it off, by pressing the ⟨OFF⟩ button....
But there is no ⟨OFF⟩ button—just press ⟨ON⟩ again.

A key whose meaning alternates between two opposites like this is called a *toggle key*. You'll see more such toggle keys, and they all behave in this on-again-off-again way. Toggle keys help to reduce the number of keys (after all, you have enough keys as it is).

(If you're already familiar with the keyboards and the display, you can skip ahead now to page 21.)

A Good First Setting

At this point, there's no telling what might be in the display. So to be sure you're starting from the same point as this Course, you're going to do a few preparatory keystrokes.

Don't worry if you don't understand these yet—you will soon. But you can't very well learn until you get the machine ready to learn with, right? So, turn your machine on, and...

Do This: Press the *gold key* (denoted here as ■), then the (EXIT) key. Now press ■ (that gold key again), then the (INPUT) key.

Next, press the (DISP) key, then *the upper-left blank white key* (right under the display), then (2) and (INPUT).

Finally, press ■ (that gold key once again), then the (÷) key.

If you've done everything right, the machine will probably beep, and then you'll see this:

```
ERROR:  ÷0
0.00
 FIN | BUS | SUM |TIME|SOLVE|TEXT
```

(If this doesn't work the first time, just try it all again.)

The Display

Even when things are going wrong, the display usually tries to tell you what's going on. When in doubt, look at the display for clues.

(If you already know all about the display, what it's telling you and how to adjust it, then skip ahead now to page 19).

The Viewing Angle

Can you see and read the display comfortably? It's hard to read if it's aimed at the wrong angle—but you can adjust that angle.

Try It: With the machine on, *press and hold down* the [ON] key. Then press and hold the [+] or the [−] key and watch how the viewing angle varies. Play around with it until you find a comfortable angle.

Messages and How to Clear Them

The **ERROR:** ÷0 is a good example of a *message*—usually telling you of an error or asking you for something. A message just *temporarily covers* part of the display. To get rid of it, simply press the [◀] key.

Do that now ([◀]).

The Number Lines

Now your display should look like this:

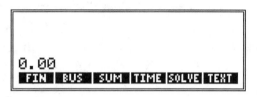

The display uses its top three lines to show numbers (and messages).

Try This: Press ③[INPUT]②[INPUT]①. See how numbers stack up?

The Menu Line

The very bottom line is the Menu Line. Each of the selections on the Menu Line is associated with the blank white key directly beneath it.

The Menu Line is the best way to tell "where" your calculator is. For example, the menu you're seeing this right now (above) is the *MAIN Menu*, the "home base" starting point. After all, it probably makes sense to start this "Driver's Course" from home.

The Keyboards

Now look at the keys (if you already know the basics of the keyboards, go ahead and jump now to page 21).

The Calculating Keyboard

Look first at the right-hand keyboard. This is where you'll find the keys for your arithmetic and other number-oriented operations. The digit and math keys are here, as are [ON] and [←], which you've seen already.

Notice that *the white keys* (including the blank white menu keys) are most directly related to "crunching" numbers.

The dark-grey keys, on the other hand, are more for controlling the display and moving numbers around. HP has designed the key colors this way, to make it easier for your eyes to find the right keys.

The Typing Keyboard

Look now at the left-hand keyboard, the "typing" keyboard. These keys are for spelling out words and names—much like a typewriter. You have a space bar at the bottom, plus some handy typing operations such as [INS] and [DEL]—all for typing *characters* (letters and symbols) into your display.

And, just like a typewriter, many keys have second ("shifted") characters too.   ...So...where's the "shift" key?

The ■ Key

The gold key on the right-hand keyboard is the shift key (shown here as ■). It's no coincidence that each key's "shifted" meaning is printed *in gold* right above it.

Try This: Press the ■ (shift) key. What happens? The ⟶ *annunciator* appears (a little signal up there in the *Annunciator Area*), telling you that the next key you press will produce its *gold* letter or operation.

Press ■ again. The ⟶ disappears. ■ is a *toggle* key—like the [ON]/[OFF] key—because it alternates its meaning.

Type a few gold characters from the left-hand keyboard. As you do, notice these things about the ■ key:

Unlike a typewriter, you don't hold it down while pressing the key you're "shifting." Just press and release the ■ key, then press the key you want. The ⟶ will always tell you when the ■ is in effect.

But the ⟶ is cancelled *after every use;* you need to re-press the ■ for every gold character you want. ■ is *not* a "Caps Lock" key.

(Press [EXIT], as the display tells you to, when you've finished "playing with the typewriter.")

Pop Quiz

Yes—a quick little stop-and-check point.

Make sure you know these things before you go on. The answers are on the next page, but don't look until you need to. Along with those answers, you'll find page numbers for re-reading, just in case. Take your time—and who cares if you re-read? It's *your* Course.

1. What's a toggle key? Name two such keys.

2. How many lines does the display have? How are they used?

3. What's an annunciator?

4. What's a message? How do you get rid of it?

5. What will happen to your calculator if you forgot to turn it off before leaving for Nepal?

Pop Answers

1. A toggle key is like a light switch: hit it once to turn something on; hit it again to turn it off. [ON] and ■ are two such keys (see pages 15 and 20 for review).

2. The display has four lines. The top three lines show numbers (and messages, sometimes). The bottom line is the Menu Line, which tells you your current calculation choices (to review all this, see pages 17-18).

3. An annunciator is a little signal, a status indicator that appears in the Annunciator area, above the display's top line, to keep you informed of the current "doings" of the machine.

   You generally can't and shouldn't do anything about it—just understand what it means. For example, the shift annunciator, ⤴, means that any key with a gold operation written above it will now produce that operation if pressed (page 20).

4. A message is a phrase or question that appears temporarily *in front of* the upper part of the display, to notify you of an error or ask you to do something. When you want a message to go away, just press ◀ (page 17).

5. After about 10 minutes, it will turn itself off. Then, when you come back and turn it on, its display (and memory) will be the same as when you left—so don't lose any sleep over it.

3. Learning to Drive

Warming Up the Arithmetic Engine

Basics first:

Arithmetic truly is the "engine" of any calculator. No matter how else you use your HP 19Bıı, it should certainly be able to add 2+2.

(At this point, if you're already very comfortable with doing arithmetic—including percentages, negative numbers, and display settings on your HP 19Bıı—then feel free to go on now to page 46.)

Ready to "crunch" a few numbers, then?

As you know, most arithmetic happens on the bottom number line (the display line right *above* the Menu Line). So turn your machine on (if it's not on already) and look at that line....

Clear For Departure?

You're starting with some numbers already in the display. Do you need to clear anything before starting a new calculation?

Try It: Press ②⑤ ■ √x̄ and see the result: **5.00**
            That **1.00** didn't mess up anything, did it?

Again: What if you now want to find $\sqrt{495,616}$? Should you clear away that **5.00**?

Nope: Full speed ahead: ④⑨⑤⑥①⑥ ■ √x̄, (<u>ans.</u>: **704.00**). Notice how the **5.00** just rode up above, out of your way.

            Anytime you finish a calculation, the machine knows it. And it will automatically "bump" that result upwards when you begin the next calculation. You don't need to clear anything!

You don't need to clear the display if you've just <u>completed</u> a calculation.

OK ?

OK, But: What if you decide to scrap a calculation midway—when it's *not* complete?

Suppose you're trying to find $\sqrt{495,616}$, as you did on the previous page, but you mistakenly key in 496561... and right then you discover your goof. How do you fix it?

Two Ways:

#1:   To back the wrong digits out, just use the ⬅ key. It's a simple backspace key, so...

First, back out the wrong digits: ⬅⬅⬅⬅.

Now key them in correctly: ⑤⑥①⑥...
...and finish the problem: ■√x̄

Or, #2:   To simply start over, you can clear the entire Calculator Line in one "swell foop:" Press ■CLEAR (that's the gold— shifted—version of the ⬅ key).

Not too tough, eh? Now that you know how to clear things if necessary, you're ready to start "driving around...."

How Many Digits Do You Have?

As you begin, notice that the display is showing exactly two digits past the decimal point on every number. Since the HP 19BΙΙ is a financially-oriented calculator, this simply makes good cents.*

But is this the best precision you can get?

> Not by a long shot.

In fact, every number has 12 digits, _no matter how many you can see at the moment._ For example, that 704.00 you just computed, is really

$$704.00\text{000000.}$$

> (Count 'em—there should be a total of 12 digits.)

You just aren't allowed to see beyond those first two zeros right now.

---

* Couldn't resist—sorry.

Ah, but...

Notice This: Key in ②①⓪·⑨⑧⑦⑥⑤④③②① and press [INPUT] (to tell the machine you've "finished").

Here's what you'll see: **210.99**

"What gives? Why did the number change?"

It didn't change. The calculator merely changed its *presentation* to you.

The entire 210.987654321 is *still in the machine*, but the display has been instructed to show you only the first 2 decimal places, rounded like this, to represent the *entire* number as accurately as possible.

Therefore the display rounds the number 210.987... *up* to 210.99. But if the 7 had been a 4 or smaller, the number would have been rounded *down* to 210.98.

Again, the point of all this is: It's the display doing the editing—for your eyes only. *Your machine will always do all your arithmetic with 12 digits in each number.*

How Many Digits Do You See?

Here's how your display probably looks right now:

```
704.00
210.99
210.99
 FIN | BUS | SUM |TIME|SOLVE|TEXT
```

Now, how do you tell the display to *change* its "editing policy?" What if you want to see 4 decimal places rather than 2?

Say the Word: Press the [DISP] key. Here's what you'll see:

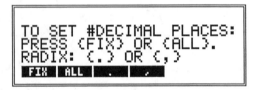

```
TO SET #DECIMAL PLACES:
PRESS (FIX) OR (ALL).
RADIX: (.) OR (,)
 FIX | ALL |  .  |  ,
```

When in doubt, follow the display's directions: You want to FIX the number of decimal places at four. So press the blank key under **FIX** .... Then follow the next set of directions: Press [4][INPUT].... Voilá!

Display

Your display now shows this:

```
704.0000
210.9877
210.9877
 FIN │ BUS │ SUM │TIME│SOLVE│TEXT
```

Just For Laughs: Set your display to show you ALL the decimal places that aren't merely trailing zeros.

Solution: Press [DISP], then **ALL**. Here's the result:

```
704
210.987654321
210.987654321
 FIN │ BUS │ SUM │TIME│SOLVE│TEXT
```

Now you see ALL decimal places except unnecessary trailing zeroes. The `704.0000` becomes simply `704`, and the `210.9877` reveals its true identity.

(Now go back to dollars and cents format, by FIXing 2 decimal places. You know how, right?)

Simple Arithmetic: A Matter of Choice

At this point, you have a choice to make. As you probably know, the HP 19BII offers you two different ways to do arithmetic.

Do This: Press ▇(MODES), then select **MORE** from the *menu* (i.e. press the blank menu key under **MORE**—on the far right). You'll see these two choices: **ALG** and **RPN**

Try each one: First, press **ALG** (notice how your display then echoes your choice: ALGEBRAIC MODE).

ALGebraic arithmetic uses the ⊟ key. For example, to add 2 and 3, you would press ⊡⊞⊡⊟ (do it now).... As you can see, this method imitates the way in which you might *say* the problem to yourself: "Two plus three equals..."

Now try the other method: Press ▇(MODES)**MORE RPN** (your display now echoes this choice: RPN MODE).

RPN stands for Reverse Polish Notation, so-named for the Polish mathematician who developed the efficient logic it uses. In this "reverse" method of arithmetic, you give the operation *last,* thus eliminating the need for an ⊟ key.

To add 2 and 3, for example, press ⊡(ENTER)⊡⊞ (in RPN mode, the ⊟ key acts as the (ENTER) key).

So, why the choice—and which way is best for you?

Long ago, HP calculators adopted the less conventional RPN style of calculation, because it's simply more efficient (for series of calculations it requires fewer keystrokes than the ALGebraic method—and no parentheses). So most users who took the time to learn RPN soon "swore by it" and became loyal to HP calculators as a result.

However, many other persons prefer to do arithmetic in the "left-to-right" ALGebraic method. And since, for a long time, HP built only RPN calculators, these persons missed out on the many other great features of HP machines.

Then, when HP *did* build some ALGebraic machines (as part of its new generation of calculators), the situation became reversed: RPN users began to wish that *they* could enjoy the latest technology and features —but without having to switch from their beloved RPN.

Well, you know the rest of the story: HP is now offering a choice within the same machine—so you don't have to "un-learn" the method of arithmetic you're now using. It's that simple.

So choose the way that's easiest for you (press ▮ MODES ▮ **MORE**, then either **ALG** or **RPN**)....

– – – – – – – – – – – – – –

...And then, once you've made your choice:

If you chose **RPN**, go now to page 40; otherwise, just turn the page....

Arithmetic with the ⊟ Key (ALGebraic Mode)

This method of arithmetic doesn't take much practice to learn. The basic rule of thumb is: "saying it = doing it."

Here's a good set of examples (and remember that you can use the ◄ or ■CLEAR keys to back out or clear any mistakes):

Example: Calculate $342 - 173 + 13$

Solution: Press ③④②⊟①⑦③⊞①③⊟   Answer: **182.00**

See? You just press the keys just as you would say the problem to yourself—left to right. And as you proceed, you automatically get intermediate results (do the problem again and watch what happens after you press the ⊞ key). Then the ⊟ key gives your final result.

Example: Find $101.00 - 47.50 \times 2$

Solution: Press ①⓪①⊟④⑦·⑤⊠②⊟ Answer: **107.00**

This left-to-right rule works even when you *mix* multiplication (and/or division) with addition (and/or subtraction)! And notice that you don't need to key in any trailing zeroes (i.e. **101.00** is just **101**).

Example: What's $342 - (173 + 13)$?

Solution: Press ③④②⊖❨❨①⑦③⊞①③❩❩⊜ Answer: **156.00**

If parentheses appear in the written problem, use them in your calculator, too. And notice how the ❨**173+13** changes to **186.00** when you close the parentheses.

Example: Calculate $\dfrac{101.00 - (47.50 \times 2)}{64 - \left(25 \times \frac{3}{4}\right)}$

Solution: ①⓪①⊖❨❨④⑦·⑤⊠②❩❩⫽
❨❨⑥④⊖❨❨②⑤⊠❨❨③⫽④⊜

Answer: **0.13** (Reminder: This is just the first two decimal places, with the second digit rounded. To see more digits, you know how to adjust the display, right?)

Notice that the keystrokes include an extra set of parentheses (around the entire denominator of the problem). After all, that's what is meant by that big horizontal line between the numerator and denominator.

Notice also that at the very end, you don't actually need to close a parenthetical expression with the right parenthesis. The ⊜ key says that you're finished, so the calculator closes all the open parentheses for you.

Changing the Sign of a Number

Try This: Find $34 \times (-19)$

Solution: Press ③④⊗⊖①⑨⊜   <u>Answer</u>: ‐646.00

         This is the simplest way to key in a negative number. And again, you *do* it just as you *say* it: "34 times negative 19 equals…" (those parentheses in the problem are simply to clarify things—they're optional).

But there's another way to do it, also.

Like This: Suppose now that you want to change that ‐646.00 into 646.00.

Solution: Press the +/− key.

         That's the "change sign" key. It changes the sign of the number you're working on. Notice that this +/− key is a *toggle* key—with alternating meanings.

So there are *two* ways to make a number negative in ALGebraic mode, the − key and the +/− key.

Playing the Percentages

Do you realize how easy it is to do percentage calculations on this HP 19Bʀ? Yes, even these—everybody's *least* favorite math problems—are a breeze.

Watch: What's 25% more than 134?

Solution: ⌈1⌉⌈3⌉⌈4⌉⌈+⌉⌈2⌉⌈5⌉⌈%⌉⌈=⌉   Answer: **167.50**

See? Whenever you want to *increase or decrease* a number by some known percentage, you just *add or subtract that percentage*—again, just as you would say it.

And how do you find an unknown percentage of any given number?

Example: What's 40% of $21.95?

Piece of Cake: Press ⌈2⌉⌈1⌉⌈·⌉⌈9⌉⌈5⌉⌈×⌉⌈4⌉⌈0⌉⌈%⌉⌈=⌉   Answer: **8.78**

To *increase* or *decrease* by a known percentage, you add or subtract. To simply find some percentage of a number, you multiply. What could be easier? Try a few more problems on your own....

Notice in all cases that the machine evaluates the percentage as soon as it can—just as it does with parentheses.

The History Stack

By now, you've probably noticed something: When you start a new problem, your previous results simply "bump upwards," don't they?

Do This: Press ①⌐②⌐③⌐④⌐. You have just "finished" four arithmetic problems, one after another.

Now notice the arrow keys, ⊤ and ⊥, and also the ▓x⩾y and ▓R⊥ keys. You can use these keys to make those four most recent results "roll around" or change sequence in the Stack (▓x⩾y swaps the bottom two values). Try them....

Now rearrange them back to their original order and press ⑤⌐. Can you now roll five results around? Try it....

Nope. This *History Stack* holds only the *last four results*. But it truly is a "Stack" of your recent calculating History, no? And notice that regardless whether you can *see* all four of those numbers, they're still there.

So the History Stack will let you see the results of previous calculations.

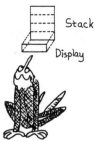

Stack

Display

Problem: Your gross incomes and total taxes for the last three years were as follows (not really—just suppose):

Gross Income	Total Taxes
$ 81,500.00	$ 28,525.00
96,850.00	39,708.50
103,700.00	38,887.50

In which year were your total taxes highest *in proportion* to your income?

Solution: To find this out, you'll need to do three separate calculations, one for each year:

⟨2⟩⟨8⟩⟨5⟩⟨2⟩⟨5⟩⟨÷⟩⟨8⟩⟨1⟩⟨5⟩⟨0⟩⟨0⟩⟨=⟩
(<u>Result</u>: **0.35**—the fraction you paid three years ago).

Next, press: ⟨3⟩⟨9⟩⟨7⟩⟨0⟩⟨8⟩⟨·⟩⟨5⟩⟨÷⟩⟨9⟩⟨6⟩⟨8⟩⟨5⟩⟨0⟩⟨=⟩
(<u>Result</u>: **0.41**—two years ago).

And: ⟨3⟩⟨8⟩⟨8⟩⟨8⟩⟨7⟩⟨·⟩⟨5⟩⟨÷⟩⟨1⟩⟨0⟩⟨3⟩⟨7⟩⟨0⟩⟨0⟩⟨=⟩
(<u>Result</u>: **0.38**—last year).

Just by looking at the Stack, you can see that you paid the biggest fraction two years ago, right?

Skip now to page 46.

Arithmetic with the [ENTER] Key (RPN Mode)

This method of arithmetic takes a little practice to learn—but the rewards are *definitely* worth the trouble.

Here's a good set of examples (and remember that you can use the [←] or [■CLEAR] keys to back out or clear any mistakes):

Example: Calculate $342 - 173 + 13$

Solution: Press [3][4][2][ENTER][1][7][3][−][1][3][+]
Answer: **182.00**

Get the idea? When you key in the numbers you're going to combine, you separate them with the [ENTER] key. And the operation comes *last*.

Another: What's $2 \times (101.00 - 47.50)$?

Solution: [1][0][1][INPUT][4][7][·][5][−][2][×]   Answer: **107.00**

Notice that you can use the [INPUT] key as an [ENTER] key also—just for convenience!

And notice that you don't need to key in any trailing zeroes (i.e. **101.00** is just **101**).

But the most important point to notice is this: *You don't need parentheses, because you do the calculations inside the parentheses first.*

One More: Find $\dfrac{101.00 \times (47.50 - 2)}{64 + \left(25 \times \frac{3}{4}\right)}$

Solution: ④⑦•⑤ ENTER ②— ①⓪① ✕
④③ ENTER ④÷②⑤✕⑥④+
÷

Answer: **55.53** (Reminder: This is just the first two decimal places, with the second digit rounded. To see more digits, you can adjust the display, right?)

See how you work from the inner parentheses outward —and how your intermediate results simply "float up above" until you're ready to use them? Do the problem again, and pay special attention to what's going on *above* the calculation line....

...Now do the problem a *third* time, and this time, notice what ENTER does: It makes a copy of the bottom number, thus allowing you to separate numbers that you need to key in "back-to-back" (without an operation between them). Don't over-use ENTER! In this problem, you need it only between the 47.5 and the 2 and between the 3 and the 4. You *don't* need it (and it would be wrong) anywhere else.

Changing the Sign of a Number

Try This: Find $34 \times (-19)$

Solution: Press ③④ [INPUT] ①⑨ [+/−] [×]   <u>Answer</u>: ⁻646.00

That's how you make a positive number negative—with the [+/−] key.

But if it's already negative, then...

Hmmm: Suppose you now want to make that ⁻646.00 into a 646.00.

Guess What: Just press the [+/−] key.

Like the shift key, the [+/−] ("change sign") key is a *toggle* key—a key with alternating meanings.

Playing the Percentages

Do you realize how easy it is to do percentage calculations on the HP 19BⅡ? Yes, even these—everybody's *least* favorite math problems—are a breeze.

Example: What's 40% of $21.95?

Piece of Cake: Press ⎡2⎤⎡1⎤⎡·⎤⎡9⎤⎡5⎤⎡ENTER⎤⎡4⎤⎡0⎤⎡%⎤   Answer: $8.78

The ⎡%⎤ operation needs two numbers—just like other arithmetic. The first number you key in is the "whole;" the second number is the "part" —the percentage of the "whole" that you want to find.

Watch: What's 25% more than 134?

Solution: ⎡1⎤⎡3⎤⎡4⎤⎡INPUT⎤⎡2⎤⎡5⎤⎡%⎤⎡+⎤   Answer: 167.50

Notice how the ⎡%⎤ calculation leaves the "whole" intact afterwards—so that you can conveniently add it to the "part" if you wish. What could be easier?

Try a few more problems on your own.

The RPN Stack

By now, you've probably noticed how your previous and intermediate results simply "bump upwards." What's happening here?

Do This: Press ⬜1⬜ (INPUT) ⬜2⬜ (INPUT) ⬜3⬜ (INPUT) ⬜4⬜—to pretend that you've just done some arithmetic problems, one after another.

Now notice the arrow keys, ⬆ and ⬇, and also the ⬛ (x≷y) and ⬛ (R↓) keys (they're the "shifted" parenthesis keys, but since parentheses are not used in RPN mode, you'll get (x≷y) and (R↓) even without pressing the ⬛ key).

You can use these keys to make the four most recent results "roll around"—change sequence—in the Stack ((x≷y) swaps the bottom two values). Try them....

Now arrange them back to the way they started and press ⬜5⬜. Can you now roll five results around? Try it....

Nope. The Stack holds only the *last four results*. But notice that regardless whether you can *see* all four of those numbers, they're still there.

So the Stack will let you see *and re-use* the results of previous calculations....

Problem: Your gross incomes and total taxes for the last three years were as follows (not really—just suppose):

Gross Income	Total Taxes
$ 81,500.00	$ 28,525.00
96,850.00	39,708.50
103,700.00	38,887.50

In which year were your total taxes highest *in proportion* to your income? What was the difference between this highest fraction and the lowest?

Solution: To find this out, you'll need to do three separate calculations, one for each year:

⟨2⟩⟨8⟩⟨5⟩⟨2⟩⟨5⟩ ⟨ENTER⟩ ⟨8⟩⟨1⟩⟨5⟩⟨0⟩⟨0⟩ ⟨÷⟩
(<u>Result</u>: **0.35**—the fraction you paid three years ago).

Next, press: ⟨3⟩⟨9⟩⟨7⟩⟨0⟩⟨8⟩⟨•⟩⟨5⟩ ⟨ENTER⟩ ⟨9⟩⟨6⟩⟨8⟩⟨5⟩⟨0⟩ ⟨÷⟩
(<u>Result</u>: **0.41**—two years ago).

And: ⟨3⟩⟨8⟩⟨8⟩⟨8⟩⟨7⟩⟨•⟩⟨5⟩ ⟨ENTER⟩ ⟨1⟩⟨0⟩⟨3⟩⟨7⟩⟨0⟩⟨0⟩ ⟨÷⟩
(<u>Result</u>: **0.38**—last year).

Just by looking at the Stack, you can see that you paid the biggest fraction two years ago and the smallest fraction three years ago, right? Then, to find the difference, just rearrange the Stack and subtract: ⟨R↓⟩⟨x≷y⟩⟨−⟩

More Math If You Want It

At this point, you may well be satisfied with your level of arithmetic on the HP 19Bɪɪ:

- clearing the display and changing its number formatting;
- addition, subtraction, multiplication and division;
- negative numbers;
- percentages;
- moving around the Stack a little bit.

If that's enough for you, skip now to the end of this chapter (page 53)....

On the other hand, you may be interested to know about some of the other, "higher math" operations this machine offers you. If so, "stick around" and work through the next few pages (the examples will have both ALGebraic and RPN solutions).

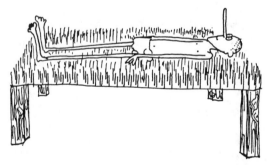

Scientific Notation

Try This: What's $2{,}000{,}000 \times 2{,}000{,}000$?

Solution: Press [2][0][0][0][0][0][0][×][2][0][0][0][0][0][0][=] (ALG mode)

       or   [2][0][0][0][0][0][0][ENTER][×]   (RPN mode)

      <u>Answer:</u> **4.00E12**

      As you may know, this shorthand way of writing very large (or very small numbers) is *scientific notation*. You would read this as "four-point-zero-zero times ten to the twelfth power." The **E** means "…times ten to the…"

Notice the little gold E above the [+/−] key. It's there so you can also use scientific notation when you *key in* numbers.

Go For It: Find "two million times two million" once again—but this time, you're not allowed to use the [0] key.

Solution: Press [2][■][E][6][×][2][■][E][6][=]   (ALG mode)

       or   [2][■][E][6][ENTER][×]   (RPN mode)

Saves a few [0]'s, doesn't it? Anyway, whether you like this notation or not, just be sure to recognize the **E** when your calculator uses it.

You might be surprised at the useful things you can do with some other MATH functions in your HP 19B<small>II</small>....

Try One: A bank account earns 6% per year, compounded constantly. If you put $100 into this account and let it grow for 6 months, how much would you have then?

Solution: The formula for continuous compounding is

Ending balance = (Beginning balance)(e^{rt}),

where r is the yearly rate (in decimal form) and t is the number of years. The other number, e, is the natural logarithm base. You will also see e^{rt} written as $\exp(rt)$, i.e. the "exponential of rt."

In this problem, $r = .06$ (that's 6%, written as a decimal) and $t = 0.5$ (half a year). So, compute (rt):

⟨·⟩⟨0⟩⟨6⟩⟨×⟩⟨·⟩⟨5⟩⟨=⟩   (the ALGebraic way), or
⟨·⟩⟨0⟩⟨6⟩⟨ENTER⟩⟨·⟩⟨5⟩⟨×⟩   (the RPN way).
Result: **0.03**

Now *exponentiate* this: Press ▮ MATH ▮ **LOGS** ▮ **EXP** ▮.
This is e^{rt} (or $\exp(rt)$). So now multiply by your beginning balance: ⟨×⟩⟨1⟩⟨0⟩⟨0⟩⟨=⟩ (ALG),   or ⟨1⟩⟨0⟩⟨0⟩⟨×⟩ (RPN)

Answer: **$103.05**

Notice that the **EXP** function *doesn't care* whether you're using ALGebraic or RPN arithmetic. And that's true in general: When you select an operation from a menu like this, it simply operates on your current number—no matter how that number got there.

Try Another: The answer from the previous problem is *not* exactly $103.05. Prove this to yourself—press **■**(SHOW)....

See? It's really 103.045453395. Your *display* is rounding its presentation of the number—"for your eyes only," because you've set a FIX 2 display setting.

If you truly want to round (i.e. actually *change*) the number *to match your current display setting,* you can use do this: (EXIT)(to leave the **LOGS** Menu), then press **RND**.

Nothing much seems to happen, right? Ah, but now SHOW full precision (**■**(SHOW)), and see 103.05.

That's a different number than before: there are no more hidden digits out past the second decimal place.

Again, notice that it doesn't matter which kind of arithmetic you use. The function simply operates on the current number.

A Trig or Two: What's sin(180°)? And what's sin π? How do you tell the machine when you want degrees and when you want radians?

Like This: Press ▉(MODES), then the ▉D/R▉ selection. See the (2π) annunciator appear at the top of the display? That means you're in *radians* mode for trig calculations. But simply press ▉D/R▉ again, and you turn it off and return to *degrees* mode.

So, to solve the problem, press (EXIT) (to get out of the MODES Menu and back to the MATH Menu), then: (1)(8)(0) ▉TRIG▉ ▉SIN▉ .
Result: **0.00**   That's sin(180°).

Now switch to radians mode (press ▉(MODES)▉D/R▉ (EXIT)(EXIT)) ...grab a ▉PI▉ , and ▉TRIG▉ ▉SIN▉ again.
Result: **-2.07E-13**.   This is what your HP 19BII gives as sin π radians—a very small number (so it's shown here in scientific notation).

"But shouldn't the sine of π radians—like sin(180°)—be *exactly zero?*"

Yes, but you didn't compute the sine of *exactly* π radians. You computed the sine of 3.14159265359 radians. The real π has an *infinite number of digits*—a lot more than the 12 digits your calculator can hold.

Nobody can compute the sine of *exactly* π radians. Your HP 19BII is giving the correct answer *for the 12 digits it is using.*

OK: What are the lengths of the legs of this right triangle? What's the length of the arc?

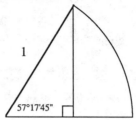

Hmm...:   Your first problem is to convert that angle into decimal degrees, rather than degrees, minutes and seconds. So [EXIT] the TRIG Menu and select **CONV**.

Next, key in ⑤⑦·①⑦④⑤ (to represent the angle in degrees, minutes and seconds), and press **▸HR**.*
Result: **57.30**   The angle is 57.30°

Now, you *could* go back to the TRIG Menu and use SIN and COS calculations to compute the triangle legs, but instead, press **MORE** and use this handy triangle menu: Store the angle by pressing **∡**. Then key in and store the radius: ① **R**. Make sure you're in *degrees* mode (use the toggle, **D/R**, if necessary). Now you're ready to compute:
The horizontal leg: **XCORD**   Result: XCOORD=**0.54**
The vertical leg: **YCORD**   Result: YCOORD=**0.84**

For the arc length, since the radius is 1, just convert the angle to radians: **∡** **MORE** **▸RAD**   Answer: **1.00**

---

*You are converting "to decimal HouRs" here, which may seem like a strange name, but notice that these functions work for *time* conversions as well as angle conversions.

Try This: If you have 21 marbles in a bag, how many possible *combinations* of 6 marbles (never mind the order) can you draw out? How about *permutations* (where the order does matter) when you draw 3 at a time?

Solution: Use a PROBability calculation: [EXIT] the CONVert Menu (from the previous problem) and press ▮PROB▮.

To find how many ways you can combine X objects, taken Y at a time, simply key in the values for X and Y. In this problem, X = 21 and Y = 6, so [2][1] ▮ X ▮ [6] ▮ Y ▮
Now solve for the number of possible combinations by pressing ▮C X,Y▮.   <u>Result</u>: C X,Y=54,264.00

For permutations, it's the same idea:
[2][1] ▮ X ▮ [3] ▮ Y ▮
Now solve for the number of possible permutations by pressing ▮P X,Y▮.   <u>Result</u>: P X,Y=7,980.00

The MATH Menu on your HP 19BII makes all this look pretty simple. Can you imagine trying to do such calculations yourself? You might end up...

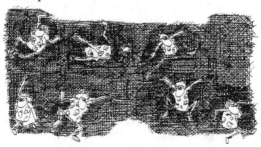

...losing your marbles.

A Rest Stop

That about does it for this chapter on arithmetic and math. Things will get more interesting soon, but you needed to know these things first:

- You know when and how to clear the calculator line;
- You know that the machine always keeps and uses 12 digits for each number in every arithmetic calculation;
- You know how to change the display setting (i.e. FIX and ALL) to see however many decimal places you want (up to 11).
- You know how to key in and use negative numbers;
- You know how ridiculously easy it is to do percentage problems;
- You know about the Stack and how it shows previous results.

And, if you went through the **More Math** section,

- You know about Scientific Notation;
- You know about the MATH Menu, including exponentiation, trigonometry and probability.

And of course, no matter what,

- You know you'll have an arithmetic quiz now....

Arithmetic Quiz*

Solve these on your HP 19Bɪɪ. As usual, the solutions are on the next pages, with some page references for review (and you'll see new twists, too). In some problems, it won't matter whether you use ALG or RPN arithmetic—the keystrokes are the same either way. But for any problems where the two methods do have different keystrokes, both solutions will be given (ALGebraic first).

1. Find $\dfrac{100/75}{(25 \times 64) + (34 \times (-19))}$

   Then find $\dfrac{(25 \times 64) + (34 \times (-19))}{100/75}$ *by two different methods.*

2. Which is greater: $4/7$ or $\dfrac{6.281}{11}$?

3. **4.00E12** is "4 trillion" (a very large number). How much is **4.00E-12**? How would you key this in?

4. Suppose that this year's income is 35% more than last year's, but next year's will be only 85% of this year's. If last year's was $25,000, what will next year's be?

---

*For more practice with RPN arithmetic specifically, see also Appendices D and E in your HP Owner's Manual.

5. Calculate $(-19) \times (-19)$ *by three different methods,* two of which don't use the $\boxtimes$ key.

6. Compute $\sqrt{4096}$ *two different ways.* Then find $\sqrt[12]{4096}$.

7. Find $\left(\dfrac{1 - 1.1^{-10}}{.1} + 100 \right)\left(1.1^{10}\right)$

(If you skipped the section called **More Math If You Want It**, you'll probably want to skip problems **8-10**, too.)

8. Find $\dfrac{\log\left(12^2 + \dfrac{2704}{3}\right)}{e^3}$

9. What's Arccot$(3\pi/4)$? Express your answer in degrees, minutes and seconds.

10. If sixteen U.S. states and five Canadian provinces meet to decide how to stop acid rain, how many ways are there to cast just the minimum majority of "no" votes to prevent any action?

Arithmetic Quiz Solutions

1. $\boxed{1}\boxed{0}\boxed{0}\boxed{\div}\boxed{7}\boxed{5}\boxed{\div}\boxed{(}\boxed{(}\boxed{(}\boxed{2}\boxed{5}\boxed{\times}\boxed{6}\boxed{4}\boxed{)}\boxed{+}\boxed{(}\boxed{3}\boxed{4}\boxed{\times}\boxed{-}\boxed{1}\boxed{9}\boxed{)}\boxed{)}\boxed{=}$(ALG),*or*
$\boxed{1}\boxed{0}\boxed{0}\boxed{ENTER}\boxed{7}\boxed{5}\boxed{\div}\boxed{2}\boxed{5}\boxed{ENTER}\boxed{6}\boxed{4}\boxed{\times}\boxed{3}\boxed{4}\boxed{ENTER}\boxed{1}\boxed{9}\boxed{+/-}\boxed{\times}\boxed{+}\boxed{\div}$
<u>Answer (to 8 decimal places)</u>: 0.00139762

The easiest way to solve the second part is to "flip" the first
answer with the ■$\boxed{1/x}$ key, taking the reciprocal of the current
number. <u>Answer (to 2 decimal places)</u>: 715.50

Of course, the other way is to start from scratch:
$\boxed{2}\boxed{5}\boxed{\times}\boxed{6}\boxed{4}\boxed{+}\boxed{(}\boxed{3}\boxed{4}\boxed{\times}\boxed{-}\boxed{1}\boxed{9}\boxed{)}\boxed{\div}\boxed{(}\boxed{1}\boxed{0}\boxed{0}\boxed{\div}\boxed{7}\boxed{5}\boxed{=}$ (ALG), *or*
$\boxed{2}\boxed{5}\boxed{ENTER}\boxed{6}\boxed{4}\boxed{\times}\boxed{3}\boxed{4}\boxed{ENTER}\boxed{1}\boxed{9}\boxed{+/-}\boxed{\times}\boxed{+}\boxed{1}\boxed{0}\boxed{0}\boxed{ENTER}\boxed{7}\boxed{5}\boxed{\div}\boxed{\div}$

(To review basic arithmetic methods, re-read pages 32-45).

2. To compare, find both answers: $\boxed{4}\boxed{\div}\boxed{7}\boxed{=}$ (ALG), *or* $\boxed{4}\boxed{ENTER}\boxed{7}\boxed{\div}$
and $\boxed{6}\boxed{\cdot}\boxed{2}\boxed{8}\boxed{1}\boxed{\div}\boxed{1}\boxed{1}\boxed{=}$ (ALG), or $\boxed{6}\boxed{\cdot}\boxed{2}\boxed{8}\boxed{1}\boxed{ENTER}\boxed{1}\boxed{1}\boxed{\div}$.

If you're looking only at the first two decimal places, they look
identical (0.57). But ask the DISPlay to FIX more than three
decimal places, and you'll see the difference: $\frac{4}{7}$ is greater (see
page 30 to brush up on FIX).

3. This is "four times ten to the negative twelfth power," or "four trillionths."
Written out fully, it would be 0.000000000004. To key this in, you
would press $\boxed{4}$■$\boxed{E}\boxed{-}\boxed{1}\boxed{2}$.

4. $\boxed{2}\boxed{5}\boxed{0}\boxed{0}\boxed{0}\boxed{+}\boxed{3}\boxed{5}\boxed{\%}\boxed{\times}\boxed{8}\boxed{5}\boxed{\%}\boxed{=}$ (ALG), *or*
$\boxed{2}\boxed{5}\boxed{0}\boxed{0}\boxed{0}\boxed{\text{ENTER}}\boxed{3}\boxed{5}\boxed{\%}\boxed{+}\boxed{8}\boxed{5}\boxed{\%}$ Answer: \$28,687.50
(See page 37 or 43 to review $\boxed{\%}$ calculations)

5. **(a)** $\boxed{1}\boxed{9}\boxed{+/-}\boxed{\times}\boxed{-}\boxed{1}\boxed{9}\boxed{=}$ (ALG), *or* $\boxed{1}\boxed{9}\boxed{+/-}\boxed{\text{ENTER}}\boxed{\times}$ (RPN)
Answer: 361.00

(b) $\boxed{1}\boxed{9}\boxed{+/-}\boxed{■ \text{X}^2}$. The $\boxed{■ \text{X}^2}$ key squares the current number.

(c) $\boxed{1}\boxed{9}\boxed{+/-}\boxed{■}\boxed{^\wedge}\boxed{2}\boxed{=}$ (ALG), *or* $\boxed{1}\boxed{9}\boxed{+/-}\boxed{\text{ENTER}}\boxed{2}\boxed{■}\boxed{^\wedge}$ (RPN).
The $\boxed{■ ^\wedge}$ key raises a number to a power. $(-19)^2$ is "negative
nineteen raised to the second power."

6. **(a)** $\boxed{4}\boxed{0}\boxed{9}\boxed{6}\boxed{■ \sqrt{x}}$. The $\boxed{■ \sqrt{x}}$ key operates on the current
number. Answer: 64.00

(b) $\boxed{4}\boxed{0}\boxed{9}\boxed{6}\boxed{■}\boxed{^\wedge}\boxed{\cdot}\boxed{5}\boxed{=}$ (ALG), *or* $\boxed{4}\boxed{0}\boxed{9}\boxed{6}\boxed{\text{ENTER}}\boxed{\cdot}\boxed{5}\boxed{■}\boxed{^\wedge}$.
The "square root" is the one-half (.5) power.

(c) $\boxed{4}\boxed{0}\boxed{9}\boxed{6}\boxed{■}\boxed{^\wedge}\boxed{1}\boxed{2}\boxed{■ 1/x}\boxed{=}$ (ALG), *or*
$\boxed{4}\boxed{0}\boxed{9}\boxed{6}\boxed{\text{ENTER}}\boxed{1}\boxed{2}\boxed{■ 1/x}\boxed{■}\boxed{^\wedge}$ (RPN).
$\sqrt[12]{4096}$ is the same as $4096^{\frac{1}{12}}$. Answer: 2.00

7. $\boxed{1}\boxed{-}\boxed{(}\boxed{(}\boxed{1}\boxed{\cdot}\boxed{1}\boxed{■}\boxed{^\wedge}\boxed{-}\boxed{1}\boxed{0}\boxed{)}\boxed{/}\boxed{\cdot}\boxed{1}\boxed{+}\boxed{1}\boxed{0}\boxed{0}\boxed{\times}\boxed{(}\boxed{1}\boxed{\cdot}\boxed{1}\boxed{■}\boxed{^\wedge}\boxed{1}\boxed{0}\boxed{=}$
(ALG), *or*
$\boxed{1}\boxed{\text{ENTER}}\boxed{1}\boxed{\cdot}\boxed{1}\boxed{\text{ENTER}}\boxed{1}\boxed{0}\boxed{+/-}\boxed{■}\boxed{^\wedge}\boxed{-}\boxed{\cdot}\boxed{1}\boxed{\div}\boxed{1}\boxed{0}\boxed{0}\boxed{+}\boxed{1}\boxed{\cdot}\boxed{1}\boxed{\text{ENTER}}$
$\boxed{1}\boxed{0}\boxed{■}\boxed{^\wedge}\boxed{\times}$ (RPN) Answer: 275.31

8. ⌨12⬛ x² + (⌨2704÷3=

   ⬛MAIN ⬛MATH LOGS LOG ÷3 EXP = (ALG), or

   ⌨12⬛ x² ⌨2704 ENTER 3÷+

   ⬛MAIN ⬛MATH LOGS LOG 3 EXP ÷ (RPN)

   <u>Answer (to 4 decimal places)</u>: 0.1503

   (To review the MATH Menu, re-read pages 47-52).

9. There's no cot (cotangent) function among the trig functions, but

   $$\cot(x) = \tan\left(\frac{1}{x}\right)$$

   In other words, $\text{Arccot}\left(\dfrac{4\pi}{3}\right) = \text{Arctan}\left(\dfrac{3}{4\pi}\right)$

   Thus, to solve the problem:

   ⬛MAIN ⬛MATH 3÷4÷ ⬛PI ⬛ =

   TRIG ATAN EXIT CONV >HMS (ALG), or

   ⬛MAIN ⬛MATH 3 ENTER 4÷ ⬛PI ⬛ ÷

   TRIG ATAN EXIT CONV >HMS (RPN)

   <u>Answer (to 4 decimal places)</u>: 13.2537

   That's 13°25'37".

10. Essentially, the question is, "How many different combinations of 11 'no' votes—the minimum majority—are possible among the 21 voters?"

You want combinations, not permutations, because the voting order doesn't matter:

▇(MAIN) **▇**(MATH) **PROB** **2****1** **▇** **X** **▇** **1****1** **▇** **Y** **▇** **C X,Y**

<u>Answer:</u> `C X,Y=352,716.0000`

There are well over a quarter-million ways to stymie any action. You wouldn't think so just by looking at the problem, would you? But your HP 19Bɪɪ makes this kind of calculation a piece of cake.

4. Your First BUSiness Trip

Road Signs: Menus and Their Keys

So much for arithmetic and math. The good news is: Most of the time, you won't need to do "manual" arithmetic on your HP 19Bɪɪ—because it has so many built-in formulas. But you do need to know how to use those formulas.*

Up to now, you've just been "driving around the block." In other words, the Menu Line has generally looked like this:

FIN | BUS | SUM | TIME |SOLVE| TEXT

This is "home"—the MAIN Menu. But now you're going to leave home and drive off for the road training you've been waiting for.

With the driving analogy, it may seem strange to be talking about maps, roads, and then *menus,* but it does make some sense: On the freeway, those big green signs showing lanes and exits are indeed a kind of menu. And how do you use these freeway menus? You choose the proper lane and exit—and you remember them for your return trip.

So you can think of the MAIN Menu on your HP 19Bɪɪ as the "freeway," from which you may exit to, say, the **FIN** or **TIME** "highways." From those, you can exit onto still smaller "routes," and so on. Reaching your destination—the formula you want to use—is just a matter of reading the "road signs" in the calculator's Menu Line.

*If you already know how to find these formulas and tools by navigating back and forth through the menus, then skip over now to page 67.

A Menu Map

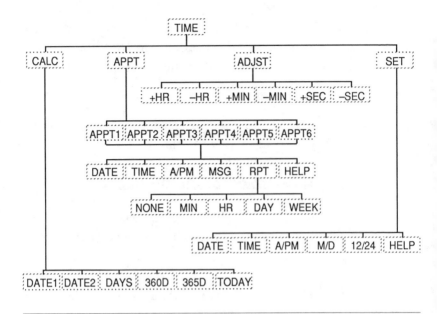

Try This: Look at the map above. This is one "major route" (the TIME Menu)—and its "suburbs." Use this map to guide you on a quick trip to the "place" called **TODAY**—starting from the MAIN Menu.

Solution: Press **TIME** **CALC** **TODAY** See what happens? **TODAY** is a *calculation* that gives you the date and day of the week.

Notice that some menu selections are merely exits to get you onto a different "road." The selections at the *ends* of the roads are your actual destinations—where the HP 19BII does its calculations.

Next Question: How do you get "home" again?

Next Answer: You can *retrace* your road route—or you can "*fly.*"

To retrace your route, use the [EXIT] key. Every time you press this key, you retrace your route back to the previous EXIT. Thus, you press [EXIT] to go from

here ⇒

| DATE! | DATE2 | DAYS | 360D | 365D | TODAY |

to here ⇒

| CALC | APPT | ADJST | SET |

and then [EXIT] once more to arrive "home" at the MAIN Menu.

To demonstrate how you can "fly" home, first go out to **TODAY** again.... Now press ■[MAIN].

■[MAIN] is the quick way home—the "When-All-Else-Fails-And-You-Can't-Figure-Out-Where-You-Are" key.

So never fear—no matter how lost you think you are, there's always a way to get back to a familiar route.

Pages in a Menu

A word about these "road signs" in the Menu Line: Sometimes there's just not enough room to list all the choices. What then?*

When this happens, the menu becomes more of the restaurant kind, because then it has more than one *page*.

Try This: Look at the menu map on the opposite page. Starting from your MAIN Menu, "move" through this map until your Menu Line looks like this:

Solution: Press ■ (MAIN) **FIN** , **DEPRC**, then **MORE** .... That **MORE** is an extra item—a "turn-the-page" key—that appears on every page of any multiple-page menu.

---

*Traffic engineers just use smaller writing on their road signs, but your HP 19BII can't do that.

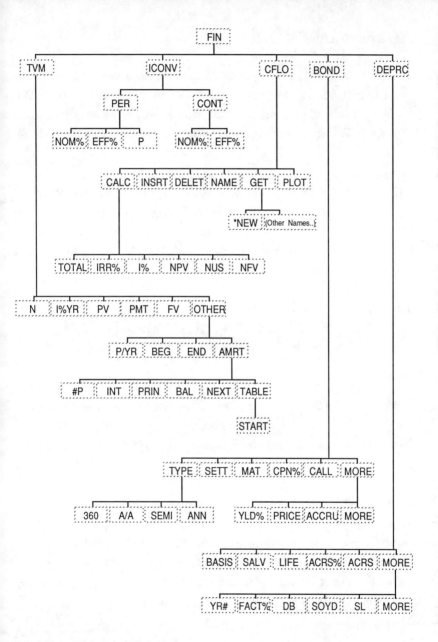

MAIN Routes vs. Side Trips

One more thing to notice about navigating through menus: Sometimes you can be working at one menu and need to take a short trip to do a "side calculation" at another menu—to get a number or adjust some mode, etc. But then you want to go back to the first menu and continue.

Like This: Suppose you're setting the current time in your calculator. You press ▮[MAIN][TIME][SET]. But then you realize that the only clock you have is a decimal chronometer that started at midnight. If it now shows 10.43 hours, to what time should you set your HP 19Bɪɪ?

Hmm...   This calls for a CONVert calculation. So you go to the ▮[MATH] Menu, select [CONV], then [1][0][·][4][3][>HMS].... Result: 10.25

Now just press [EXIT][EXIT] and voilá!—you're back at the TIME SET Menu directly—not at the MAIN Menu; the machine knows where you were before your CONVert calculation. So you just press [TIME] and you're done.

Except for ▮[MAIN] and [EXIT], any operation that's available to you *on the keyboard* (i.e. *not* via menu keys) is regarded as a temporary side trip. So while you do arithmetic, use the Stack, change the DISPlay setting, use the PRINTER or MATH Menus, etc., your HP 19Bɪɪ doesn't forget "where you were" in the menu system—and it returns you there when you finish with the keyboard.

Playing "What-If?" with Menu Keys

So now you know the basics of *moving around* in the menus.

But of course, menu keys are not just "traveling keys." They're also keys that can give you *answers*—hard numbers. For example, you've already used the **TODAY** key to give you the date and day of the week.

But the real beauty of menu calculations is how they let you play with complicated formulas—which often have several different variables in them. And since each variable has its own key on the menu, *you can vary them*—one at a time—to see the effect on your answer.

This means that you can play the "What-If?" game that's so useful in making good decisions! You can ask questions like *"what if* the rent goes up by $100?" *"What if* that interest rate were 2 points higher?"

And your calculator will show you the answers.

Watch This: From the MAIN Menu, press **BUS** and then **%CHG**:

```
┌─────────────────────────────────┐
│                                 │
│                                 │
│                                 │
│ ▓OLD▓│▓NEW▓│▓%CH▓               │
└─────────────────────────────────┘
```

And here's the problem you want to solve:

The retail trade per square foot in one shop was $75 this year. Last year it was $64. By what percentage did this trade increase in a year?

Related question: *What if* you were looking for a 20% increase—what level of trade would this have required this year?

Solution: ⁶⁴ **OLD** ⁷⁵ **NEW** **%CH**

<u>Answer</u>: %CHANGE=17.19

That was the actual percentage increase in the per-square-foot retail trade.

Now specify the 20% target increase: ²⁰ **%CH**
And find what the NEW trade (i.e. this year's) would have had to be in order to meet that target: **NEW**

Answer: NEW=76.80

The General Idea

See the basic pattern?

With the first calculation, you specified known values for two variables, OLD and NEW, and calculated the unknown variable, %CH. Then, for the second part, you specified your desired %CH and OLD values and calculated NEW instead.

> You can calculate any one of the three values
> —if you know the other two.

And Notice: You can *review* the current values in each of the variables—anytime you want.

Here's How: Press [RCL] **OLD** and see: `OLD=64.00`
Press [RCL] **NEW** and see: `NEW=76.80`
Press [RCL] **%CH** and see: `%CHANGE=20.00`

You use the [RCL] key to *ReCaLl* values from variables. There are actually three storage *registers* built into the machine, registers named OLD, NEW, and %CH. This is where the calculator stores the values you give it when you're playing "What-If?"

That's the heart of it, then: You store values in all menu variables except one, then calculate that one. And you can play this "What-If?" with *any* of the menu variables.

Now press EXIT to back up one level to the BUSiness Menu... and try some more examples....

If: A broker buys a property for $12/ft² and then sells it for $15/ft². What's the markup as a percentage of cost?

What is the markup as a percentage of price?

Solution: From the BUSiness Menu, press **MU%C**. This is the "MarkUp as a % of Cost" Menu.

So use it: Press ①② **COST** and ①⑤ **PRICE**.
Then calculate: **M%C**

Answer: MARKUP%C=25.00

To find the markup as a percentage of price, go back to the BUSiness Menu (EXIT) and press **MU%P**.

Then press **M%P**.

Answer: MARKUP%P=20.00

Hmmm...

Question: Why didn't you need to key in the **COST** and **PRICE** in the MU%P Menu, as you did in the MU%C Menu?

Answer: Simple: The **COST** and **PRICE** variable registers in the MU%P Menu *are the same* as in the MU%C Menu. That is, they are *shared variables*—shared between more than one menu.

Thus, since you had already stored the 12 and the 15 in the COST and PRICE registers, those values were still there, ready to calculate *either* **M%C** or **M%P** !

And they're still there now—which you can prove by recalling them:

Press [RCL] **COST** and see COST=12.00
Press [RCL] **PRICE** and PRICE=15.00

One More: If the appraised value of a property decreased by 36% this year and 25% last year, what was its total percentage decrease in value over these two years?

Solution: From the BUS Menu, choose the **%CHG** option. Then, since you don't have the actual values to work with, just start with a convenient number—say, 100—to represent the property's value two years ago: Press ①⓪⓪ **OLD**

One year later, the value was 36% less than that. That is, the %CH was -36. So press ③⑥+/– **%CH** .

Now solve for the NEW level: **NEW**.... NEW=64.00 So if the value was 100 two years ago, then it was just 64 one year later.

Now do the second year. The NEW value from the first year is the OLD value for the second year, so you would press ⑥④ **OLD** . Next, you key in the value decrease in the second year: ②⑤+/– **%CH** , and solve for the NEW (and that's the current) value: **NEW**....NEW=48.00

So, what was the percent change for the two years? Your NEW level is now correct, but your OLD level needs to be 100 for the entire two-year period, right?

Press ①⓪⓪ **OLD** **%CH**
Answer: %CHANGE=-52.00

The property's value dropped 52% over two years.

Review

That's what you need to know about menus and "moving around" in your HP 19BII. Just keep in mind these few important things:

- When in doubt, look at your display. It will orient you, showing you your current menu choices, error messages, instructions, etc.

- You can always get "Home" to the MAIN Menu quickly, via ■ MAIN.

- You can always "retrace your steps" (toward Home) with EXIT.

- When there are more than six menu items, you'll find a second "page" for that menu, by choosing **MORE**.

- You can play "What-If?" with the formulas you find in the menu system. Each variable is matched with a *register*, where you store the value you want to use in the formula.

- Even short quizzes can be helpful....

Menu Quiz

Take a "solo drive" with some percentage problems and with some "What-Iffing." Try these (the answers are on the next page, as usual):

1. There's a calculation key called **PRICE** in the **BOND** Menu. Your mission: Starting from the MAIN Menu, find it (don't bother to calculate with it), then report back to the MAIN Menu ASAP.

2. Using what you know about menus, see if you can figure out how to set the correct time and date in your calculator.

3. If you're in the middle of an arithmetic problem and you suddenly decide to change menus ("move") for some reason, what happens to your calculation?

4. In general, what happens to your most recent calculation result when you change menus? How about the rest of the Stack?

5. A holder of a note wished to sell it and offered a 10% discount off of the face value. The buyer then turned around and re-sold the note by adding 10% to the price he had just paid for it. Did he sell it for face value?

6. The most severe drop in the history of the U.S. stock market occurred in the period between September 3, 1929 and July 8, 1932. During that time, an industrial stocks average fell from 452 to 58. If the same percentage drop happened with a beginning average level of, say, 2735, where would the bottom level be?

7. A football field is 100 yards long. If it's 45 yards wide and you increase both its width and its length by 9%, by what percentage would this increase its area?

Menu Quiz Answers

1. From the MAIN Menu, press **FIN** **BOND** **MORE**, and there on the second page of the **BOND** Menu, you'll see the choice called **PRICE**. Notice that, as usual, if you press **MORE** at this point, you'll flip-flop between the pages of the **BOND** Menu (see page 64 if you don't remember this). Then press ■(MAIN) to "fly home" again.

2. From the Main Menu, press **TIME** (obviously), and then **SET** (because you want to *set* the time and date). That brings you to another menu. Now, just pressing **DATE** or **TIME** on that menu *won't* set the correct time or date in the display. What do you do?

   Ask for **HELP**! ...See? It shows you how to key in the number to represent the correct time and date. For example, if today is February 28, 1990, and it's 2:25 p.m., press ②·②⑧①⑨⑨⓪ **DATE**, then ②·②⑤ (then **A/PM** if necessary) and **TIME** to get 2:25 in the afternoon. Now set your *correct* date and time, and watch the information in the display change.

3. Absolutely nothing happens to your calculation-in-progress—try it: Press ②⊕③ (or ②(ENTER)③, for RPN), change menus (e.g. (EXIT)), then ⊜ (or ⊕, for RPN), to finish your addition.

4. When you change menus, your current calculation will remain undisturbed, but the values above it in the Stack may disappear.

5. Use the MU%P Menu and, say, a $100 note: Press `1` `0` `0` `PRICE` `1` `0` `M%P` `COST`.... <u>Result</u>: `COST=90.00`

That's what the buyer paid for the note. Then he re-sold it simply by adding 10% to this figure. That is, he used the MU%C Menu and, since the `90.00` was already stored in the COST register, he did this: `1` `0` `M%C` `PRICE`.... <u>Result</u>: `PRICE=99.00` That's *not* the face value.

6. This is a %CHG problem. From the BUS Menu, press `%CHG`, then `4` `5` `2` `OLD` `5` `8` `NEW` `%CH`. <u>Result</u>: `%CHANGE=-87.17`

That's the *percent change* of the 1929-1932 crash (negative because the change was *down*ward). Now key in the hypothetical high level, `2` `7` `3` `5` `OLD`, and calculate what the corresponding low level would be: `NEW`.... <u>Result</u>: `NEW=350.95`

7. You need a %CHANGE calculation, so go to the %CHG Menu. Then start by computing the area before the enlargement:
`4` `5` `×` `1` `0` `0` `=`   (or `4` `5` `ENTER` `1` `0` `0` `×` for RPN)
<u>Answer</u>: `4,500.00` Press `OLD`—this is the OLD area.

Next, you need to find the dimensions of the enlarged field:
`(` `(` `1` `0` `0` `+` `9` `%` `)` `×` `(` `(` `4` `5` `+` `9` `%` `=`   (for ALG), or
`1` `0` `0` `ENTER` `9` `%` `+` `4` `5` `ENTER` `9` `%` `+` `×`   (for RPN)
<u>Answer</u>: `5,346.45` This is the NEW area; press `NEW`.

Finally, `%CH` gives you the increase in area: `%CHANGE=18.81` (If you had *decreased* it, the %CH would have been negative).

Where Do You Want To Go Next?

You've come to a fork in the road.

Since you now know the basics of arithmetic and menus on your HP 19Bɪɪ, it's really up to you now to decide where to read next.

Of course, the recommended choice is to keep going, straight through the book. Each topic takes only a short amount of time to cover, but it teaches you a lot about the calculator and how versatile and powerful it really is.

But granted, you may not be interested in all the topics, so here's where you can read the road signs and make your own choice.

(You'll find similar "forks in the road" at the ends of later chapters, too, so you'll have this kind of choice through the rest of the Course....)

4. YOUR FIRST BUSINESS TRIP

Basic Arithmetic...............24	TVM.............................94
Using Menus.....................60	The CFLO Menu..................202
	SUM Lists.......................258
	TIME, Dates and Appts.....280
	The SOLVE Menu...............294
	TEXT Lists.....................409
	Appendix........................424

Where Do You Want To Go Next?

The Bread Value Of Money:
CURRency EXchanges

So you're going to continue with your first BUSiness trip? Fine. Then here's a look at another useful item on the BUS Menu....

Suppose you're an economist comparing the living standards of three countries—the United States, Costa Rica, and Peru. One way to do this is to compare average per-capita incomes to the costs of a basic food commodity—i.e. "daily bread," or something comparable.

There are several common foodstuffs you could choose as an indicator (and actually, wheat bread isn't one of these, since most countries use far more rice than wheat). Suppose you choose chicken.

That fine, but there's a slight problem: Annual income reports are usually given in U.S. dollars, while food prices (which may fluctuate daily) are not. So you need to do some conversions before making the comparisons. Here are the numbers you're using:

Country	Currency	Cost of Chicken (per kg)	Exch. Rate (per $US)	Avg. Annual Per-Capita Incm. ($US)
U.S.A.	Dollar	1.95	1.0000	$17,800
Costa Rica	Colón	168.00	87.0000	$ 1,810
Peru	Inti	45,000.00	18,000.0000	$ 965

So how does the HP 19Bɪɪ do currency conversions?...

From the MAIN Menu (remember that **MAIN** will always get you there), press **BUS**, then **CURRX**. Here's what you'll see....

```
1 US$ = 1.0000 YEN
ENTER A RATE
0.00
 US$ | YEN | RATE |C.STO|C.RCL|SELCT
```

The idea is this: The HP 19BII lets you select the *names* of two currencies—and the conversion *rate* between them. Right now, the two selected names are US$ and YEN, but that's not what you want. So press **SELCT**, and see this:

```
SELECT CURRENCY 1


 US$ |CAN$| DM | FF | UK£ |MORE
```

Now choose **US$** from the menu of currency names—and notice how the display then verifies your choice and tells you what to do next....

```
CURRENCY 1 IS: US$
SELECT CURRENCY 2

 US$ |CAN$| DM | FF | UK£ |MORE
```

Use **MORE** to "page" through the menu to find (and choose) **INTI**:

```
1 US$ = 1.0000 INTI
ENTER A RATE
0.00
 US$ | YEN | RATE |C.STO|C.RCL|SELCT
```

OK, now that your currency names are both correct, you're ready to **ENTER A RATE**.

Notice that the exchange is always in terms of *one* unit of Currency 1. That is, you always ask the calculator, *"One* unit of Currency 1 equals *how many* units of Currency 2?" So key in ①⑧⓪⓪⓪, press **RATE**, and notice again how the display will echo your choice.

Now, if a kilogram of chicken costs you 45,000 Intis in Peru, how much would that be in US dollars?

At this point, it's simply a matter of playing "What-If?" to find out:

④⑤⓪⓪⓪ **INTI** **US$** ....   Answer: US$=2.50

And if chicken were to cost the *same* (in dollars) as it does in the US, what would that price be in Intis?

①·⑨⑤ **US$** **INTI** ....   Answer: INTI=35,100.00

See? You can go in either direction for the conversion. Simply key in one known currency value and then solve for its corresponding value in the other currency.

Easy, right? But the best news of all is this: Once you associate two given currency names with their corresponding conversion rate, you can *save* this combination for easy recall later. Press **C.STO** to see this:

```
PRESS A MENU KEY TO
STORE CURRENCIES/RATE
```

As the instructions explain, simply by selecting one of these six blank menu keys, you can *store* a currencies/rate combination.

Try it: Press, say, the second blank key.... Instantly you're back at the main CURRency eXchange Menu.

And now suppose you convert some other currencies. For example, suppose you convert between Canadian dollars and German deutsche marks, pressing **SELCT** **CAN$** **DM** ④ **RATE** (do this now). The display will show you this:

```
1 CAN$ = 4.0000 DM
RATE=4.00
CAN$  DM  RATE C.STO C.RCL SELCT
```

Ah, but you can *instantly* reset to US$/INTI exchanges by pressing **C.RCL** and choosing **US:IN**...!

You can save up to six such combinations on this store/recall Menu.

Try Another: Now compute the price of a kilogram of chicken in Costa Rica, using the data on page 80.

Solution: At the CURRency EXchange Menu, press `SELCT` `US$` `MORE` `MORE` `MORE` `MORE` `MORE` `MORE` `MORE` (...there doesn't seem to be a built-in name for Colones). So use the final selection on the last page of the menu: `CURR2`. That's the "last-resort," the "generic" name to use when there's no better one.

Now enter the rate and solve the problem:

`8` `7` `RATE` `1` `6` `8` `CURR2`
`US$` .... Answer: <u>US$=1.93</u>

Save this exchange combination: Press `C.STO`, then the first blank key on the menu. Now you have two such combinations to use whenever you need them.

As you can see, the prices of a kilogram of chicken in the three countries are "in the same ballpark," dollar-for-dollar:

U.S.: $1.95   Costa Rica: $1.93   Peru: $2.50

But how hard are those dollars to *earn?* To see the *real* cost of this food in each country, you must compare it to the average income....

The Real Costs: Calculate what a kilogram of chicken would cost in the U.S. if it cost the same *in proportion to income* as in Costa Rica and Peru.

Solution: ①·⑨③÷①⑧①⓪×①⑦⑧⓪⓪=(ALG), or
①·⑨③ENTER①⑧①⓪÷①⑦⑧⓪⓪× (RPN)

<u>Answer</u>: $18.98 That's the *real* cost (i.e. the relative cost) of a kilo of chicken in Costa Rica— nearly 10 times the cost in the U.S.

②·⑤⓪÷⑨⑥⑤×①⑦⑧⓪⓪=(ALG), or
②·⑤⓪ENTER⑨⑥⑤÷①⑦⑧⓪⓪× (RPN)

<u>Answer</u>: $46.11 That's the *real* cost (i.e. the relative cost) of a kilo of chicken in Peru—nearly 24 times the cost in the U.S.

Loaves and Fishes: Getting Your UNITS Right

The last item on the BUSiness Menu is **UNITS**. The idea behind it is very simple—to help you answer questions such as this:

Hmm...: With seven one-pound fishes and eleven 26-oz. loaves of bread, to how many persons can you feed 100 grams of food?

Ahh...: At the MAIN Menu (■ MAIN), select **BUS UNITS**. You will see something like this:

```
┌─────────────────────────────┐
│                             │
│  UNIT CONVERSIONS           │
│                             │
│  LENG  AREA  VOL  MASS  TEMP │
└─────────────────────────────┘
```

To convert weight, or *mass,* press **MASS**, and then:

Press ②⑥ **OZ** **LB**.   Result: LB=1.63
This is the weight of each loaf of bread, in *pounds.*
Then ⊗①①⊕⑦⊜ (ALG) or ①①⊗⑦⊕ (RPN)
Result: 24.88   —the total pounds of food you have.

Now: **LB** **GRAM**.   Result: GRAMS=11,283.11
That's how many *grams* of food you have, so now simply
divide by 100: ⊜①⓪⓪⊜ (ALG) or ①⓪⓪⊜ (RPN)....

You can feed a multitude—nearly 113 persons (112.83).

Get the idea? You just key in the value in the known units and solve for that same value in other units. It's very similar to the way you convert currencies.

For some more practice with both of those conversion menus, try this...

Conversion Quiz

1. At the close of foreign exchange trading today, the British pound sterling (£) would buy $1.6325. The dollar was going for 1.7002 dm (deutsche marks), and the dm was trading for 93.4¥ (Yen). Find and store all six conversion rates between these four currencies.

2. Besides converting currencies, what other conversion uses might you find for the CURRency EXchange Menu?

3. Which is more economical—a car that averages 12 kilometers per liter of fuel, or a car that averages 30 miles per gallon?

4. In certain sections of Tokyo, the real estate market is so ferocious that if you lay a $1000 bill down on the ground, it will just pay for the area it covers(!) Calculate that price per square foot. What is it in Yen per square meter, assuming the currency exchange rates given in problem **1**, above?

Conversion Quiz Solutions

1. First, do the ones you're given: Press ▮ (MAIN) **BUS** **CURRX**, then
    SELCT **UK£** **US$** (1)(·)(6)(3)(2)(5) **RATE** **C.STO**, then the **first** key
    on the Rate storage Menu.

    Next: **SELCT** **US$** **DM** (1)(·)(7)(0)(0)(2) **RATE** **C.STO**, then select
    the **second** key on the Rate storage Menu (group all the dollar
    conversions together at the left, for convenience).

    Next: **SELCT** **DM** |MORE| |MORE| |MORE| |MORE| |MORE| **YEN** (9)(3)(·)(4)
    RATE **C.STO**. Select the **fourth** key on the Rate storage Menu.

    Notice how you choose CURRENCY 1 to be the currency whose
    unit value (e.g. 1 dm, or 1 dollar) you know from the problem, thus
    making the input easier.

    Now use these three known rates to calculate the others. The
    idea is to calculate in a currency chain, like this:
    C.RCL **US:DM** (1) **US$** **DM** (Result: DM=1.70)

    Now, keep that number there on the Stack, to use with the next
    rate: **C.RCL** **DM:YE** (STO) **DM** **YEN** (Result: YEN=158.80)

    Keep this number, too, to use as the new rate: **SELCT** **US$** |MORE|
    |MORE| |MORE| |MORE| |MORE| **YEN** (STO) **RATE** **C.STO**. Now select the
    third key on the Rate storage Menu.

Do likewise on the other two rates:

C.RCL **UK:US** **1** **UK£** **US$** (Result: US$=1.63).

Now, keep that number there on the Stack, to use with the next rate: **C.RCL** **US:YE** (STO) **US$** **YEN** (Result: YEN=259.24)

Keep this number, too, to use as the new rate: **SELCT** **UK£** **MORE** **MORE** **MORE** **MORE** **MORE** **YEN** (STO) **RATE** **C.STO**. Store this rate on the **fifth** key on the Rate storage Menu.

C.RCL **UK:US** **1** **UK£** **US$** (Result: US$=1.63).

Now, keep that number right there on the Stack, to use with the next rate: **C.RCL** **US:DM** (STO) **US$** **DM** (Result: DM=2.78)

Keep this number, too, to use as the new rate: **SELCT** **UK£** **DM** (STO) **RATE** **C.STO**. Store this rate on the **sixth** key on the Rate storage Menu.

Now, every day, as the currencies fluctuate, you can simply adjust each rate, thus keeping current on all these exchanges!

2. The CURRency EXchange Menu is really good for converting between *any* two known values. For example, you can use an exchange rate between the dollar and 1 share of a common stock or a mutual fund, or 1 carload of pork bellies, or 1 ounce of gold.... You get the idea—the possibilities are endless.

In fact, you can use the CURRency EXchange Menu to convert between *any* units—even physical units, like the UNITS Menu.

For example, you can convert between various lengths: 1 parsec = 153 trillion furlongs. Or, convert units of *time:* 1 day = 86,400 seconds, or 1 year = 26.09 fortnights, or 1 minute = 40 winks(?), etc.

3. This is a problem for the UNITS Menu:

Press ▉`MAIN` ▉`BUS` ▉`UNITS`, then ▉`LENG` ▉`MORE` `1``2` ▉`KM` ▉`MILE`
Result: `MILES=7.46`
(The full precision is `7.45645430685`, as ▉`SHOW` tells you.)

So the car that gets 12 km/liter is getting 7.46 *miles*/liter. Now, how many gallons are in a liter?

Press `EXIT` ▉`VOL` `1` ▉`LITER` ▉`GAL`
Result: `GALLONS=0.26`
(The full precision is `0.264172052358`)

So this car is getting about 7.46 miles/0.26 gallons of fuel, right? Now just do the division to get an answer in miles per gallon:

`7``·``4``5``6``4``5``4``3``0``6``8``5``÷`
        `·``2``6``4``1``7``2``0``5``2``3``5``8``=` (ALG),*
or `x≷y``R↓` `÷` (RPN—isn't the RPN Stack great?)

Answer: `28.23` miles per gallon.

So while a 12 km/liter car is pretty good—28.23 miles/gallon—a 30 mpg car is still a little more economical.

---

*Changing sub-menus within the UNITS Menu seems to be a case where the RPN Stack is preserved, but the ALG Stack is not. While you could have *stored* the `7.46`... value in a *storage register,* then recalled it later, you may not yet have been introduced to storage registers, so the ALG solutions here are simply to re-enter earlier values by hand.

4. First of all, you need to decide on the dimensions of a \$1000 bill...
To save you a trip to the bank (or your mattress), just assume that
it's about 6.1250 inches by 2.5625 inches.

Knowing that, you can calculate its area in square inches and use
the UNITS Menu to find the equivalent area in square feet: Press
■(MAIN) **BUS** **UNITS** **AREA**, then

[6][.][1][2][5][×][2][.][5][6][2][5][=](ALG), or
[6][.][1][2][5][ENTER][2][.][5][6][2][5][×](RPN)
<u>Result:</u> **15.70**

(The full precision is **15.6953125**, as ■(SHOW) tells you.)

Now **SQ.IN** to store this and **SQ.FT** to calculate....
<u>Result:</u> SQ.FT=**0.11**

(The full precision is **0.108995225694**)

So the price of this precious real estate is "\$1000 per 0.11 sq. ft." Now
just do the division:

[÷][1][0][0][0][=]■[1/x] (ALG),   or   [1][0][0][0][x≷y][÷] (RPN)
<u>Answer:</u> **9,174.71**   (Gulp)

That's \$9,174.71 *per square foot*....   ...Quite a lot, really.

Next, find the dollars per square *meter:*

[1] **SQ.FT** **SQ.M** <u>Result:</u> SQ.METERS=**0.09**   Then:
[÷][9][1][7][4][.][7][1][=]■[1/x] (ALG),   or   [x≷y][R↓][÷] (RPN)
<u>Answer:</u> **98,755.80**   That's \$98,755.80 per square meter.

Now hotfoot it over to the CURRency EXchange Menu and convert that dollar figure to Yen:

EXIT EXIT **CURRX** **C.RCL** **US:YE** STO **US$** **YEN**

<u>Answer:</u> `YEN=15,682,290.26`
This real estate costs 15,682,290.26¥/square meter.

Hope you brought your checkbook....

Checking the Map Again

Here's another "fork in the road."

As usual, the recommended choice is to keep going straight on through the book. But here's you chance to "skip around," if you wish.

Read the road signs now and make your own choice....

Basic Arithmetic.............24

Using Menus...................60

TVM.........................94

The CFLO Menu..............202

SUM Lists....................258

TIME, Dates and Appts.....280

The SOLVE Menu.............294

TEXT Lists...................409

Appendix.....................424

Checking the Map Again

5. THE TIME VALUE OF MONEY: TVM

Problem Understanding = Problem Solving

Now that you know the basics of math and arithmetic, it's time to start on financial problem solving. But first, consider this:

> *"You never really understand something*
> *until you can explain it to someone else."*

This is certainly true for solving problems on your HP 19BII. To get it to solve your problems, you must explain the problem to it—in the "picture language" it understands. And of course, that means you need to figure out that picture *for yourself* first.

> You must understand and define a problem
> for yourself before you can possibly "explain"
> it to your calculator.

This Course trains you to do exactly that—understand and define problems. That makes the actual button-pushing very easy—almost an afterthought. So don't be too impatient to start hitting keys here. Just park your calculator for a moment, sit back, and consider carefully the details that surround even simple finance calculations.

And don't skip over this part! Even if you've seen some of this before, it will pay you to review it now....

What Is TVM?

TVM, of course, stands for the Time Value of Money.

TVM assumes that money earns *interest* simply through the passage of time. When you're not using it, you're renting it out (loaning it) for someone else to use. Therefore, when you ask "How much money do I have?" you must also ask "What time is it?" Under TVM's assumption, the first question is meaningless without the second one.

So for the purposes of calculations, the old cliché is very useful:

Time is money.

Thus, even when *amounts* of money differ, they may still be equivalent because of the *time* difference between them. For example, if $1.00 today earns 10% annual interest, it will be worth $1.10 this time next year. And you can say this with an "equals" in it:

"$1.00 now *equals* $1.10 next year."

Time adds the extra Value to the Money. So (assuming that 10% annual interest rate), you could correctly view the face value of a dollar-bill as being any one of these equivalent amounts of money:

$$\$1.00_{\text{now}} \ = \ \$1.10_{\text{next year}} \ = \ \$2.59_{\text{ten years from now}}$$

How Does Interest Behave?

OK, so borrowed money earns interest over time. Everybody knows that. But *how*, exactly? If you were to watch the pennies of interest accrue in your bank account, what would the pattern look like?

It all depends on what kind of interest you're earning.

Basically, there are two forms of interest: **Simple** and **Compound**. Here's how they differ:

Simple Interest is the less common method: The amount of money earned periodically as interest is defined as a set percentage of the amount *originally loaned*.

Example: Suppose you earn **Simple Interest** at 1% per month in your bank account (not bad). And suppose you deposit $100.00 there for 12 months. How much interest will you earn over the entire 12 months?

Solution: There will be exactly $12.00 in interest, because you earn 1% of the *original* $100.00 every month. That's $1 per month for 12 months. Simple to calculate—just like the name—**Simple Interest.**

Compound Interest, on the other hand, is much more widely used: The amount of money earned as interest per period is defined as a set percentage of the amount owed *as of the beginning of that particular period*—including any past interest earned but not yet paid.

Example: Take that same $100.00 for 12 months, earning 1% per month, but this time it's **Compound Interest**. How much is earned over 12 months?

Solution: The first month is easy: 1% of $100.00 = $1.00
So after one month, the total amount owed is $101.00.

Now comes the second month: 1% of $101.00 = $1.01
So after 2 months, the total owed is $102.01. Etc.:

After	Amount Owed
Month 3	$ 103.03
Month 4	$ 104.06
Month 5	$ 105.10
Month 6	$ 106.15
Month 7	$ 107.21
Month 8	$ 108.29
Month 9	$ 109.37
Month 10	$ 110.46
Month 11	$ 111.57
Month 12	$ 112.68

So if it's not paid immediately, Compound Interest earns *more* than Simple Interest.

Again, here's the difference between the two types of interest:

With **Simple Interest**, no matter what month you're talking about, the interest earned in that month is always based upon the *original amount*—the amount owed *at the beginning of the loan.*

With **Compound Interest**, the interest earned in any given month is based upon the amount owed at the beginning of *that month.* Therefore, interest is earned not only on the original amount but also on all other interest already earned (but not yet paid). Hence the name, *Compound* Interest.

(Don't worry—you're going to put these ideas into practice in just a few more pages. Just grin and bear it for now; it's very important to cover these things first.)

Here's a pictorial summary of the behaviors of each of these types of interest:

Simple Interest

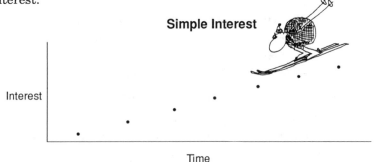

Interest

Time

Compound Interest

Interest

Time

As you know (and illustrated here), Compound Interest grows faster than Simple Interest. That's why Compound Interest is used much more widely—and on your HP 19Bɪɪ.

So you won't hear much more about Simple Interest here; anytime you see just the word "interest," it will mean Compound Interest.

Again, all this may seem obvious. But don't overlook these subtleties:

Subtlety #1: In either form of interest, there is only one time period which is the Defined Interest Period (D.I.P.), and only one Defined Interest Rate (D.I.R.) corresponding to that period. No other numbers can be used to calculate compounding interest. Don't be mislead by quoted annualized values! They may be *nominal*—not *effective*—rates.

The examples with the $100.00 for 12 months stated specifically that interest accrues at 1% per month. Therefore the D.I.P. is 1 month, and the corresponding D.I.R. is 1%. But it's conventional to quote interest rates on an annual basis, using a simplified, "thumbnail" approximation, called a *nominal* rate. For example, a bank would quote the above rate as "12% A.P.R. (Annual Percentage Rate)."

That's the nominal rate. But now ask the bank for your *effective* (i.e. your actual) interest earned on $100.00 over 12 months. They do not simply multiply your starting $100.00 by 12% A.P.R. (that would be simple interest). Instead, they divide the quoted A.P.R. by the number of D. I. P.'s per year (12), to get the D.I.R.* Then they go through exactly the same compounding calculation as you did on page 99—one period at a time.

To put it succinctly: A *nominal* rate is a *simple-interest* annualized approximation often used to *quote* interest rates. The *effective* rate it stands for is then *calculated*—by *compounding* the D.I.R. for a year's worth of D.I.P.'s.

---

*Canadian lenders do it slightly differently. The Appendix shows you how to convert between the Canadian method and the U.S. method—which is used by the HP 19Bɪɪ.

Subtlety #2: In your 12-month account problem, you never stopped to ponder how much interest you had earned after, say, 2.5 months, or 5.79 months, or 9.61 months.

And why not?

Because you weren't given any rules.

The D.I.R. and D.I.P. define only what the loan balance will be at *one point* in each period (the end). There must be other definitions to determine how that balance goes *between* points.

That's why the points on the graph on page 100 aren't connected with lines. Knowing only the D.I.R. and the D.I.P., nobody can tell you how those lines should be drawn. For all you know, those lines might be drawn like this:

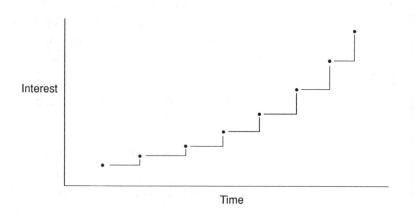

Or maybe interest might accrue like this....

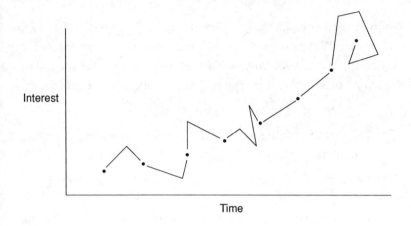

...Or who-knows-what-else. All you know is the balance at one point in each Defined Interest Period.

"Then how <u>do</u> I picture my $100.00 compound-interest bank account—if I can't draw a nice smooth curve of some kind?

"And what if I deposit into—or withdraw from—my account during those 12 months? How do I include that information in the picture?

"And how does this apply for other kinds of investments?"

Funny you should ask.... ☞

Getting the Picture Right

Whether it's a note, mortgage, lease or another financial scenario, the underlying TVM principles are the same. But each financial industry may use its own set of terms, so it's best to omit the words altogether—*draw a picture*—to analyze the scenario. The picture must show:

- The numerical *value* of the transaction;
- The *direction* of the transaction (*paying* or *receiving* the money), usually shown with (), or ±, or a debit/credit designation.
- The *time* of the transaction. Time adds value to money!

There are many ways to "draw the picture." Here are two of them:

Using a T-Bar

Suppose you invest $100 now, then $10 more at the end of every month for 6 months. In return you receive $40 at the end of month 2, and then your original $100, plus $30 more, at the end of month 6. Here's how a *T-bar*—a chronological table of cash-flows—would represent this:

Month (m)	$Cash-flow
0	(100.00)
1	(10.00)
2	(10.00) + 40.00
3	(10.00)
4	(10.00)
5	(10.00)
6	(10.00) + 100.00 + 30.00

To be sure you build a correct T-bar, follow these rules:

1. "Either a borrower or a lender be!" When buying money market shares or putting money into a savings account, you're a *lender*. If you're taking out a mortgage to buy or build a piece of property, then clearly you're a *borrower*. The same scenario will look different, depending upon which view you take. So pick one perspective and *stick with it*.

2. The signs (negative vs. positive) of the cash-flows denote the directions of the transactions. A *positive* amount means that you *receive* money; a *negative* amount means you *pay* money.

3. The cash-flows proceed forward in time from top to bottom in the chart—and the *same period of time* separates each cash-flow. This period must be the D.I.P. (Defined Interest Period) to match the assumptions of your HP 19Bₚ.

4. When multiple transactions occur simultaneously, *you combine them* into one net transaction. For example, these two scenarios are entirely equivalent:

m	$	m	$
0	(100.00)	0	(100.00)
1	(10.00)	1	(10.00)
2	(10.00) + 40.00	2	30.00
3	(10.00)	3	(10.00)
4	(10.00)	4	(10.00)
5	(10.00)	5	(10.00)
6	(10.00) + 100.00 + 30.00	6	120.00

Using a Cash-Flow Diagram

A **cash-flow diagram** is a good way to represent and understand an investment scenario *visually*. For example, observe how a cash-flow diagram would represent this same T-bar scenario:

Month (m)	$Cash-flow
0	(100.00)
1	(10.00)
2	(10.00) + 40.00
3	(10.00)
4	(10.00)
5	(10.00)
6	(10.00) + 100.00 + 30.00

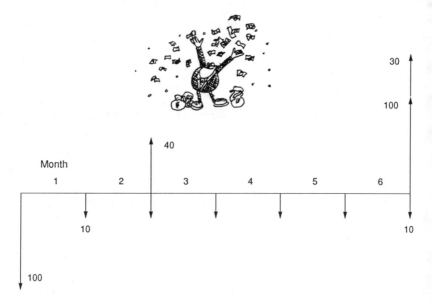

Of course, just as with T-bars, there are certain rules for drawing cash-flow diagrams—and you'll notice a lot of similarities:

1. "Either a borrower or a lender be!" In drawing the diagram, *pick one perspective and stick with it.*

2. The cash-flows proceed forward in time from left to right on the diagram—and the *same period of time* separates each cash-flow. This period must be the D.I.P. (Defined Interest Period) to match the assumptions of your HP 19Bᴵᴵ.

3. The *directions* of the vertical arrows denote the directions of the transactions. An *upward* arrow means that you *receive* money; a *downward* arrow means that you *pay* money:

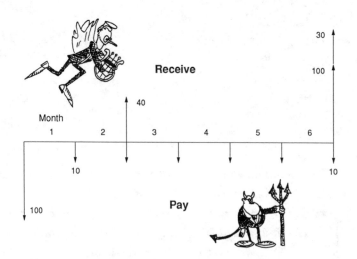

4. Whenever multiple transactions occur simultaneously, *you can net them together.* This:

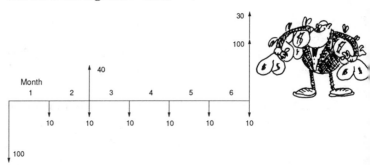

is the same as this:

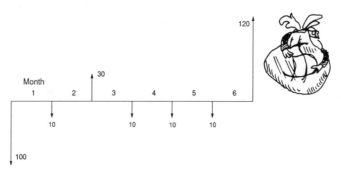

Whichever method you choose—T-bar or diagram—use it! You can't solve a problem if you can't describe it correctly first.

> *The first thing to do in any financial calculation is to*
> **Get the Picture Right.**
> *Either create a T-bar or draw a cash-flow diagram.*

Discounting Cash-Flows

One of the real values of TVM is that you can use it to make the scenario simpler—actually *adjust* cash-flow amounts to get a clearer picture of the situation. Go back to your $100.00 sitting in the bank account for 12 months. Of course, you can withdraw your money from the account at any time, but suppose you want to see your options for withdrawing at the end of each of the first six months. Here's how those six options look on T-bars:

m	$	m	$	m	$
0	(100.00)	0	(100.00)	0	(100.00)
1	101.00	1	0.00	1	0.00
2	0.00	2	102.01	2	0.00
3	0.00	3	0.00	3	103.03
4	0.00	4	0.00	4	0.00
5	0.00	5	0.00	5	0.00
6	0.00	6	0.00	6	0.00

m	$	m	$	m	$
0	(100.00)	0	(100.00)	0	(100.00)
1	0.00	1	0.00	1	0.00
2	0.00	2	0.00	2	0.00
3	0.00	3	0.00	3	0.00
4	104.06	4	0.00	4	0.00
5	0.00	5	105.10	5	0.00
6	0.00	6	0.00	6	106.15

Each of these withdrawal amounts is equivalent to any other, *considering the time involved*. This is indeed the *Time* Value of Money.

And here's how these same six variations look on cash-flow diagrams—
it's like playing "What-If?" with your withdrawal:

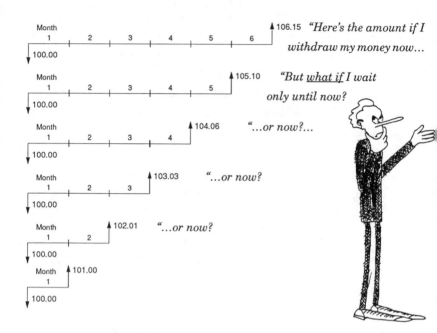

Month 1 2 3 4 5 6 ▲ 106.15 *"Here's the amount if I withdraw my money now...*

100.00

Month 1 2 3 4 5 ▲ 105.10 *"But <u>what if</u> I wait only until now?*

100.00

Month 1 2 3 4 ▲ 104.06 *"...or now?...*

100.00

Month 1 2 3 ▲ 103.03 *"...or now?*

100.00

Month 1 2 ▲ 102.01 *"...or now?*

100.00

Month 1 ▲ 101.00

100.00

The point is, each of these scenarios is entirely equivalent. You are
really just "sliding" one cash-flow (your proposed withdrawal) *across
time.* The earlier in time the cash-flow's position becomes, the smaller
its amount becomes. This process is called **discounting**, and it's one
of the fundamental tools offered by TVM analysis.

To repeat: You can slide any cash-flow across a cash-flow diagram (or
up/down the list of a T-bar) and retain complete accuracy as long as you
adjust it according to the prevailing interest rate. If the cash-flow is
sent forward in time, it increases in amount; if it goes back in time, it
decreases (and is said to be *discounted*).

So here's what you know about the Time Value of Money so far:

- You know the difference between the two types of interest. Rates are often *quoted* with *nominal* (simple-interest) annual values but *calculated* via *effective* (compound-interest) periodic values;

- You know that the HP 19BII's TVM uses Compound Interest;

- You know how to draw T-bars and/or cash-flow diagrams;

- You know that you can slide cash-flows along the timeline and keep the picture entirely accurate, as long as you adjust those cash-flows according to the prevailing interest rate.

What you *don't* know (yet) is how to draw a diagram for your HP 19BII. After all, it's supposed to do the calculating. How can the machine possibly "see" or "understand" a picture that you've drawn on paper?

Drawing the Picture for Your Calculator

Time to rev up your machine. From the MAIN Menu, choose these menu selections: **FIN** **TVM** .

You'll see something like this:

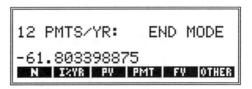

```
12 PMTS/YR:    END MODE
-61.803398875
 N   I%YR   PV   PMT   FV  OTHER
```

(Change the display setting back to FIX 2, also)

This is the TVM Menu. The first five selections here are the keys you use to draw a cash-flow diagram for your calculator:

N	Number of Defined Interest Periods (D.I.P.'s)
I%YR	Interest % rate per YeaR
PV	Present Value
PMT	PayMenT
FV	Future Value

You're soon going to be very adept with these keys.

The keys form a picture frame over a cash-flow scenario:

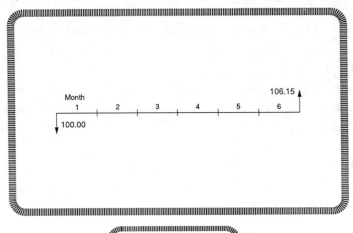

or:

m	$
0	(100.00)
1	0.00
2	0.00
3	0.00
4	0.00
5	0.00
6	106.15

The first thing to look for in this picture is a pattern of steady, regular cash-flows—one per D.I.P.—throughout the time line. If you have *uneven* or *irregular* cash-flows along the timeline (except for the ends), you can't use TVM (as shown above, the cash-flows may be $0.00, but they must be level and regular throughout).

The reason for this restriction is TVM's **PMT** (PayMenT) key. When describing a cash-flow scenario to your calculator, you must put this steady, level cash-flow amount into the PMT register on the TVM Menu.

And here's what the other four TVM keys mean to your picture frame:

N represents the Number of periods (D.I.P.'s) from one side of the picture frame to the other.

PV is the Present Value, which is the net cash-flow (if any) that occurs at the *left* side of the picture frame, *over and above* any PMT cash-flow that may *also* occur there.

FV is the Future Value, which is the net cash-flow (if any) that occurs at the *right* side of the picture frame *over and above* any PMT cash-flow that may *also* occur there.

So, for example, to describe the diagram under your picture frame on the previous page (your $100 bank account, assuming you wait until after month 6 to withdraw), here's what you would tell your HP 19Bₙ:

$$
\begin{array}{lcl}
\text{N} & = & 6 \\
\text{PMT} & = & 0.00 \\
\text{PV} & = & -100.00 \\
\text{FV} & = & 106.15 \\
\end{array}
$$

Notice that anytime you have a cash-flow paid *out* (i.e. from you to the other party), you show it on your diagram with a *downward* arrow, and you *tell it to your calculator with a minus sign* (remember the +/– key?). By opening your bank account, you *loan* the bank $100.00, so this is an *out*flow of cash (downward) on your diagram—and a *negative* 100.00 in your calculator.

But what about I%YR—the fifth key on your TVM Menu? The interest is the "glue" that holds the picture frame together.

All you really know is that the D.I.R. is 1% per month, right? But notice that **OTHER** item on your menu. Press it. Here's what you'll see:

```
12 PMTS/YR:    END MODE
-61.80
P/YR  BEG  END  AMRT
```

This is the second page of the TVM Menu. Here you can vary certain parameters that affect the outcome of TVM calculations.

For example, notice the message: **12 PMTS/YR:** Your HP 19Bɪɪ is telling you its current assumption about the "picture" you're "drawing" for it: 12 payments per year.

Is this correct for your bank account problem? You don't really make any PMT's (withdrawals or deposits), do you? No, but there *are* 12 PMT's per year, nevertheless—*because the number of payments per year is always the number of periods (D.I.P.'s) per year.* There's *always* one PMT per period—even if it's zero; that's what you mean by a PMT— that steady, level, once-per-period cash-flow.

Since the D.I.P. is one month, there are 12 payments per year—no need to change that message (which you could do by using the **P/YR** key).

Now (EXIT) to return to the TVM Menu.

OK, so there are 12 PMT's per year. How does this help you determine the interest rate in your "picture frame?"

It helps a lot: It means that you can *key in the I%YR as an A.P.R.* (recall the discussion on page 101). That is, I%YR is the annualized approximation you use to *conveniently specify* the interest rate. And, just like the bank* with its quoted, *nominal* A.P.R., the calculator knows that it's supposed to divide the I%YR by the number of PMT's per year to get the actual D.I.R. to do its compounding:

Therefore, saying that   A.P.R. ÷ D.I.P.'s/Year = D.I.R.

...is really saying that   I%YR ÷ PMTS/YR = D.I.R.

And in this problem, that's   12% ÷ 12 = 1%

Seem complicated? The point is, *all you need to key in* is the 12%—the I%YR. Then, as long as the machine knows the right number of PMTS/YR, it knows how to convert the annualized I%YR to the actual D.I.R.

---

*Just like a *U.S.* bank, that is. For a Canadian mortgage, you need to perform a quick conversion to arrive at the correct A.P.R. to match the HP 19Bɪɪ's U.S. assumptions. See the Appendix.

So now you know all five TVM variables in the picture of your bank account—the scenario where you withdraw after the sixth month:

<u>N</u>	<u>I%YR</u>	<u>PV</u>	<u>PMT</u>	<u>FV</u>
6	12.00	0.00	-100.00	106.15

And here's the completed picture frame around the scenario:

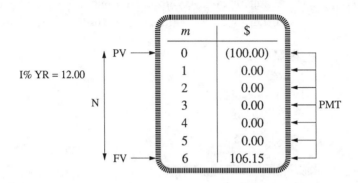

or:

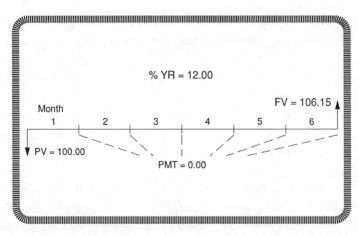

Of course, normally, you need the calculator to *compute* one of these five variables for you—after you tell it the values for the other four. But you can always test your calculator to see if it agrees with these values. Do that now: Give it any four of the five values and see if it comes up with the missing value—the missing piece of the "picture...."

Verify: Try solving for Future Value. That means you need to key in the other four TVM values. From the TVM Menu, press

⑥ ▊ **N**
① ② ▊ **I%YR**
① ⓪ ⓪ [+/−] ▊ **PV**
⓪ ▊ **PMT** ▊ **FV** .... Result: **FV=106.15** Right on!

Things to notice and remember:

1.   Remember that pressing a menu key can mean either to store or to calculate—depending upon what you did just previously.

2.   You could have keyed in the N, the I%YR, the PV, and the PMT *in any order*—just so you have them all in there when you ask for the FV. *You may solve for any of the five variables, but you must always specify the other four.* Never ignore a variable or assume that it's zero and therefore irrelevant!

3.   The machine obeyed its own sign convention: Since your PV was negative (meaning cash out of your pocket), it figured that FV must be the pay-off—when the cash comes back—there-

fore, positive. In fact, the machine *insists* that PV and FV be of opposite sign—to keep this idea of investment and return. If you give it a PV and FV of the same sign (when solving for PMT, for example), it beeps with a `NO SOLUTION` message, because you *must* have at least one investment and one return in any meaningful TVM problem.

4. **Most importantly**, now that you have all the parameters in the TVM registers, you can play "What-If" simply by changing the number of months you leave your money in there. For example, by pressing `1` `N` `FV` , you change the analysis to the case where you withdraw your money after 1 month. By pressing `2` `N` `FV` , you do the 2-month scenario, etc. You use the TVM keys to "slide" a cash-flow (your withdrawal) up and down the timeline—just as you did on paper (page 113).

So, what if you let your account grow for a full 12 months? How about 50 years (600 months)? The answers to each of these are merely variations on the same procedure. You're varying one parameter (N, the number of periods), preserving three others, and checking to see how this affects the fifth parameter (Future Value). And remember: as with all menus, you never need to re-key in any number once it's stored in a TVM Menu register. It's there to be used—or varied—over and over again.

A Typical Mortgage Problem

Now it's time to put TVM into practice with something more exciting than a bank account. After all, what's life without a good mortgage?

Like This One: You're buying a $120,000 property by paying down $20,000 and financing the rest on a 30-year mortgage with monthly payments. The quoted A.P.R. is 12.00%. What is the monthly payment?*

Solution: You can't solve this problem until you fill in some details that aren't specifically spelled out:

- Is the monthly payment at the beginning or at the end of the month?

- What is the D.I.P.?

- What is the D.I.R.?

- Why do you care about these things?

---

*If you already know how to solve this, go to page 128. Note: Laws for quoting mortgage rates in Canada differ slightly from the U.S. To use the HP 19Bii under Canadian rules, see the Appendix.

BEGIN or END?

Does it make any difference whether the payment is at the beginning or at the end of a month? After all, isn't the beginning of one month the same as the end of the previous one? Compare the two scenarios:

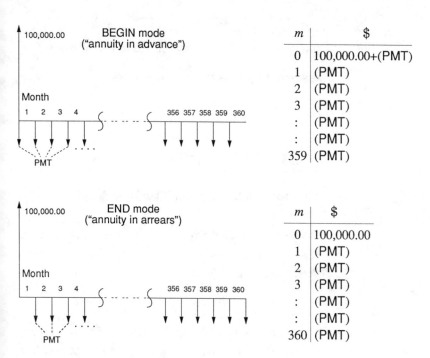

As you can see, in the first case, a payment is due at the beginning of the loan—right when you sign the papers. This reduces the balance sooner, so there is *less interest* to be paid on the borrowed money. With less interest to be paid, the PMT amount (which covers both principal and interest) will be less; indeed it does matter whether the payment is at the beginning or at the end of the month.

So what about your mortgage? Which is it—BEGIN or END?

In a real contract, it would have to be stated, of course, but for this problem, just assume the more common case—the END of the month. So, how do you tell your HP 19BII to assume this too?

Like This: From the TVM Menu, press **OTHER** and see this again:

```
┌─────────────────────────────────┐
│                                 │
│  12 PMTS/YR:    END MODE         │
│                                 │
│  P/YR  BEG  END  AMRT            │
└─────────────────────────────────┘
```

Notice the two keys, there, **BEG** and **END**.

Press them alternately and notice the change in the message in your display (but be sure to leave it in END MODE for this problem).

Don't forget to set this mode to match the specifications of the loan you're computing. And remember to check this for each new TVM problem; except when you first arrive at the TVM Menu, you can't usually tell which of these two modes your calculator is using.

Next detail to clear up:

What's the D.I.P.?

The problem says 12% A.P.R.—and it's compound interest, of course—but it doesn't say how *often* this interest compounds. Is it yearly? After all, A.P.R. does stand for <u>Annual</u> Percentage Rate.*

Well, yes and no: Yes—that's what A.P.R. means, but no—the compounding isn't yearly. It's monthly.

How do you know? Because the payments are specified as monthly, and unless told otherwise, you can assume that the payment period is the same as the compounding period (and vice versa).

Thus, the Defined Interest Period (D.I.P.)—the period over which interest *actually* compounds—is a month. And now you need to tell your HP 19Bıı this detail also....

Clue It In: From the second "page" of the TVM Menu (use **OTHER** to get there), press 1 2 **P/YR**.

(Your display probably already shows 12 PMTS/YR, but do this anyway, just for practice.)

---

*Remember that Canadian quoted rates must be converted to an equivalent U.S. A.P.R., which will be different than this 12%. For details, see the Appendix.

And so what's the D.I.R.? What's the monthly rate of interest that corresponds to an A.P.R. of 12.00%?

It's "12% divided by 12 months/year," or 1%/month (recall the discussions on pages 101 and 116). You may sleep better tonight knowing this, but you don't need to tell your calculator—it will *assume* it.*

> *The nominal A.P.R. used to compute a loan payment*
> *is exactly what I%YR means to the HP 19B$_{II}$.*

That is, to arrive at the actual interest rate to use in its calculations, a bank would take this *nominal* A.P.R. and divide it by the number of compounding periods in a year.

So whenever you see a nominal A.P.R. specified for the purposes of computing a payment or a balance, just make sure that your P/YR is set properly and then use that A.P.R. as your I%YR.*

---

*It's this assumption that forces Canadian lenders and borrowers to do a little interest conversion before supplying the HP 19B$_{II}$ with an "A.P.R." Again, see the Appendix for details.

The Typical Solution

Finally, you're ready to solve this mortgage problem. Here's the scenario in diagrams again. Notice how it takes your perspective—the borrower. The loan amount is shown as positive (you *receive* it), and each PMT amount is negative (you *pay* it).

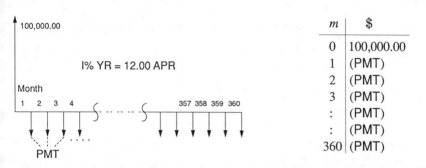

m	$
0	100,000.00
1	(PMT)
2	(PMT)
3	(PMT)
:	(PMT)
:	(PMT)
360	(PMT)

Simply by looking at the picture, you can read off the values you need for the TVM registers:

Read 'em Off: At the TVM Menu: ③⓪✕①②⑤ (ALG) *or*

                          ③⓪[INPUT]①②✕ (RPN) **N**

                          ①② **I%YR** ①⓪⓪⓪⓪⓪ **PV** ⓪ **FV**.

                   Then press **PMT** to calculate the payment.

                   <u>Answer</u>: PMT=-1,028.61

Note how the HP 19BII knows that this PMT must be negative (a cash *out*flow). It, too, obeys the sign convention.

Question: How did you know that FV (Future Value) was zero?

Answer: The problem didn't specifically *say* there's anything left to pay at the end of the 30 years, so you can safely assume there isn't. That is, the payments completely *amortize* (literally: "kill") the loan in 360 months.

If it were otherwise, the problem would have specified an amount then due in a lump-sum payment—called a *balloon* payment—at the end of the 360-month term.

So you know that FV is zero. *But even so, don't ignore it.* Zero is a number just like any other, and your calculator always uses four TVM numbers to solve for the fifth. If you had forgotten to specify your FV for this problem, your machine would *not* have *assumed* zero. It would have used the number it found in the FV register—no matter what that value was or when it was put in there.

Remember! A number in the continuous memory of the HP 19Bɪɪ is like a budget deficit: It won't melt back to zero just because you ignore it.

The Typical Mortgage Checklist

Review in your mind the checklist of all the little invisible steps you took to actually calculate the payment on that $100,000 mortgage.

1.   You got a verbal description of the loan.

2.   You decided on the *annuity* mode. In other words, do the payments come at the END of the month (also called "annuity in arrears") or at the BEGINning of the month (also called "annuity in advance")?

3.   You interpreted the terms of the loan in order to arrive at the proper D.I.P. and thus the D.I.R. You set the P/YR accordingly and observed that the A.P.R. given in the problem can be used directly as your I%YR.

4.   You drew the correct picture of the problem from your perspective as a borrower, thus establishing the directions of the cash-flows (up or down on the diagram, + or - in your calculator).

5.   You observed that since no mention was made of any balloon payment, the mortgage must be completely amortized after the 360th payment. So the Future Value (FV) was zero.

6.   You plugged in all known values: N = 360 months, I%YR = 12.00, PV = 100,000, FV = 0. Then you solved for PMT.

7.   You realized that most of the real problem is in defining it; the keystrokes are easy.

Variations on a Theme

So there you have it: a $1028.61 monthly mortgage payment, assuming that your payment comes due at the END of the month.

Question: *What if* it were at the BEGINning of the month? What would your payment amount be? From the comparison diagrams on page 121, can you tell whether it's more or less than the END mode payment?

Solution: Don't touch any of the values you now have in the five TVM registers. Just go to the OTHER Menu and change the annuity mode from END to BEGIN.

Now (EXIT) back to the TVM Menu, and solve for PMT. <u>Answer</u>: PMT=-1,018.43

About ten bucks a month *less*—not a whole lot, you might think. But over 360 months, that works out to be over $3,600 in interest saved.

And keep in mind how you're saving this interest—it's not from a lower rate: With BEGIN mode, you're still paying the same interest *rate*, but you save money, because you are borrowing for a slightly shorter *time*.

From the diagram on page 121, you can see that you're actually making each payment one month earlier than in the END mode scenario.

Well, in either BEGIN or END mode, that payment's a little steep for your budget. But you do want the house, so now you're going to use the "What-If?" abilities of your HP 19Bɪɪ to shop for better loan terms....

O Joy: Up jumps a lender who offers you all the same terms—360 months, payment at the end of each month, etc.—*and* it's only a 10.5% A.P.R.(!) What will your payment be?

Easy: Again, leave all your TVM parameters alone, except for the ones you're now going to vary:

Press **OTHER** **END** , to set the annuity mode. Then (EXIT). Now, the only thing you need to change is the I%YR, right?

Prove this by *recalling* each of the five TVM registers (menu variables are just registers you (STO) into and (RCL) from):

(RCL) **N**	N=360.00	Don't change this.
(RCL) **I%YR**	I%YR=12.00	Change this.
(RCL) **PV**	PV=100,000.00	Don't change this.
(RCL) **PMT**	PMT=-1,018.43	Recalculate this after changing I%YR.
(RCL) **FV**	FV=0.00	Don't change this.

OK, so change the interest rate: (1)(0)(·)(5)**I%YR** .... And recalculate **PMT** : PMT=-914.74

Well… that's better—about $100 lower on the payment. But what if it's still too high? Suppose your absolute limit for a principal-and-interest payment is $900.00. That's fine—but it will mean that at the end of the 360th month, you'll have a lump-sum balloon payment to make—to pay off the remaining balance. After all, you *know* there'll be a remaining balance—the machine just told you that it will take $914.74/month to *completely* amortize this loan in 360 months. If you pay even slightly less per month than that, there'll be some leftover to pay at the end.

So here's how the scenario looks:

m	$
0	100,000.00
1	(900.00)
2	(900.00)
3	(900.00)
:	(900.00)
:	(900.00)
360	(900.00)+(FV)

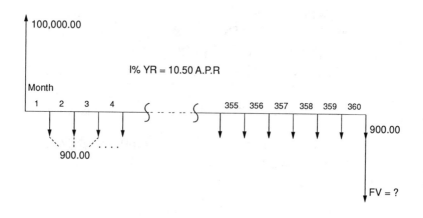

What you want to know is: *How much* is that final balloon payment?

Find Out: Again, three of the five TVM parameters are already correct (the term, N; the interest rate, I%YR; and the Present Value, PV). What you will do now is *specify* the payment (rather than calculate it), and then find the Future Value that would result.

Press ⑨⓪⓪[+/-] **PMT** (remember why this should be negative?), and solve for the remaining balance: **FV**

Answer: FV=-37,089.98

Remember the definition of Future Value! This represents the amount you would have to pay *over and above* your final (360th) payment—and it's negative, as it should be, to indicate who's paying it (yep—it's you). Since this is an END mode problem, your last PMT occurs at the same time as this balloon payment.

As you can see, then, you *could* lump those last two cash-flows together and write just one check if you wanted. Just be sure that you don't forget what each part means. Sometimes, the terms of a contract won't itemize this final combined payment, and if you try to confirm such terms by using that *combined* total as your Future Value ... well, that's not what your HP 19BII means by Future Value. You need to subtract out the amount of the final PMT.

Looking at the T-bar and cash-flow diagram on the previous page here, you can see how clearly and succinctly it shows all this information. *You'll never get confused if you get the picture right.*

So, here's what you've decided: You want to borrow $100,000.00 at 10.5% A.P.R., repaying it in 360 end-of-month installments of $900.00, plus a final balloon payment of $37,089.98 ...OK?...

No? *Now* what's wrong?

Oh—the balloon's a bit much, eh? It's amazing what "a little less" each month adds up to over thirty years, isn't it? All right, but you realize, of course, that a lower balloon will demand a slightly higher monthly payment; you'll be breaking your $900.00 monthly payment ceiling—by few more bucks a month now—to save thousands over thirty years.

How big a balloon payment could you stand—say, $20,000? Fine. Now check to see what PMT this will demand.

Not Much More: As usual, change only the values you need to (this is routine by now, no?): Press ⓄⓄⓄⓄⓄ ⊕⊖ **FV** to specify the balloon amount. Then press **PMT** to find the corresponding payment.

Answer: PMT=-906.79

See how powerful this "What-If?" ability is? And you can review your variables at any time with the [RCL] key ([RCL] **N**, [RCL] **I%YR**, etc.):

360	10.50	100,000.00	−906.79	−20,000.00
N	I% YR	PV	PMT	FV

So you can live with those terms. The only problem is, your lender with the 10.5% A.P.R. won't agree to anything less than full amortization— no balloons. In fact, he's encouraging you to consider even *higher* payments, to shorten the term of the loan down to 25, 20, even 15 years.

Of course, you already know you can't afford this much every month, but now that you've got a machine like the HP 19Bɪɪ, it doesn't hurt to play some more "What-If?" So, *what if* you had the same financing rate and amount, but only, say, a 20-year term? Your scenario would be:

m	$
0	100,000.00
1	(PMT)
2	(PMT)
3	(PMT)
:	(PMT)
:	(PMT)
240	(PMT)

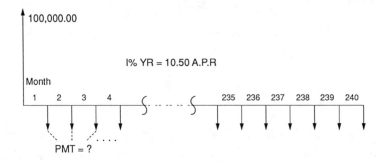

Play With the Term: Find the payment amount necessary to fully amortize this loan in 25, 20, and 15 years.

Solution: Change only what you need to, and leave the rest of the five parameters alone:

[2][5][×][1][2] (ALG) or [2][5][INPUT][1][2][×] (RPN) **N** (a shorter term). Then [0] **FV** (no balloon), and solve for **PMT** ....

Answer: PMT=-944.18

Not much more than the $914.74—for 5 years' fewer payments! What about 20 years?

[2][0][×][1][2] (ALG) or [2][0][INPUT][1][2][×] (RPN) **N**, then **PMT** ....

Answer: PMT=-998.38

Try 15 years:

[1][5][×][1][2] (ALG) or [1][5][INPUT][1][2][×] (RPN) **N**, then **PMT** ....

Answer: PMT=-1,105.40

Did you realize that for less than $200 more per month, you could cut your mortgage term in *half*? Not bad—if you could scrape together that extra $200/month. But you can't, so you shake the fellow's hand, thank him for his eye-opening offer, and head on down the road....

Feeling slightly discouraged at this point, you start to wonder if you can really afford this house after all....

Sigh: You had set your upper monthly payment limit at $900.00, but even that was pushing it. What you *really* wanted to get away with was about $800.00 or less—and no balloon.

Check: How much house could you finance at 10.5% A.P.R., with 30 years of $800 end-of-month payments?

Here's how the TVM registers should look right now (and you can verify these with the RCL key, remember?):

180	10.50	100,000.00	–1,105.40	0.00
N	I% YR	PV	PMT	FV

This time, you're varying the PMT and calculating the Present Value—the amount you can finance over 30 years:

$3$$0$$\times$$1$$2$ (ALG) *or* $3$$0$ INPUT $1$$2$$\times$ (RPN) ▮ **N** ▮
$8$$0$$0$ +/– **PMT**   (the payment you'd like to make)
▮ **PV** ▮   (find how much you could finance)
<u>Answer</u>: PV=87,456.61

So if you could come up with about $22,500 for a down-payment on that $110,000 house, you'd have an $800.00 monthly payment. But you've only got $10,000 for a down-payment, and you *do* want the house, so stick to your $900 limit (with a $20,000 balloon) and keep looking....

The next bank down the road seems to have a better deal for you. Here's a lender who will loan you $100,000 in exchange for $906.79 end-of-month payments for 360 months. Period.

Same payments—but no $20,000 balloon—what a deal!

"Uh... what's the catch?"

This: There's a *loan fee* (also known as "points") due and payable at the moment you sign the papers. This fee is 2% of the amount financed, but it's not an early installment on the loan; you still have to pay 360 full payments of $906.79 each.

Is this really a better deal than the $20,000 balloon? Better find out. Start with the T-bar and diagram:

m	$
0	100,000.00+(2,000.00)
1	(906.79)
2	(906.79)
:	(906.79)
360	(906.79)

Still, it's hard to tell which is the better deal for you. How can you use your TVM calculations to help?

Think about it: On page 132, you *know* you're paying 10.5% A.P.R.—
that's what you specified to calculate your PMT. But this lender here
just pulled a payment amount out of the air. What's the interest rate
he was using to do this?

Hmm... Let your HP 19Bɪɪ tell you. Here are the current contents
of the TVM registers:

360	10.50	87,456.61	–800.00	0.00
N	I% YR	PV	PMT	FV

You need to change only PV and PMT. First, press ⑨⑧⓪⓪⓪
PV. Since you net together all simultaneous cash-flows,
what with the $2000 fee (2% of $100,000), you're *not* getting
a $100,000 loan. It's a $98,000 loan—but you're still paying
$906.79 a month for 30 years.

So press ⑨⓪⑥·⑦⑨+/– **PMT** then **I%YR** to find the *real*
A.P.R.... <u>Answer:</u> I%YR=10.64

Aha! That loan fee effectively raised the rate *above* 10.5%
A.P.R. you're looking for—not so good!

By using just fundamental TVM skills and your HP 19Bɪɪ's "What-If?"
ability, you saved yourself from an expensive mistake (and the calculator probably paid for itself several times over)!

Interest _CONVersions_

More confident now, you continue your search for the elusive Perfect Mortgage.... Finally, you find a bank that agrees to your payments, balloon, and a 10.35% rate(!)—but this is a rate that compounds _daily_.

That calls for a little thought.... An _effective_ yield is higher than a _nominal_ (quoted) rate, since interest compounds. For example, your $100 bank account yields you $112.68 after one year—because the 12% quoted A.P.R. is actually compounded at 1% per month for 12 months.

But when competing for borrowers, a lender wants to put his rates in the best possible light. So, if he's allowed to quote a 10.35% nominal rate alongside its higher effective yield, he'll probably want to emphasize the nominal rate—the lower number is simply more attractive to the loan shopper.

The point is, the more often you compound, the bigger this difference becomes—between the nominal rate and the effective yield. And you can prove this.

Prove It: Use the HP 19Bπ to find the *effective* yield on a nominal annual rate of 10.35%, compounded:

(i) annually; (ii) semi-annually; (iii) quarterly;
(iv) monthly; (v) semi-monthly; (vi) weekly; (vii) daily

Like So: [EXIT] from the TVM Menu and notice the **ICONV** selection. This is a side-calculations menu for converting between interest rates. So press **ICONV** ... Then, since you want *periodic* interest conversions (converting from one period to another), press **PER**. Here's what you'll see:

```
EFF%=NOM% COMPOUNDED
P TIMES PER YEAR
10.64
NOM%|EFF%|  P
```

Just like any other "What-If?" menu, you key in any two variables and solve for the third. Here you know the NOMinal rate (10.35%) and you have some values to try for P (the number of Periods to be compounded) to see what EFFective yields they produce:

[1][0][·][3][5] **NOM%** [1] **P** **EFF%** .... EFF%=10.35
10.35% compounded once a year is just 10.35%.
But now try [2] **P** **EFF%** .... EFF%=10.62
That's the effective yield for *semi-annual* compounding.
And [4] **P** **EFF%** .... EFF%=10.76 (quarterly)
Well, you get the idea. Try the rest of the compounding periods (P = 12, 24, 52, and 365) on your own.

As you'll see, the effective rate for 10.35% compounded daily is **10.90**.

"This lender is charging me 10.90% ??? That's way too high!"

Not so fast. That's the *effective* rate. You're trying to compare that to a 10.5% *nominal* rate—like comparing apples and oranges. Besides, it's a nominal rate that the HP 19Bɪɪ needs for its I%YR, since it then converts this to a D.I.R. according to its assumptions.

So, what nominal rate—compounded monthly—*is* equivalent to 10.35% compounded daily? Use the ICONV Menu to find out....

Do It: At the (periodic) interest conversion Menu: `1` `0` `·` `3` `5` **NOM%**
`3` `6` `5` **P** **EFF%** ....   EFF%=10.90
You've already done this much.

Now just `1` `2` **P** **NOM%** ....   NOM%=10.39

See? You can use this menu to work in either direction—from nominal to effective or vice versa.

That's the A.P.R. this bank is really quoting you. It's higher than it looked—but it's still less than the A.P.R. you were hoping for! And that means you'll actually have a slightly *smaller* payment or balloon than you were willing to accept.

Go for the smaller payment....

Choose: Leaving the interest conversion (10.39) right where it is, go back into the TVM Menu ($\boxed{\text{EXIT}}$$\boxed{\text{EXIT}}$ $\boxed{\text{TVM}}$). Then, once you're there, the first thing you do is press $\boxed{\text{STO}}$ $\boxed{\text{I\%YR}}$ (don't just press $\boxed{\text{I\%YR}}$, because that would be asking the calculator to *calculate* I%YR, which is not what you want).

Now you're ready to figure your payment:

N=360.00   (don't touch it)

I%YR=10.39   (you just stored this—don't touch it)

PV=100,000.00   (you'll probably need to key this in)

FV=-20,000.00   (key this in, too)

Solve for $\boxed{\text{PMT}}$:   PMT=-898.64

That's less than your $906.79 for the monthly compounding case, which makes sense: The equivalent A.P.R. here is 10.39, rather than 10.5.

At last—a mortgage with a $20,000.00 balloon <u>and</u> payments of less than $900! All your shopping around and "What-Iffing" with your HP 19Bɪɪ has finally paid off. Congratulations (take a bow).

Interest CONVersion Review

Here's a summary of how to convert an interest rate with differing compound and payment periods, using the ICONV Menu. Remember that the idea is to find the rate to use in TVM (with TVM's assumptions) that produces the same *effective* result as the quoted rate:

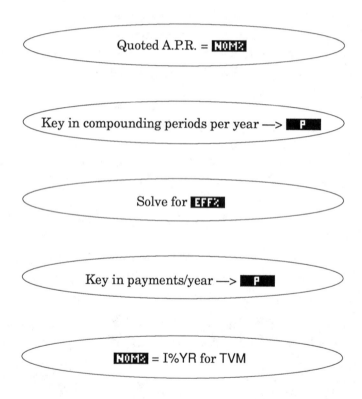

Quoted A.P.R. = **NOM%**

Key in compounding periods per year —> **P**

Solve for **EFF%**

Key in payments/year —> **P**

NOM% = I%YR for TVM

And keep in mind that this conversion can go in either direction.

One more conversion example—just to be sure you've got it....

Example: You're making monthly payments on a $88,500 loan for
25 years. The rate is 12.75%, compounded *daily*. What's
the equivalent I%YR you would use in TVM?

Solution: At the ICONV Menu, convert the daily-compounding
rate to an equivalent monthly-compounding rate:

1️⃣2️⃣•7️⃣5️⃣ **NOM%**
3️⃣6️⃣5️⃣ **P**
EFF%.... (EFF%=13.60)
1️⃣2️⃣ **P**
NOM%.... <u>Answer:</u> NOM%=12.82

Notice that each step here matches the step on the opposite page—no
magic, no mystery.

By now, you should know how to handle these types of problems:

- A simple, fully-amortized loan with annuity either in arrears (END) or in advance (BEGIN);

- A loan with a balloon payment;

- A loan with prepaid fees (also called "prepaid finance charges" or "points up front");

- Conversion of an interest rate that compounds over a different period of time than the payment period;

If those are the typical kinds of problems you face each day, then you might wish to skip now to the quiz (on page 160).

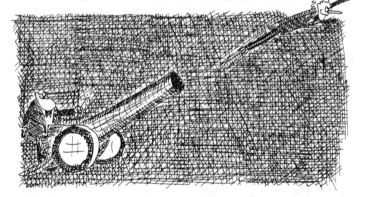

Or, if you want to explore some other kinds of TVM before you try the quiz, then just continue on right here....

AMoRTization Schedules

The most common questions you'll want to answer after you know the terms of a mortgage are:

"How much interest and principal am I paying every year? And what's my remaining balance?"

Well, the HP 19BII has an additional feature on the TVM Menu to help you answer these very questions.

Try This: From the TVM Menu, select **OTHER**. Notice an item here that you haven't used yet: Press **AMRT**, and see this:

```
KEY IN #PAYMENTS TO
AMORTIZE; PRESS {#P}
┌────┬─────┬──────┬─────┬──────┬───────┐
│ #P │ INT │ PRIN │ BAL │ NEXT │ TABLE │
└────┴─────┴──────┴─────┴──────┴───────┘
```

An AMoRTization schedule is an itemized computation of the amounts of principal and interest ("P and I") paid over any given number of periods within the term of a mortgage. You'll want to know at least the amount of interest you've paid each year, because it's usually tax-deductible.

The AMRT Menu is a set of side calculations—much like the ICONV Menu—but AMRT has an added advantage: *It uses the values directly from your TVM registers;* that's why it's located on the TVM Menu.

To get a feel for AMRT, look at your original house loan again: It was a 30-year, fully-amortized mortgage for $100,000 at 10.5% A.P.R., with monthly payments in arrears, and a balloon of $20,000 at the end (this was before you found that attractive 10.35% loan).

Try This: Use the AMRT Menu to find the principal and interest you would pay in each of the first three years—and the remaining balance still due after the third year.

Solution: First, fill in the usual TVM parameters:

(EXIT)(EXIT) to return to the TVM Menu, then
(3)(6)(0) **N**
(1)(0)(·)(5) **I%YR**
(1)(0)(0)(0)(0)(0) **PV**
(2)(0)(0)(0)(0)(+/−) **FV**
OTHER(1)(2) **P/YR** **END** (EXIT)
PMT ....   <u>Result</u>: PMT=-906.79

This payment ought to look familiar. It was what you had settled on as "acceptable," with a $20,000 balloon.

Now go to the AMRT Menu, by pressing **OTHER** **AMRT**. Then just follow the displayed directions:

```
KEY IN #PAYMENTS TO
AMORTIZE; PRESS (#P)
```

Since you want to look at 12 payments (one year) at a time, just press ⌈1⌉⌈2⌉ **#P** ....

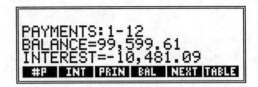

There are the remaining balance and the total interest paid in payments 1-12 (the first 12 months of the loan)! To see the principal paid in this same period, just press **PRIN** .... PRINCIPAL=-400.39

Notice that your payments show as negative numbers here—because AMRT follows the same sign conventions as the rest of the TVM Menu. That makes sense, right?

But here's the best part: To amortize the NEXT set of 12 payments, just press **NEXT** .... Not bad, eh?

You can go all the way through the life of the loan this way. To start over from the beginning of the loan, just ⌈EXIT⌉ from the AMRT Menu, then re-enter it again with the **AMRT** key.

Play around with the AMRT Menu items on your own a little bit. Notice especially the selection called **TABLE**. It lets you *print* any portion of the amortization schedule, if you have a printer.

One other note about AMRT: As you know, your HP 19BII uses 12 digits in its arithmetic, including the TVM calculations. *But AMRT is a rare exception to this rule.*

Look: Recall the current value in the PMT register (from TVM, press
[RCL] **PMT**). You'll see this: PMT=-906.79

But now SHOW all of its digits (press ■[SHOW]).... That's what the payment *really* works out to be (to nine decimal places, at least): PMT=-906.791435594

But nobody writes a check for that much, right? So even though this is the amount you would need to pay every month to *exactly* amortize that 30-year mortgage, you won't be paying that. To be accurate, you need to use the true amount to the nearest penny (here it would be rounded down: 906.790000000).

So key it in: [9][0][6][·][7][9][+/−] **PMT** . And now *recalculate* the **FV** ....

You get FV=-20,003.61 What does this mean?

This: Since you had to round your payment down slightly (by a fraction of a penny), you've technically (mathematically) *underpaid* your loan by $3.61. Therefore, your $20,000 balloon payment at the end of the loan is *increased* slightly.

AMRT uses the TVM values, too, but it doesn't use unrealistic "penny fragments" that those TVM registers may hold. Except for the I%YR variable (which is always used to 12 digits), the AMRT Menu uses TVM values only up to the *displayed* number of digits.

In other words, if you have your display set to FIX 2 digits (for dollars and cents), the AMRT calculations will automatically round its own copies of PV and PMT in the same way—so that you always end up with a realistic and verifiable amortization schedule.

Prove It: Go back and run the AMRT example on pages 146-147 again—but with a DISP ALL setting.... Then try it with a FIX 4 setting.... See how the results differ slightly?

So although you'll normally keep a FIX 2 setting, it's instructive to see and understand this difference—to avoid any unnecessary misunderstandings with the bank.

Other Side Calculations

The TVM Menu is designed to handle one basic kind of interest-bearing situation—an amortized installment loan (such as a mortgage). The TVM Menu can handle *only* regular installments over regular periods, with interest compounding each period. So while it's very useful for analyzing investments with cash-flow diagrams, sometimes you need to do other, preliminary calculations simply to construct those diagrams. That's where the "side calculations" menus come in handy.

You've already seen how to use one of these side calculations menus—the ICONV Menu—when you need to determine a proper I%YR to use in the TVM Menu. But there are a couple other such side calculations menus that you ought to look at now....

Do This: Go to the MAIN Menu (press ▓MAIN▓). Press ▐FIN▌....
There, alongside the TVM selection you've come to know and love, you'll see several other choices:

```
┌─────────────────────────────────────┐
│ SELECT A MENU                        │
│                                      │
│                                      │
│ ▐TVM▌▐ICONV▌▐CFLO▌▐BOND▌▐DEPRC▌      │
└─────────────────────────────────────┘
```

You've already seen the ICONV Menu. And CFLO is another major cash-flow diagram analysis tool (like TVM)—the subject of the next chapter. But the two other choices are indeed side calculations menus: ▐BOND▌ and ▐DEPRC▌.

Bonds

A bond is just another kind of loan, but it has different conventions than those of the TVM Menu. A bond is simply a piece of paper that acknowledges an interest-bearing debt from the *issuer* of the bond (the borrower) to the *holder* (the lender). The issuer usually makes *interest-only* payments once or twice a year. The bond specifies the amount of this interest (the *coupon rate*), when it is paid (the *coupon dates*), and when the principal amount is to be repaid (the *maturity date*):

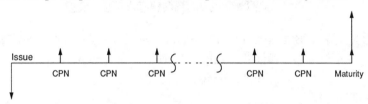

Furthermore, bonds are generally designed to be *negotiable*. That is, they may be freely traded at any time* and for any price.* Thereafter the issuer must pay the interest (and the principal, at maturity) to the *new* holder. This makes for some complications when calculating your yield or the price you should pay, because the dates upon which you buy or sell a bond may not coincide with its coupon dates or maturity date:

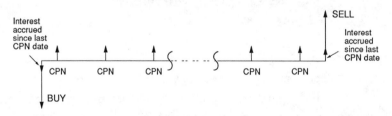

This is why you can't put a bond scenario on a TVM-compatible cash-flow diagram—because the time periods may be *irregular*.

*within all applicable laws and the terms of the bond's original issuance, of course.

Try One: On July 3, 1990, you buy a municipal bond that matures on August 30, 1994 for $100. The bond's coupon rate is 6.75%, with semi-annual payments, calculated on a 30/360-day basis (30 days/month and 360 days/year). What is your yield to maturity if you paid a price of $96.50?

Solution: Press the BOND selection and see this menu:

TYPE SETT MAT CPN% CALL MORE

Specify the TYPE of bond you have: Press TYPE SEMI and 360 to select the coupon payment frequency and the calendar basis, respectively.

Now EXIT and key in the SETTlement date (the date when you buy the bond): 7 • 0 3 1 9 9 0 SETT...
...and the MATurity date: 8 • 3 0 1 9 9 4 MAT...
...and the CouPoN percentage rate: 6 • 7 5 CPN%...
...and the CALL (maturity) value: 1 0 0 CALL....

Now MORE, 9 6 • 5 PRICE YLD%....
Answer: YLD%=7.75

Easy, no? There's not a lot more to say about calculating with bonds. Just key in all the particulars and grind out the answers. You'll get some more hands-on practice in the upcoming quiz, but here are some reminders and things to consider about the BOND Menu:

- No matter whether the coupon is paid annually or semi-annually, the rate you key in is the *annual* coupon rate.

- Key in dates according to the current date format. This example assumed that your HP 19Bɪɪ was in MM.DDYYYY date mode.*

- Sometimes a bond may have one or more optional "pay-off" dates—earlier than the maturity date. This is a *call date,* and the HP 19Bɪɪ allows for it (just key it in as the MATurity date) *as long as it coincides with a coupon date* (a date when interest is paid).

- A call value may be different from $100, but the maturity value must be $100, the conventional basis for face value. Thus, all calculated values represent *percentages of the face value* of your bond. The "pay-off" value—whether it's the face value or some other call value—must always go into the CALL register. However, for convenience, the calculator *automatically* puts 100.00 into the CALL register whenever you press ▓[CLEAR DATA].

- Unlike some of the other "What-If?" menus you've seen, most of the values on the BOND Menu are for input only; you can't solve for them. Only PRICE or YLD% may be your unknown—and you must key in one to get the other.

- When you buy a bond on any date other than a coupon date, in addition to the price, the seller is also due the as-yet-unpaid interest accrued since the last coupon date. So after calculating either the price or yield (whichever is your unknown), just press **ACCRU**. Result (for this example): ACCRU=2.31

---

*You can change this format: Press ▓**MAIN**TIME**SET**M/D**, then ▓**MAIN**FIN**BOND** to return to the BOND Menu. Date formats are covered in Chapter 8.

Depreciation

The final topic of this chapter is another "side-calculation" menu you may need when constructing a TVM diagram.

Usually, when you think of the Time Value of Money, it's an investment or account that gains value over time. But depreciation occurs when an asset _loses_ value over time. It starts at its cost or other BASIS value, then, over its useful LIFE, depreciates to its SALVage value. The total value lost over the LIFEtime is called the _total depreciable value._

Example: You're buying a piece of equipment for $40,000. You estimate it to have a useful life of 5 years and a salvage value of $10,000. What amounts should you recognize as depreciation in each of those five years?

Answer: First of all, identify the BASIS value. Usually, this is the cost: $40,000. You know the SALVage value is $10,000, and so the total depreciable value—the difference—is $30,000. This is the total capital value you expect the asset to _lose_ over its 5-year LIFE.

Now, that doesn't answer the main question: What fraction (percentage) of the depreciable value should you depreciate each year—for tax and accounting purposes—for this asset? There are several standard methods to compute this—different methods for different assets. The HP 19BII gives you four such methods. Consider each, as it would treat your $40,000 asset:

SL: **Straight Line.** This is the easiest method to compute (and to understand). It simply *prorates* the total depreciable value, reducing it evenly over the LIFE of the asset. That is, the same percentage of the original value is taken each year. Your asset has a total depreciable value is $30,000, so you simply depreciate $6,000/year for each of the 5 years of its useful life.

Do It: From the MAIN Menu, press **FIN** **DEPRC**.... This is the "side-calculations" DEPReCiation Menu.

First, key in the values you know: 4 0 0 0 0 **BASIS** 1 0 0 0 0 **SALV** 5 **LIFE**. Then press **MORE** to see the menu's next page.

Now just key in each year you're interested in and ask for the SL amount of depreciation for that year:

1 **YR#** **SL**	Result:	SL=6,000.00
2 **YR#** **SL**	Result:	SL=6,000.00
3 **YR#** **SL**	Result:	SL=6,000.00
4 **YR#** **SL**	Result:	SL=6,000.00
5 **YR#** **SL**	Result:	SL=6,000.00
6 **YR#** **SL**	Result:	SL=0.00

As you can see, Straight-Line depreciation is just that—steady and uniform. And notice that it's smart enough to catch your "Year 6" error. The HP 19Bii won't let you take depreciation beyond the asset's SALVage value—provided that you don't change depreciation methods in midstream.

DB: **Declining Balance.** This method reduces the *total remaining* value of the asset by the same *fraction* each year. That fraction is expressed as a percentage of the fraction necessary for a *Straight-Line* depreciation to *zero* (no salvage value).

For example, with your five-year asset, a straight-line depreciation to zero Salvage Value would require that you depreciate 20% (of the original value) per year. A Declining Balance factor of, say, "150%" would therefore depreciate 30% (that's 1.5 times—or 150%—as fast as the SL 20%) per year.

But *unlike SL,* DB is depreciating this 30% off of the *Remaining* Depreciable Value. As that value declines, so does the amount of depreciation in each successive year. Here are the two methods, side by side:

	Straight Line (20% of *total BASIS value* per year)		**Declining Balance** (30% of *total remaining value* per year)	
Year	$ deprec.	Remaining Value	$ deprec.	Remaining Value
0	--	$40,000	--	$40,000
1	$8,000	32,000	$12,000	28,000
2	8,000	24,000	8,400	19,600
3	8,000	16,000	5,880	13,720
.				
.				
.				

And so on.

Do It: From the previous example, you're already within the DEPRC Menu, with your known values already in the BASIS, SALV and LIFE registers.

So press **MORE**, if necessary, and key in the Declining Balance FACTor, as a percentage: (1)(5)(0) **FACT:**. This is how fast the declining balance rate begins its depreciations, compared to a Straight-Line/no-salvage pace. Then, as usual, key in each year and ask for the amount of depreciation for that year:

(1) **YR#** **DB**   Result: RDV=18,000.00
                              DB=12,000.00

(2) **YR#** **DB**   Result: RDV=9,600.00
                              DB=8,400.00

(3) **YR#** **DB**   Result: RDV=3,720.00
                              DB=5,880.00

(4) **YR#** **DB**   Result: RDV=0.00
                              DB=3,720.00

(5) **YR#** **DB**   Result: RDV=0.00
                              DB=0.00

Notice that the calculator forces the Remaining Depreciable Value (RDV) to finish at the SALVage value:

If the depreciation rate is too fast, there may be one or more years at the end in which the depreciation is *zero*—as in year 5 here—since all RDV has already been used. Or, if the rate is too slow, then there may be a big chunk of depreciable value left for the final year—and it will *all* be taken that year.

SOYD: Sum Of the Years' Digits. This method—like the DB method—weights the depreciation toward the beginning. But it does so by depreciating a *decreasing* percentage of the total *depreciable* value (whereas DB takes a *constant* percentage of the total *remaining* value). The pattern of SOYD's percentage decreases is determined by the Sum Of the Years' Digits. For example, your $40,000 asset has a total depreciable value of $30,000 and a 5-year LIFE. And the *sum* of those five years' *digits* is 1+2+3+4+5 = 15. *So:*

Year	fraction depreciated	$ amount of deprec.
1	5/15	$10,000
2	4/15	8,000
3	3/15	6,000
4	2/15	4,000
5	1/15	2,000
Total	15/15	$30,000

Go: Using the existing asset data (BASIS, LIFE and SALVage), key in each year and ask for the depreciation for that year:

1 **YR#** **SOYD**	Result: RDV=20,000.00
	SOYD=10,000.00
2 **YR#** **SOYD**	Result: RDV=12,000.00
	SOYD=8,000.00
3 **YR#** **SOYD**	Result: RDV=6,000.00
	SOYD=6,000.00
4 **YR#** **SOYD**	Result: RDV=2,000.00
	SOYD=4,000.00
5 **YR#** **SOYD**	Result: RDV=0.00
	SOYD=2,000.00

ACRS: Accelerated Cost Recovery System. This method isn't really much of a calculation. ACRS simply *assigns* percentages of the total depreciable value to be taken in each year in the asset's LIFE. These percentages don't necessarily follow a mathematical formula, but they must add up to 100% of the *BASIS* value over the asset's LIFE (*ACRS ignores the SALVage value*). Here's an example of how ACRS depreciation percentages and amounts might look for your 5-year asset:

Year	percentage depreciated	$ amount of deprec.
1	25	$10,000
2	15	6,000
3	20	8,000
4	20	8,000
5	20	8,000
Total	100	$40,000

So: Using the existing asset data (the BASIS value) do this:

②⑤ **ACRS%** **ACRS**	Result: ACRS=10,000.00
①⑤ **ACRS%** **ACRS**	Result: ACRS=6,000.00
②⓪ **ACRS%** **ACRS**	Result: ACRS=8,000.00
②⓪ **ACRS%** **ACRS**	Result: ACRS=8,000.00
②⓪ **ACRS%** **ACRS**	Result: ACRS=8,000.00

As you can see, these ACRS calculations are little more than simple percentage calculations—where *you* key in the percentages. So beware: The HP 19BⅡ doesn't check these percentages to see if they add up to 100—nor does it check to see if the BASIS or LIFE has been exceeded.

TVM Quiz

It's time to put it all together. On the following pages are quiz problems that combine and reinforce the various TVM concepts and tools you've studied in this chapter.

Don't blur over these problems! This is where you'll do most of your real learning. You don't know how much you really understand until you do some problems where the answers aren't given right away.*

The problems are grouped according to subject matter, so that you can concentrate on one area, if that's your main concern. Most problems will require you to build a cash-flow diagram or T-bar—and you may need to do "side-calculations" to get those values.

You will learn far more if you try them all, rather than concentrating on your immediate interest, because all the problems give you lots of practice with menus, problem-solving, and—in most cases—with the TVM Menu and cash-flow diagrams. Whatever else you do, be sure to use a diagram or a T-bar for any situation where you need any help in visualizing the timing of the cash-flows!

Enjoy these—and take all the time you need to understand them *well*. There's nobody looking over your shoulder here.

_____

* The answers *are* given here—they're just collected all together, following the problems.

TVM Review

1. If Benjamin Franklin saved (and thus earned) one penny, investing it on January 1, 1750, in a tax-free account earning 5% per year (compounded annually), what would that account balance be on January 1, 2000? When would it reach $1,000? What if the interest compounds *daily*?

2. How much will you need to invest every month for 5 years, in a fund that typically earns 12% (compounded monthly), to accumulate a 15% down payment on a $130,000 home? What if home prices are rising at 6% per year in the meantime?

3. If your money can earn 10% interest (compounded daily) in a liquid account, and you win a $1 million lottery jackpot, would you rather receive it tax-free but paid out at $50,000/year over 20 years, or in a taxable lump-sum now? Your tax bracket is 33%.

4. A fast-food hamburger that went for $0.89 twenty years ago now costs $2.59. Using this as a cost-of-living index, what has been the average annual inflation rate over those twenty years?

5. How long does it take to pay down a 30-year, $100,000 mortgage at 10%, (monthly payments in arrears) to 75% of the original balance? How about 50% of the balance? 25%?

6. What is the balance after 48 end-of-month payments of $188 on a loan of $7,500 at 12.5%, compounded monthly? What if the first payment is due three months from the date of the loan?

7. If you can earn 6.5% in an account (compounded daily), and you are selling a truck for $15,000, would you accept $500 down and a note for $15,000 more—due in 1 year?

8. How long would it take to double your money in each of these accounts?

    a. 7.5%, compounded monthly;

    b. 7.5% compounded daily;

    c. 5% compounded annually;

    d. 10% compounded annually;

    e. 15% compounded annually;

What yearly-compounded rate doubles your money in 10 years?

9. If, on your 25th birthday (happy birthday), you begin to pay $2000 per year for 7 years into a (tax-deferred) IRA yielding a 10% A.P.R., and then you *stop* paying into that account for 28 subsequent years, how does the resulting year-end balance compare with a similar account that you open on your 32nd birthday, into which you pay $2000 for *every year* up through your 60th year?

10. As a lessor, what should you pay for a 5-year office lease with monthly rent (due in advance) of $900? Your discount rate is 8%. Then, for a 12% yield, what should you sell the lease for in 3 years?

11. A mortgage was written at 9.5% A.P.R. It amortizes totally in 30 years of monthly payments (in arrears). If the payment amount is $924.94, what was the loan amount?

12. If the loan from the previous problem instead had $850 payments—and annuity in advance—what would the remaining balance be after the 360th month? After the 120th month?

13. Compare these interest rates: A $20,000 car lease with monthly payments of $440 (in advance) and a buyout of $5000 in five years; or a credit card charging 16.5% A.P.R., compounded daily.

14. A finance company charges 2 points for a $100,000 loan at 12% A.P.R., compounded daily (on a 360-day year), with quarterly payments (in arrears) that will amortize the loan in 15 years.

    a. What is the payment amount?

    b. What is the remaining balance after 10 years?

    c. If the balance is actually paid in a balloon payment at that 10-year point, what is the A.P.R. earned by the finance company? Would that A.P.R. be different if the loan is carried to term (15 years)? Why?

Residential Real Estate

15. You're buying a $103,000 home, putting 10% down and financing the balance at 11% A.P.R., with monthly payments in arrears. Your maximum payment (principal and interest) is $900.

    a. Can you totally amortize this loan in 20 years?

    b. If you were to make the payment necessary to amortize the loan in 20 years, how much interest would you save, compared to a 30-year amortization?

16. How long will it take to pay off a 30-year, $100,000 mortgage at 10%, if you make 26 payments/year, each *half* the normal monthly payment? What is this payment amount? Calculate the amortization schedule for each of the first two years.

17. A prospective home-buyer wants to accelerate the pay-down of her mortgage by adding an extra $20 of payment toward principal in each monthly installment. The $85,000, 9.5% mortgage would normally amortize in 30 years of monthly payments (in arrears), how much sooner will the borrower pay this off? Calculate the amortization schedule for each of the first two years.

18. What is the amount of the first payment on a 30-year, $72,000 loan at 12% (monthly payments, in arrears), with constant payments to principal? How much is the last payment?

19. The rates for a 30-year, $90,000 Adjustable Rate Mortgage (ARM) are:

Year 1: 9.0%   Year 2: 9.5%   Year 3: 10.0%

Year 4: 10.5%   Year 5: 11.0%

Find the payments and year-end balances for the first five years.

20. A couple is buying a $90,000 home. Their gross monthly income is $3500. They pay $200 per month toward other long-term debt. Insurance on the home will be about $30/month; taxes are $2,250 annually. With a 30-year mortgage at a fixed rate of 10%, for what amount of financing could they qualify under each of the following four sets of qualifying rules?* Calculate the corresponding principal-and-interest payments, also.

(*Note:* Applicable qualifying rules may now be different):

<u>Conventional</u>:   *Maximum* PITI (Principal, Interest, Taxes and Insurance, plus any mortgage insurance/association dues) is the *lesser* of

- 28% of Gross Income ($GI)   *or*
- 36% of $GI, less long-term debt pmt. ($LTD).

Use 25% of $GI and 33% of $GI, respectively, if the down-payment is less than 10%.

<u>FNMA</u>:   Maximum PITI is 28% of $GI.

<u>GNMA</u>:   Maximum PITI is 36% of $GI, less $LTD.

<u>FHA</u>:   Maximum PITI is the *lesser* of

- 29% of Gross Income ($GI)   *or*
- 41% of $GI, less long-term debt pmt. ($LTD).

*Assume no mortgage insurance or other association dues in this example.

Commercial Investment

21. For a 10% yield-to-maturity, what price (and accrued interest) can you pay on 7/28/90 for a 7% bond (semiannual coupons, actual calendar basis) maturing on 9/9/99? Then what's your yield-to-call if the bond is callable at 88.125 on 3/9/95?

22. At the beginning of a tax year, you buy a small office building with improvements valued at $75,000, a $10,000 computer, and then landscape the property with $5000 in shrubs. Estimated salvage values for these new assets: $15,000, $500 and $0, respectively. What depreciation can you take for each in tax years 3 and 4?:

Property examples	Class	Allowed Depr. Method
vehicles, office/lab equip.	5 years	200% DB or SL
roads, shrubbery,	15 years	150% DB or SL
nonresidential real prop.	31.5 years	SL

23. Use the Band of Investment method (weighting current market expectations for mortgage and equity funds by the Loan-to-Value ratio on a property) to compute the NOI, cap rate and value of this property:

	Office	Warehouse
Rent ($/ft²/year)	7.80	4.07
Floor area (ft²)	2,277	2,005
Vacancy rate (%)	0.5	1.0

Taxes: $3,647   Mngmt: $3,060   Maint.: $2,318

Insurance: $773   Loan-to-Value: 70%

Mortgage rate: 12.75%   Equity return rate: 14%

24. An investor is considering the purchase of a small office building appraised at $750,000, of which 70% is improved.

The proposal:

    $250,000 cash down
    First mortgage: $350,000 at 10.5% for 20 years (1.5 points)
    Second mortgage: $150,000 at 12% for 10 years (2 points)
    Costs of closing and acquisition: $2,000

    Maximum gross rent potential: $125,000/yr
    Projected vacancy/loss rate: 6%
    Insurance: $3,000/yr
    Maintenance and management: $12,000/yr

    Property tax rate: 2.5%
    Rent, expenses and prop. values to follow inflation: 5%/yr.

In five years, the investor expects to sell the property (through a broker, for a 6% commission), at a cap rate of 11.5% on the Net Operating Income projected for Year 6. The investor's income tax bracket is 33%; capital gains are 100% taxable.

Find the net (after-tax) cash-flow for the initial investment and for each of the five years of operation. For Year 1, find the Gross Rent Multiplier, cap rate, equity return rate, and the after-tax cash return rate.

Personal Finance

25. If inflation is 5% per year, and your tax bracket is 27%, what will be the real value (i.e. the buying power in terms of today's dollars) of a $1000 investment (today) into a taxable account earning 10% per year—for 25 years? 40 years?

26. Assuming a 5% annual inflation rate and an income tax rate of 28%, if you invest $2,000 of *buying power* at the end of each year into a growth-oriented mutual fund that earns 15% per year, what buying power will accumulate in this account over 30 years? What is the equivalent annual growth rate of this buying power? What if the account were tax-deferred—like an IRA?

27. Your monthly salary is $3333.20 per month, with annual cost-of-living raises (5% a year). If, for 35 years, you invest 5% of each monthly paycheck into a growth-oriented mutual fund IRA (tax-deferred until withdrawal) averaging 15% growth per year, what gross income (today's dollars) could then you draw for 30 years of retirement if you roll the account into a more secure bond fund at 10%? What is the rollover amount? What if, in addition to that 5%, you were also allowed to invest the 7.65% that now goes for Social Security and Medicare? Repeat the problem for a taxable account (28% income tax bracket).

TVM Quiz Solutions

1. From the investor's perspective:

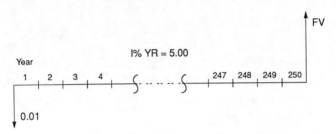

From the TVM Menu, press **OTHER** and set your annuity mode (to **END MODE**) and PMTS/YR (to **1**). Then (EXIT) to TVM, and:

②⑤⓪ **N** ⑤ **I%YR** ·⓪①+/− **PV** ⓪ **PMT**
FV .... <u>Answer:</u> FV=1,983.01 (in the year 2000)

Then ①⓪⓪⓪ **FV** **N** .... <u>Result:</u> N=235.97
①⑦⑤⓪+ <u>Result:</u> 1985.97
So the account balance reaches $1000 toward the end of 1985.

For daily compounding, just change the number of payments per year: Press **OTHER** and set PMTS/YR to **365** (ignore leap years). Then (EXIT) to TVM, and:

②⑤⓪×③⑥⑤ (ALG) *or* ②⑤⓪(INPUT)③⑥⑤× (RPN) **N**
FV .... <u>Answer:</u> FV=2,681.08 (in the year 2000)

Then ①⓪⓪⓪ **FV** **N** .... <u>Result:</u> N=84,050.11
÷③⑥⑤+①⑦⑤⓪= (ALG) *or* ③⑥⑤÷①⑦⑤⓪+ (RPN)
<u>Result:</u> 1980.27 The balance reaches $1000 in early 1980.

2. From your perspective:

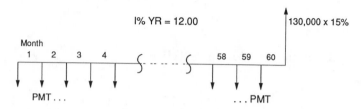

From the TVM Menu, press **OTHER** and set your annuity mode (to BEG MODE) and PMTS/YR (12). Then EXIT to TVM, and:

5×12 (ALGebraic) *or* 5 INPUT 12× (RPN) **N**
12 **I%YR** 0 **PV**
130000×15% (ALGebraic) *or*
130000 INPUT 15% (RPN) **FV**

Then solve: **PMT** .... <u>Answer</u>: PMT=-236.40

But, if the price of houses is increasing at 6% per year, then you must first compute what a 15% down payment will be in 5 years:

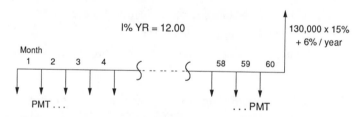

From the TVM Menu, press **OTHER** and set PMTS/YR to 1. Then EXIT and: 5 **N** 6 **I%YR** RCL **FV** +/- **PV** 0 **PMT**
FV .... <u>Answer</u>: FV= 26,095.40

Now re-calculate your monthly investment: **OTHER** 12 **P/YR**
EXIT 5×12 (ALGebraic) *or* 5 INPUT 12× (RPN) **N**
12 **I%YR** 0 **PV**

Then solve: **PMT** .... <u>Answer</u>: PMT=-316.36

3. The question is: "Which is greater—a lump sum of $1 million, less 33%, or the Present Value of this scenario, discounted at 8%?"

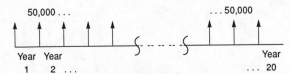

I% YR = 8.00 (daily)

50,000 50,000

Year   Year   Year
1   2 20

The lump-sum: [1][0][0][0][0][0][0][−][3][3][%][=] (ALGebraic) *or*
[1][0][0][0][0][0][0][INPUT][3][3][%][−] (RPN)   Result: **670,000.00**
To analyze the above scenario, first you must find the equivalent *yearly* discount rate: [EXIT] from TVM, and press **ICONV** **PER** [8]
NOM% [3][6][5] **P** **EFF%** ....   Result: **EFF%=8.33**
Then [EXIT][EXIT] **TVM**, [STO] **I%YR**. Then press **OTHER** and set your annuity mode (to BEG MODE) and PMTS/YR (to 1).
Then [EXIT] and: [2][0] **N** [5][0][0][0][0] **PMT** [0] **FV**
PV ....   Answer: **PV=−519,064.88**
So those 20 later payments are equivalent to $519,064.88 now.
Looks like the lump-sum is the better deal.

4. A simple rate calculation problem—but the TVM sign conventions still need to treat it as an investment/return scenario:

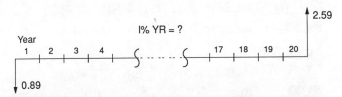

                                    ↑ 2.59
        I% YR = ?
Year
1   2   3   4   17 18 19 20

↓
0.89

From the TVM Menu, press **OTHER** and set PMTS/YR to 1. Then
[EXIT] [2][0] **N** [·][8][9][+/−] **PV** [0] **PMT** [2][·][5][9] **FV**
Then solve: **I%YR** ....   Answer: **I%YR=5.49**

5. The basic picture:

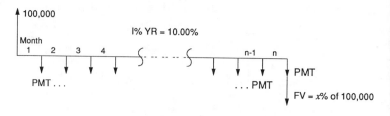

First, find the payment amount: At the TVM Menu, press **OTHER** and set END MODE and 12 PMTS/YR. Then EXIT and:

3 0 × 1 2 (ALGebraic) *or* 3 0 INPUT 1 2 × (RPN) **N**
1 0 **I%YR** 1 0 0 0 0 0 **PV** 0 **FV**
PMT ....   Result: PMT=-877.57

Now find the number of payments (months) to reach those specified balances (Future Values):

RCL **PV** +/-
× 7 5 % = (ALGebraic) *or* 7 5 % (RPN) **FV**
N ....Result: N=209.92   (about 17.5 years)

RCL **PV** +/-
× 5 0 % = (ALGebraic) *or* 5 0 % (RPN) **FV**
N ....   Result: N=282.40   (about 23.5 years)

RCL **PV** +/-
× 2 5 % = (ALGebraic) *or* 2 5 % (RPN) **FV**
N ....   Result: N=327.34   (a little more than 27 years)

<u>Note</u>: If you do a lot of this sort of calculation, you might want to try the formula on page 364 in Chapter 9.

6. The conventional loan, from the borrower's perspective:

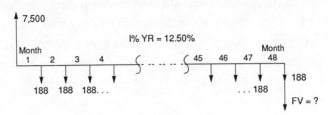

From the TVM Menu, press **OTHER** and set END MODE and 12
PMTS/YR. Then EXIT and:

4 × 1 2 (ALGebraic) *or* 4 INPUT 1 2 × (RPN) **N**
1 2 · 5 **I%YR** 7 5 0 0 **PV** 1 8 8 +/− **PMT**
Then solve: **FV** .... Answer: FV=−702.21

The same loan, but with 90 days before the first payment is due:

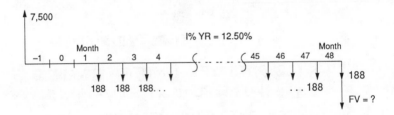

First you calculate how much $7500 becomes with 2 months of
accrued interest: 2 **N** 0 **PMT**
FV ....   Result: FV=−7,657.06

Now use this result as the "amount loaned" (after a sign change)
for a repeat of the above conventional loan calculation:

+/− **PV** 4 8 **N** 1 8 8 +/− **PMT**
FV ....   Answer: FV=−960.49

7. You're looking for $15,000 now, and the buyer is offering $500 now. So, is the *present* value of $15,000 *one year from now* equal to the difference ($14,500)? Or, to put it differently, what rate of interest are you earning if you *assume* this equivalency? Is it better or worse than 6.5% compounded daily? Here's the picture:

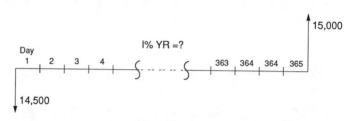

From the TVM Menu, press ▉OTHER▉ and set PMTS/YR to 365. EXIT to TVM, and:

③⑥⑤ ▉ N ▉ ①④⑤⓪⓪+/- ▉ PV ▉ ⓪ ▉ PMT ▉ ①⑤⓪⓪⓪ ▉ FV ▉
▉ I%YR ▉.... Answer: I%YR=3.39   Better insist on cash now.

8. Just double a dollar: ①+/- ▉ PV ▉ ⓪ ▉ PMT ▉ ② ▉ FV ▉

  a. Set 12 PMTS/YR and EXIT⑦·⑤ ▉ I%YR ▉ ▉ N ▉....
  Result: N=111.25 (111.25 *months*—about 9.27 years)

  b. Set 365 PMTS/YR and EXIT ▉ N ▉....
  Result: N=3,373.66 (3,373.66 *days*—about 9.24 years)

  c. Set 1 PMTS/YR and EXIT⑤ ▉ I%YR ▉ ▉ N ▉....
  Result: N=14.21

  d. ①⓪ ▉ I%YR ▉ ▉ N ▉....   Result: N=7.27

  e. ①⑤ ▉ I%YR ▉ ▉ N ▉....   Result: N=4.96

In 10 years exactly : ①⓪ ▉ N ▉ ▉ I%YR ▉   Result: I%YR=7.18

9. You're comparing the Future Values of these two scenarios:

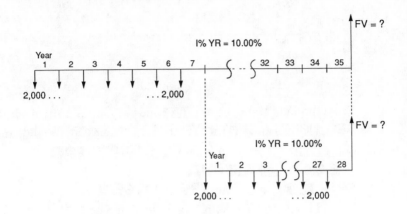

From TVM, press `OTHER` `1` `P/YR` `BEG` `EXIT`.

To begin in the first scenario, find the account balance after 7 years of saving: `7` `N` `10` `I%YR` `0` `PV` `2000` `+/−` `PMT` `FV` ....   Result: FV=20,871.78

Now let that amount accrue for another 28 years, with no further payments into the account. This FV becomes the PV now (i.e. you are moving the entire TVM "picture frame" forward in time):

`+/−` `PV` `0` `PMT` `28` `N` `FV`

Answer: FV=300,991.75

The second scenario: `0` `PV` `2000` `+/−` `PMT` `FV`
Answer: FV=295,261.86

Just 7 early years of saving are better than 28 later years.
       That's the Time Value of Money.

10. The first problem, from your (the new lessor's) perspective:

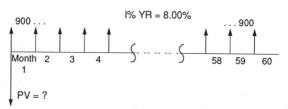

From the TVM Menu, press **OTHER** and set your annuity mode (to
BEG MODE) and **PMTS/YR** (to **12**). Then [EXIT] to TVM, and:
[5][×][1][2] (ALGebraic) *or* [5][INPUT][1][2][×] (RPN) **N**
[8] **I%YR** [9][0][0] **PMT** [0] **FV**
Solve: **PV** .... Answer: PV=-44,682.50
To find its price for sale in 3 years to yield you 12%:
[3][×][1][2] (ALGebraic) *or* [3][INPUT][1][2][×] (RPN) **N**
[1][2] **I%YR** **FV** .... Answer: FV=24,773.44

11. From the lender's perspective:

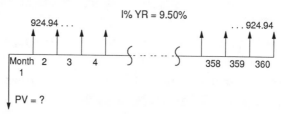

From the TVM Menu, press **OTHER** and check your annuity mode
(should be **END MODE**) and **PMTS/YR** (should be **12**). Then
[EXIT] to TVM, and:
[3][0][×][1][2] (ALGebraic) *or* [3][0][INPUT][1][2][×] (RPN) **N**
[9][·][5] **I%YR** [9][2][4][·][9][4] **PMT** [0] **FV**
Then solve: **PV** .... Answer: PV=-110,000.04

12. A variation on the previous problem:

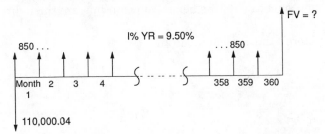

Change only what you have to from the previous problem: At the TVM Menu, press **OTHER** **BEG** (EXIT). Then (8)(5)(0) **PMT** **FV** to find the balloon payment after 30 years: FV=138,675.02

Yikes! What's *that*? How can a $110,000 mortgage produce this howling monster $138,000 balloon?

It can—if the monthly mortgage payment is not enough to cover all of the monthly interest. And $850 a month just doesn't do it. Instead of covering all interest plus paying a little principal (like a normal mortgage payment), $850 pays only *part* of the interest and never touches the principal. That astronomical balloon is the result of the unpaid interest compounding for 30 years.*

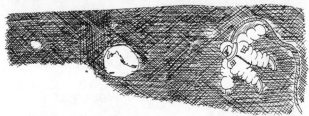

Indeed, look how far this *negative amortization* gets in just 10 years: (1)(2)(0) **N** **FV** .... FV=112,807.98

---

*Once, when asked to name the most awesome force in the universe, Albert Einstein is said to have replied, "compound interest."

13. This is just a comparison of two interest rates, but you'll need to do some calculating before you can compare them directly.

Here's the car loan diagram:

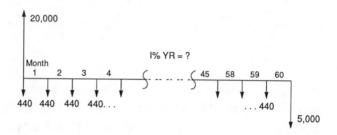

At the TVM Menu (set 12 P⁄YR and BEGIN MODE):
⑥⓪ **N** ②⓪⓪⓪⓪ **PV** ④④⓪(+/−) **PMT**
⑤⓪⓪⓪(+/−) **FV**
I%YR <u>Answer:</u> I%YR=17.22

As for the credit card rate, you don't even need a TVM calculation —just a quick trip to the ICONV Menu:
From the TVM Menu, press (EXIT)**ICONV** **PER**, then ③⑥⑤ **P**
①⑥•⑤ **NOM%**, and solve:
EFF% .... <u>Result:</u> EFF%=17.93
Now find the corresponding nominal rate in a 12-period year:
①② **P** **NOM%** .... <u>Result:</u> NOM%=16.61

That's better than the 17.22% of your car loan.

14. Here's the situation:

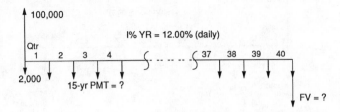

Your first problem is to match the interest rate (daily) to the payment schedule (quarterly). That's an Interest CONVersion side calculation: From the TVM Menu, press [EXIT] **ICONV PER**

Then [1][2] **NOM%** [3][6][0] **P** **EFF%**   `EFF%=12.75`
And [4] **P** **NOM%**   `NOM%=12.18`
Now [EXIT][EXIT] **TVM** and [STO] **I%YR**.

a. The payment amount: Press **OTHER END** and [4] **P/YR**, then [EXIT] to TVM and [6][0] **N** [1][0][0][0][0][0] **PV** [0] **FV** **PMT** ....   <u>Answer:</u> `PMT=-3,648.16`

b. The remaining balance after 10 years (40 payments): [4][0] **N** **FV** ....   <u>Answer:</u> `FV=-54,050.52`

c. The finance company really loaned $98,000: [9][8][0][0][0] **PV** **I%YR** ....   <u>Answer:</u> `I%YR=12.59`

d. Same calculation, but take the loan to term: [6][0] **N** [0] **FV** **I%YR** ....   <u>Answer:</u> `I%YR=12.56`

The term of the loan *does* affect the A.P.R. The finance charge is the same in either case, but its impact on the yield percentage is "distributed" over more time in the latter case. (Analogy: The same $3 tip adds 15% to a $20 dinner tab but only 10% to a $30 tab.)

15. Here's the scenario:

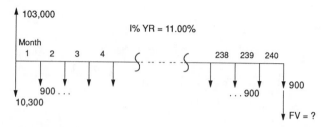

If FV comes up negative, it represents a balloon you'll have to pay at the end of the term. If FV is positive, this means that you have actually *overpaid* the loan (thus it shows a positive balance). Set 12 PMTS/YR and END mode. Then, at the TVM Menu: 2 0 × 1 2 (ALG) *or* 2 0 INPUT 1 2 × (RPN) ▬ N ▬ 1 1 I%YR 1 0 3 0 0 0 and − 1 0 % (ALG) *or* INPUT 1 0 % − (RPN) ▬ PV 9 0 0 +/− ▬ PMT ▬ FV …. <u>Answer</u>: FV=-49,201.69

This is a balloon that you'd need to *pay* (it's negative), so $900 is *not* enough to amortize the mortgage in 20 years. And how much interest would a true 20-year amortization save? Compare these:

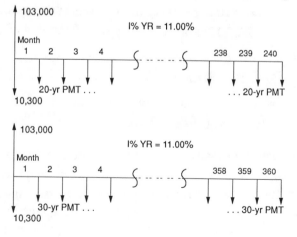

Each amortizing PMT pays all interest accrued on the loan balance in that period, *plus* it pays a little on the principal. The next month, there's a little less interest to pay and so a little more room to pay on principal, etc. Look at this diagram:

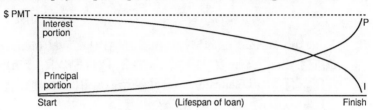

Since in both cases, the loan is totally amortized, the principal paid is the same—the amount financed: $92,700. So the difference in interest paid is simply the difference in totals paid:

Press ⓪ **FV** to specify total amortization of the 20-year case, then **PMT** .... <u>Result</u>: PMT=-956.84

Then ⓧ RCL **N** ⊜(ALGebraic) *or* RCL **N** ⓧ(RPN) and STO ① to store this (to read more about storage registers, see Ch. 7).

The 30-year case: ③⓪ⓧ①② (ALG) *or* ③⓪ INPUT ①②ⓧ (RPN) **N** **PMT** (<u>Result</u>: PMT=-882.80)

And ⓧ RCL **N** ⊜(ALGebraic) *or* RCL **N** ⓧ (RPN), then ⊖ RCL①⊜(ALGebraic) *or* RCL①⊖ (RPN)

<u>Answer</u>: -88,168.09

That's the *face value* of the difference in interest paid. But you can't equate amounts of money unless they are transacted at the same time—not true here. You can't say simply that "the 20-year case saves $88,168.09 in interest." After all, an extra $882.80/month for ten years can earn a lot of interest—far more than its face value. You can earn the added value of *time*.

16.

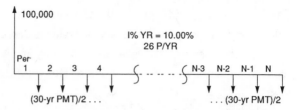

Find the normal monthly payment: At the TVM Menu, press **OTHER**, then set END MODE and 12 PMTS/YR. EXIT and:
③⓪⊗①② (ALGebraic) or ③⓪INPUT①②⊗ (RPN) **N**
①⓪ **I%YR** ①⓪⓪⓪⓪⓪ **PV** ⓪ **FV**
PMT .... Result: PMT=-877.57

Now divide this in half to get the bi-weekly payment amount:
÷②= (ALGebraic) or ②÷ (RPN) Answer: -438.79
Press **PMT**, then **OTHER** to set 26 PMTS/YR. Now EXIT and solve for **N** .... Result: N=544.93

That's about 545 *bi-weekly* periods. Divide this by 26, to find that it will take just under 21 years to amortize the loan with 26 "half-monthly-payments" per year.

The amortization schedule: Press **OTHER AMRT**

②⑥ **#P**   PAYMENTS: 1-26
            BALANCE=98,521.62
            INTEREST=-9,930.16
PRIN   PRINCIPAL=-1,478.38
NEXT   PAYMENTS: 27-52
            BALANCE=96,888.06
            INTEREST=-9,774.98
PRIN   PRINCIPAL=-1,633.56

Note: If you do a lot of this sort of calculation, you might want to try the formula on page 360 in Chapter 9.

17.

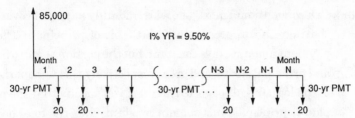

First, find the normal monthly payment amount: At the TVM Menu, press **OTHER**, then set END MODE and 12 PMTS/YR. Then (EXIT) and:

(3)(0)(×)(1)(2) (ALGebraic) *or* (3)(0)(INPUT)(1)(2)(×) (RPN) ▇N▇

(9)(•)(5) **I%YR** (8)(5)(0)(0)(0) **PV** (0) **FV**

PMT .... <u>Result</u>: PMT=-714.73

Now include the extra $20: (−)(2)(0)(=) (ALGebraic) *or* (2)(0)(−) (RPN)

<u>Result</u>: -734.73   Now use this as the PMT (press **PMT**),

and solve for ▇N▇ .... <u>Result</u>: N=313.92

That's about 314 *months*. Divide this by 12, to find that it will take a little over 26 years to amortize the loan with this additional $20 monthly payment toward principal.

The amortization schedule: Press **OTHER** **AMRT**

(1)(2) **#P**   PAYMENTS:1-12

        BALANCE=84,225.09

        INTEREST=-8,041.85

PRIN   PRINCIPAL=-774.91

NEXT   PAYMENTS:13-24

        BALANCE=83,373.25

        INTEREST=-7,964.92

PRIN   PRINCIPAL=-851.84

<u>Note</u>: If you do a lot of this sort of calculation, you might want to try the formula on page 360 in Chapter 9.

18. In a conventional mortgage, each monthly payment covers all of that month's interest, plus a little bit of principal. The total payment amount stays constant, but the portions paid to interest and principal shrink and grow, respectively, throughout the term of the loan (recall page 181). But if you specify that the portion paid to principal must remain constant, then the total payment will not—it will shrink as the interest portion shrinks.

To find the steady amount of each monthly payment that goes to principal, divide the starting principal by the number of months:
⁷⁷[7][2][0][0][0]÷[3][6][0] (ALG) *or* [7][2][0][0][0][INPUT][3][6][0]÷ (RPN)
Result: **200.00**   Knowing that, you know this:

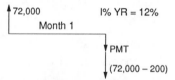

At the TVM Menu, press **OTHER**, set **END MODE** and **12 PMTS/ YR**. Then [EXIT] and: [1] **N** [1][2] **I%YR** [7][2][0][0][0] **PV** and [–][2][0][0][=][+/–] (ALG) *or* [2][0][0][–][+/–] (RPN) **FV** **PMT** .... Result: **PMT=-920.00**   The first payment.

For the last payment, you know that this is the situation:

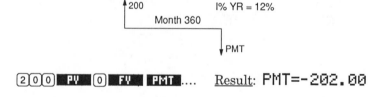

[2][0][0] **PV** [0] **FV** **PMT** .... Result: **PMT=-202.00**

Note: If you do a lot of this sort of calculation, you might want to try the formula on page 366 in Chapter 9.

19. Each time the rate changes in an ARM, you recompute the payment, using the new rate and the remaining term of the loan to amortize the remaining balance. At the TVM Menu, set **END MODE** and **12 PMTS/YR**. Then [EXIT] and:

Year 1: [3][0][×][1][2](ALGebraic) *or* [3][0][INPUT][1][2][×](RPN) **N**
[9] **I%YR** [9][0][0][0][0] **PV** [0] **FV** **PMT** ....

    Result: PMT=-724.16   Monthly payment.
[1][2] **N** **FV** ....FV=-89,385.12   Year-end balance.

Year 2: [+/−] **PV** [9][.][5] **I%YR** [0] **FV**
[2][9][×][1][2](ALGebraic) *or* [2][9][INPUT][1][2][×](RPN) **N** **PMT** ....
    Result: PMT=-756.26   Monthly payment.
[1][2] **N** **FV** ....FV=-88,775.47   Year-end balance.

Year 3: [+/−] **PV** [1][0] **I%YR** [0] **FV**
[2][8][×][1][2](ALGebraic) *or* [2][8][INPUT][1][2][×](RPN) **N** **PMT** ....
    Result: PMT=-788.29   Monthly payment.
[1][2] **N** **FV** ....FV=-88,166.10   Year-end balance.

Year 4: [+/−] **PV** [1][0][.][5] **I%YR** [0] **FV**
[2][7][×][1][2](ALGebraic) *or* [2][7][INPUT][1][2][×](RPN) **N** **PMT** ....
    Result: PMT=-820.21   Monthly payment.
[1][2] **N** **FV** ....FV=-87,551.99   Year-end balance.

Year 5: [+/−] **PV** [1][1] **I%YR** [0] **FV**
[2][6][×][1][2](ALGebraic) *or* [2][6][INPUT][1][2][×](RPN) **N** **PMT** ....
    Result: PMT=-851.99   Monthly payment.
[1][2] **N** **FV** ....FV=-86,927.97   Year-end balance.

Note: If you do a lot of ARM calculations, you might want to try the formula on page 362 in Chapter 9.

20. For conventional, FNMA and GNMA loans, the comparison is generally between 28% of $GI and 36% of $GI less $LTD—unless the amount of financing is 90% or more of the home value:

[3][5][0][0][×][2][8][%][=] (ALGebraic) *or* [3][5][0][0][INPUT][2][8][%] (RPN)
Result: **980.00**
and [3][5][0][0][×][3][6][%][−][2][0][0][=] (ALGebraic) *or*
[3][5][0][0][INPUT][3][6][%][2][0][0][−] (RPN)
Result: **1,060.00**

For FHA loans, compare 29% of $GI and 41% of $GI less $LTD:
[3][5][0][0][×][2][9][%][=] (ALGebraic) *or* [3][5][0][0][INPUT][2][9][%] (RPN)
Result: **1,015.00**
and [3][5][0][0][×][4][1][%][−][2][0][0][=] (ALGebraic) *or*
[3][5][0][0][INPUT][4][1][%][2][0][0][−] (RPN)
Result: **1,235.00**

Conventional: Maximum PITI is $980—unless the financing is 90% or more. Now find the maximum mortgage payment by subtracting the monthly insurance and taxes:

[9][8][0][−][3][0][−][(][2][2][5][0][÷][1][2][=] (ALGebraic) *or*
[9][8][0][INPUT][3][0][−][2][2][5][0][INPUT][1][2][÷][−] (RPN)
Result: **762.50**
At the TVM Menu, press [+/−] **PMT** . Then press **OTHER**, set END MODE and 12 PMTS/YR. Then [EXIT] and:
[3][0][×][1][2] (ALGebraic) *or* [3][0][INPUT][1][2][×] (RPN) **N**
[1][0] **I%YR** [0] **FV** **PV** ....
Result: PV=86,887.50
But this is over 90% of the value of the $90,000 home ($81,000), so test whether the 25%/33% limits can improve upon this 90% limit:
[3][5][0][0][×][2][5][%][=] (ALGebraic) *or* [3][5][0][0][INPUT][2][5][%] (RPN)

Result: **875.00**

and ③⑤⓪⓪✕③③%−②⓪⓪= (ALGebraic) *or*

③⑤⓪⓪[INPUT]③③%②⓪⓪− (RPN)

Result: **955.00**

So maximum PITI is $875:

⑧⑦⑤−③⓪−（②②⑤⓪÷①②= (ALGebraic) *or*

⑧⑦⑤[INPUT]③⓪−②②⑤⓪[INPUT]①②÷− (RPN)

Result: **657.50**   At the TVM Menu, press +/− **PMT**.

Then **PV**....   Result: **PV=74,922.66**

So the maximum conventional financing is 90%, or $81,000.

FNMA: Maximum PITI is $980, so the maximum financing is $86.887.50, as you just calculated for the conventional case.

GNMA: Maximum PITI is $1,060:

①⓪⑥⓪−③⓪−（②②⑤⓪÷①②= (ALGebraic) *or*

①⓪⑥⓪[INPUT]③⓪−②②⑤⓪[INPUT]①②÷− (RPN)

Result: **842.50**   At the TVM Menu, press +/− **PMT**.

Then **PV**....   Result: **PV=96,003.57**

FHA: Maximum PITI is $1,015:

①⓪①⑤−③⓪−（②②⑤⓪÷①②= (ALGebraic) *or*

①⓪①⑤[INPUT]③⓪−②②⑤⓪[INPUT]①②÷− (RPN)

Result: **797.50**   At the TVM Menu, press +/− **PMT**.

Then **PV**....   Result: **PV=90,875.78**

Note: If you do a lot of these home loan qualifying calculations, you might want to try the formula on page 352 in Chapter 9.

21. Just a quick review problem with bonds: From the Main Menu,
press **FIN** **BOND** **TYPE** **A/A** **SEMI** (EXIT).
Then ⑦·②⑧①⑨⑨⓪ **SETT** ⑨·⓪⑨①⑨⑨⑨ **MAT** ⑦ **CPN%**
MORE ①⓪ **YLD%** **PRICE**....PRICE=82.31 For a 10% YTM.
ACCRU.... ACCRU=2.68
MORE ③·⓪⑨①⑨⑨⑤ **MAT** ⑧⑧·①②⑤ **CALL**
MORE **YLD%** .... YLD%=9.75 The yield-to-call.
Note: If you often need bond calculations that also account for
taxes and commissions, see the formula on page 370 in Ch. 9.

22. Take the greater of the two allowed depreciations whenever you
have a choice. From the Main Menu, press **FIN** **DEPRC**.

The building: ⑦⑤⓪⓪⓪ **BASIS** ①⑤⓪⓪⓪ **SALV**
③①·⑤✕①② (ALG) *or* ③①·⑤ (INPUT) ①②✕ (RPN) **LIFE**
The HP 19BII won't accept non-integer input, but SL depreciation
is uniform; just multiply the *monthly* depreciation by 12:
Pick any period: **MORE** ① **YR#** **SL** ....SL=158.73
✕①②= (ALG) *or* ①②✕.... 1,904.76

The computer: **MORE** ①⓪⓪⓪⓪ **BASIS** ⑤⓪⓪ **SALV** ⑤ **LIFE**
MORE ②⓪⓪ **FACT%**
③ **YR#** **DB** ....DB=1,140.00 **SL** ....SL=1,900.00
④ **YR#** **DB** ....DB=864.00 **SL** ....SL=1,900.00*

The shrubs: **MORE** ⑤⓪⓪⓪ **BASIS** ⓪ **SALV** ①⑤ **LIFE**
MORE ①⑤⓪ **FACT%**
③ **YR#** **DB** ....DB=405.00 **SL** ....SL=333.33
④ **YR#** **DB** ....DB=364.50 **SL** ....SL=333.33

---

*Caution! The RDV of the computer is only $1200 in Year 4, if you've been using 200% DB in the
previous years. If you do a lot of MACRS calculations, see the formula on page 390 in Chapter 9.

23. The gross rents, less vacancies:

$\boxed{7}\,\boxed{\cdot}\,\boxed{8}\,\boxed{\times}\,\boxed{2}\,\boxed{2}\,\boxed{7}\,\boxed{7}\,\boxed{-}\,\boxed{\cdot}\,\boxed{5}\,\boxed{\%}$

$\boxed{+}\,\boxed{(}\,\boxed{(}\,\boxed{4}\,\boxed{\cdot}\,\boxed{0}\,\boxed{7}\,\boxed{\times}\,\boxed{2}\,\boxed{0}\,\boxed{0}\,\boxed{5}\,\boxed{-}\,\boxed{1}\,\boxed{\%}\,\boxed{=}$ (ALG) *or*

$\boxed{7}\,\boxed{\cdot}\,\boxed{8}\,\boxed{\text{INPUT}}\,\boxed{2}\,\boxed{2}\,\boxed{7}\,\boxed{7}\,\boxed{\times}\,\boxed{\cdot}\,\boxed{5}\,\boxed{\%}\,\boxed{-}$

$\boxed{4}\,\boxed{\cdot}\,\boxed{0}\,\boxed{7}\,\boxed{\text{INPUT}}\,\boxed{2}\,\boxed{0}\,\boxed{0}\,\boxed{5}\,\boxed{\times}\,\boxed{1}\,\boxed{\%}\,\boxed{-}\,\boxed{+}$ (RPN)

(<u>Result</u>: **25,750.54**)

Less operating expenses:

$\boxed{-}\,\boxed{3}\,\boxed{6}\,\boxed{4}\,\boxed{7}\,\boxed{-}\,\boxed{3}\,\boxed{0}\,\boxed{6}\,\boxed{0}\,\boxed{-}\,\boxed{2}\,\boxed{3}\,\boxed{1}\,\boxed{8}\,\boxed{-}\,\boxed{7}\,\boxed{7}\,\boxed{3}\,\boxed{=}$ (ALG) *or*

$\boxed{3}\,\boxed{6}\,\boxed{4}\,\boxed{7}\,\boxed{-}\,\boxed{3}\,\boxed{0}\,\boxed{6}\,\boxed{0}\,\boxed{-}\,\boxed{2}\,\boxed{3}\,\boxed{1}\,\boxed{8}\,\boxed{-}\,\boxed{7}\,\boxed{7}\,\boxed{3}\,\boxed{-}$ (RPN)

<u>Result</u>: **15,952.54**   The NOI—leave it in the Stack.

Now find the cap rate by weighting each portion of the investment by its expected return rate (this is the Band of Investment method for determining a cap rate):

$\boxed{\cdot}\,\boxed{1}\,\boxed{2}\,\boxed{7}\,\boxed{5}\,\boxed{\times}\,\boxed{7}\,\boxed{0}\,\boxed{\%}\,\boxed{+}\,\boxed{(}\,\boxed{\cdot}\,\boxed{1}\,\boxed{4}\,\boxed{\times}\,\boxed{3}\,\boxed{0}\,\boxed{\%}\,\boxed{=}$ (ALG) *or*

$\boxed{\cdot}\,\boxed{1}\,\boxed{2}\,\boxed{7}\,\boxed{5}\,\boxed{\text{INPUT}}\,\boxed{\cdot}\,\boxed{7}\,\boxed{\times}\,\boxed{\cdot}\,\boxed{1}\,\boxed{4}\,\boxed{\text{INPUT}}\,\boxed{\cdot}\,\boxed{3}\,\boxed{\times}\,\boxed{+}$ (RPN)

<u>Result</u>: **0.13**   The cap rate, as a decimal.

Then divide the NOI by the cap rate:

$\boxed{\div}\,\boxed{\blacksquare}\,\boxed{\text{LAST}}\,\boxed{=}\,\boxed{\blacksquare}\,\boxed{1/x}$ (ALG) *or*

$\boxed{\div}$ (RPN)

<u>Result</u>: **121,543.19**   The property value.

<u>Note</u>: If you do a lot of this sort of calculation, you might want to try the formula on page 378 in Chapter 9.

24. At TVM , press **OTHER**. Set END MODE and 12 PMTS/YR.
EXIT and amortize the first mortgage:

2 0 × 1 2 (ALG) *or* 2 0 INPUT 1 2 × (RPN) **N**
1 0 · 5 **I%YR** 3 5 0 0 0 0 **PV** 0 **FV**
Then solve: **PMT** .... <u>Answer:</u> PMT=-3,494.33

The amortization schedule: Press **OTHER AMRT**, then:

1 2 **#P**	PAYMENTS: 1-12	(Year 1)
	BALANCE=344,561.24	
	INTEREST=-36,493.20	
PRIN	PRINCIPAL=-5,438.76	
NEXT	PAYMENTS: 13-24	(Year 2)
	BALANCE=338,523.11	
	INTEREST=-35,893.83	
NEXT	PAYMENTS: 25-36	(Year 3)
	BALANCE=331,819.56	
	INTEREST=-35,228.41	
NEXT	PAYMENTS: 37-48	(Year 4)
	BALANCE=324,377.23	
	INTEREST=-34,489.63	
NEXT	PAYMENTS: 49-60	(Year 5)
	BALANCE=316,114.75	
	INTEREST=-33,669.48	

Now **EXIT EXIT** and do the second mortgage:

1 0 × 1 2 (ALGebraic) *or* 1 0 INPUT 1 2 × (RPN) **N**
1 2 **I%YR** 1 5 0 0 0 0 **PV** 0 **FV**
Then solve: **PMT** .... <u>Answer:</u> PMT=-2,152.06

The amortization schedule: Press **OTHER** **AMRT**, then:

1 2 #P   PAYMENTS: 1-12   (Year 1)
                 BALANCE=141,730.24
                 INTEREST=-17,554.96
PRIN   PRINCIPAL=-8,269.76

NEXT   PAYMENTS: 13-24   (Year 2)
                 BALANCE=132,411.66
                 INTEREST=-16,506.14

NEXT   PAYMENTS: 25-36   (Year 3)
                 BALANCE=121,911.28
                 INTEREST=-15,324.34

NEXT   PAYMENTS: 37-48   (Year 4)
                 BALANCE=110,079.16
                 INTEREST=-13,992.60

NEXT   PAYMENTS: 49-60   (Year 5)
                 BALANCE=96,746.46
                 INTEREST=-12,492.02

Annual debt service:

3 4 9 4 . 3 3 + 2 1 5 2 . 0 6 × 1 2 = (ALG) *or*
3 4 9 4 . 3 3 INPUT 2 1 5 2 . 0 6 + 1 2 × (RPN)
Result: **67,756.68**   The mortgage payments.

Annual depreciation:

7 5 0 0 0 0 × 7 0 % ÷ 3 1 . 5 = (ALG) *or*
7 5 0 0 0 0 INPUT 7 0 % 3 1 . 5 ÷ (RPN)
Result: **16,666.67**   The 31.5-year SL cost recovery.

Annual deduction for points:

⎡3⎤⎡5⎤⎡0⎤⎡0⎤⎡0⎤⎡0⎤⎡×⎤⎡2⎤⎡•⎤⎡5⎤⎡%⎤⎡+⎤⎡(⎤⎡(⎤⎡1⎤⎡5⎤⎡0⎤⎡0⎤⎡0⎤⎡0⎤⎡×⎤⎡2⎤⎡%⎤⎡)⎤⎡)⎤⎡÷⎤⎡5⎤⎡=⎤ (ALG)

or ⎡3⎤⎡5⎤⎡0⎤⎡0⎤⎡0⎤⎡0⎤⎡INPUT⎤⎡•⎤⎡0⎤⎡1⎤⎡5⎤⎡×⎤⎡1⎤⎡5⎤⎡0⎤⎡0⎤⎡0⎤⎡0⎤⎡INPUT⎤

⎡•⎤⎡0⎤⎡2⎤⎡×⎤⎡+⎤⎡5⎤⎡÷⎤ (RPN)

Result: **1,650.00**   The annual points deduction.

Initial Cash-Flow ("Year 0"): Down-payment, points and COA:

⎡2⎤⎡5⎤⎡0⎤⎡0⎤⎡0⎤⎡0⎤⎡+⎤⎡(⎤⎡(⎤⎡3⎤⎡5⎤⎡0⎤⎡0⎤⎡0⎤⎡0⎤⎡×⎤⎡1⎤⎡•⎤⎡5⎤⎡%⎤⎡)⎤⎡)⎤

⎡+⎤⎡(⎤⎡(⎤⎡1⎤⎡5⎤⎡0⎤⎡0⎤⎡0⎤⎡0⎤⎡×⎤⎡2⎤⎡%⎤⎡)⎤⎡)⎤⎡+⎤⎡2⎤⎡0⎤⎡0⎤⎡0⎤⎡0⎤⎡=⎤⎡+/−⎤ (ALG) *or*

⎡2⎤⎡5⎤⎡0⎤⎡0⎤⎡0⎤⎡0⎤⎡INPUT⎤⎡3⎤⎡5⎤⎡0⎤⎡0⎤⎡0⎤⎡0⎤⎡INPUT⎤⎡•⎤⎡0⎤⎡1⎤⎡5⎤⎡×⎤⎡+⎤

⎡1⎤⎡5⎤⎡0⎤⎡0⎤⎡0⎤⎡0⎤⎡INPUT⎤⎡•⎤⎡0⎤⎡2⎤⎡×⎤⎡+⎤⎡2⎤⎡0⎤⎡0⎤⎡0⎤⎡+⎤⎡+/−⎤ (RPN)

Result: **−260,250.00**   The initial cash-flow.

Year 1: Each yearly cash-flow is the NOI (rents less operating expenses), less income taxes, plus tax relief for depreciation and interest and prorated points (and, for Year 1, costs of acquisition), less debt service:

⎡1⎤⎡2⎤⎡5⎤⎡0⎤⎡0⎤⎡0⎤⎡−⎤⎡6⎤⎡%⎤	(rent)
⎡−⎤⎡3⎤⎡0⎤⎡0⎤⎡0⎤	(− insurance)
⎡−⎤⎡1⎤⎡2⎤⎡0⎤⎡0⎤⎡0⎤	(− mnt./mgmt.)
⎡−⎤⎡(⎤⎡(⎤⎡7⎤⎡5⎤⎡0⎤⎡0⎤⎡0⎤⎡0⎤⎡×⎤⎡2⎤⎡•⎤⎡5⎤⎡%⎤⎡)⎤⎡)⎤	(− prop. taxes)
⎡=⎤	(= NOI: 83,750.00)
⎡−⎤⎡3⎤⎡3⎤⎡%⎤	(−income taxes)
⎡+⎤⎡(⎤⎡(⎤⎡1⎤⎡6⎤⎡6⎤⎡6⎤⎡6⎤⎡•⎤⎡6⎤⎡7⎤	(+ tax relief...
⎡+⎤⎡3⎤⎡6⎤⎡4⎤⎡9⎤⎡3⎤⎡•⎤⎡2⎤⎡+⎤⎡1⎤⎡7⎤⎡5⎤⎡5⎤⎡4⎤⎡•⎤⎡9⎤⎡6⎤	...
⎡+⎤⎡2⎤⎡0⎤⎡0⎤⎡0⎤⎡+⎤⎡1⎤⎡6⎤⎡5⎤⎡0⎤⎡×⎤⎡3⎤⎡3⎤⎡%⎤⎡)⎤⎡)⎤	...)
⎡−⎤⎡6⎤⎡7⎤⎡7⎤⎡5⎤⎡6⎤⎡•⎤⎡6⎤⎡8⎤	(− debt serv.)
⎡=⎤(ALG)	

or (RPN): `1 2 5 0 0 0 INPUT 6 % −`   (rent)

   `3 0 0 0 −`   (− insurance)

   `1 2 0 0 0 −`   (− mnt./mgmt.)

   `7 5 0 0 0 0 INPUT . 0 2 5 × −`   (− prop. taxes)

                                                    (= NOI: **83,750.00**)

   `3 3 % −`   (−income taxes)

   `1 6 6 6 6 . 6 7 INPUT`   (+ tax relief...

      `3 6 4 9 3 . 2 + 1 7 5 5 4 . 9 6 +`   ...

      `2 0 0 0 + 1 6 5 0 + . 3 3 × +` ...)

   `6 7 7 5 6 . 6 8 −`   (− debt serv.)

<u>Result:</u> **12,896.21**   The Year 1 cash-flow.

<u>Year 2:</u> Each year, the NOI increases by the inflation rate:

`8 3 7 5 0 + 5 %`   (NOI + inflation adj.)

   `− 3 3 %`   (−income taxes)

   `+ ( 1 6 6 6 6 . 6 7 + 3 5 8 9 3 . 8 3`   (+ tax relief...

      `+ 1 6 5 0 6 . 1 4 + 1 6 5 0 × 3 3 % )` ...)

   `− 6 7 7 5 6 . 6 8`   (− debt serv.)

`=` (ALG) *or* (RPN):

`8 3 7 5 0 INPUT 5 % +`   (NOI + inflation adj.)

   `3 3 % −`   (−income taxes)

   `1 6 6 6 6 . 6 7 INPUT 3 5 8 9 3 . 8 3 +`   (+ tax relief...

      `1 6 5 0 6 . 1 4 + 1 6 5 0 + . 3 3 × +` ...)

   `6 7 7 5 6 . 6 8 −`   (− debt serv.)

<u>Result:</u> **14,497.94**   The Year 2 cash-flow.

<u>Year 3</u>: Each year, the NOI increases by the inflation rate:

⌨ 8 3 7 5 0 + 5 % + 5 %   (NOI + inflation adj.)
   − 3 3 %   (− income taxes)
   + (1 6 6 6 6 · 6 7 + 3 5 2 2 8 · 4 1   (+ tax relief...
      + 1 5 3 2 4 · 3 4 + 1 6 5 0 × 3 3 %)) ...)
   − 6 7 7 5 6 · 6 8   (− debt serv.)
= (ALG) *or* (RPN):
8 3 7 5 0 INPUT 5 % + 5 % +   (NOI + inflation adj.)
   3 3 % −   (− income taxes)
   1 6 6 6 6 · 6 7 INPUT 3 5 2 2 8 · 4 1 + (+ tax relief...
      1 5 3 2 4 · 3 4 + 1 6 5 0 + · 3 3 × + ...)
   6 7 7 5 6 · 6 8 −   (− debt serv.)

<u>Result</u>: **16,834.26**   The Year 3 cash-flow.

<u>Year 4</u>: Each year, the NOI increases by the inflation rate:

8 3 7 5 0 + 5 % + 5 % + 5 %   (NOI + inflation adj.)
   − 3 3 %   (− income taxes)
   + (1 6 6 6 6 · 6 7 + 3 4 4 8 9 · 6 3   (+ tax relief...
      + 1 3 9 9 2 · 6 + 1 6 5 0 × 3 3 %)) ...)
   − 6 7 7 5 6 · 6 8   (− debt serv.)
= (ALG) *or* (RPN):
8 3 7 5 0 INPUT 5 % + 5 % + 5 % +   (NOI + inflation adj.)
   3 3 % −   (− income taxes)
   1 6 6 6 6 · 6 7 INPUT 3 4 4 8 9 · 6 3 + (+ tax relief...
      1 3 9 9 2 · 6 + 1 6 5 0 + · 3 3 × + ...)
   6 7 7 5 6 · 6 8 −   (− debt serv.)

<u>Result</u>: **19,244.19**   The Year 4 cash-flow.

Year 5: When the property sells (at a price based upon a cap rate and projected Year 6 NOI), the lenders are repaid from the net sale proceeds, and capital gains are realized on the difference between the net proceeds and the unrecovered cost:

`8 3 7 5 0 + 5 % + 5 % + 5 % + 5 % + 5 %`   (Year 6 NOI)
`÷ . 1 1 5 − 6 % =`   (net sale proceeds: **873,697.97**)
`− 3 1 6 1 1 4 . 7 5 − 9 6 7 4 6 . 4 6`   (−mortgage balances)
`− ( ( 8 7 3 6 9 7 . 9 7 −`   (− tax on capital gains...
　`( ( 7 5 0 0 0 0 − ( ( 5 × 1 6 6 6 6 . 6 7 ) ) × 3 3 % ) )` ...)
`+ ( ( 8 3 7 5 0 + 5 % + 5 % + 5 % + 5 %`   (+ Year 5 NOI)
　`− 3 3 %`   (−income taxes)
　`+ ( ( 1 6 6 6 6 . 6 7 + 3 3 6 6 9 . 4 8`   (+ tax relief...
　　`+ 1 2 4 9 2 . 0 2 + 1 6 5 0 × 3 3 % )` ...)
　`− 6 7 7 5 6 . 6 8 )`   (− debt serv.)
`=` (ALGebraic)

or (RPN):

`8 3 7 5 0 INPUT 5 % + 5 % + 5 % + 5 % + 5 % +`   (Year 6 NOI)
`. 1 1 5 ÷ 6 % −`   (net sale proceeds: **873,697.97**)
`3 1 6 1 1 4 . 7 5 − 9 6 7 4 6 . 4 6 −`   (−mortgage balances)
`8 7 3 6 9 7 . 9 7 INPUT`   (− tax on capital gains...
`5 INPUT 1 6 6 6 6 . 6 7 × +/− 7 5 0 0 0 0 + − . 3 3 × −` ...)
`8 3 7 5 0 INPUT 5 % + 5 % + 5 % + 5 % +`   (NOI + infl. adj.)
　`3 3 % −`   (−income taxes)
　`1 6 6 6 6 . 6 7 INPUT 3 3 6 6 9 . 4 8 +`   (+ tax relief...
　　`1 2 4 9 2 . 0 2 + 1 6 5 0 + . 3 3 × +` ...)
　`6 7 7 5 6 . 6 8 −`   (− debt serv.)
`+`

Result: **414,242.63**   The Year 5 cash-flow.

The GRM (Gross Rent Multiplier) is Price÷Rents$_{max}$:

[7][5][0][0][0][0]÷[1][2][5][0][0][0][=] (ALG) *or*

[7][5][0][0][0][0][INPUT][1][2][5][0][0][0][÷] (RPN)

Result: **6.00**   The GRM.

The cap rate is NOI$_1$÷Price:

[8][3][7][5][0]÷[7][5][0][0][0][0][×][1][0][0][=] (ALG) *or*

[8][3][7][5][0][INPUT][7][5][0][0][0][0]÷[1][0][0][×] (RPN)

Result: **11.17**   The cap rate, as a percentage.

The equity return rate is the ratio of the net cash-flow, mortgage principal payments and appreciation, to the down-payment:

[1][2][8][8][5][·][4][1][+][5][4][3][8][·][7][6][+][8][2][6][9][·][7][6][+]

[(][7][5][0][0][0][×][5][%][)]÷[2][5][0][0][0][0][×][1][0][0][=] (ALG) *or*

[1][2][8][8][5][·][4][1][INPUT][5][4][3][8][·][7][6][+][8][2][6][9][·][7][6][+]

[7][5][0][0][0][INPUT][·][0][5][×][+][2][5][0][0][0][0]÷[1][0][0][×] (RPN)

Result: **25.64**   The equity return rate, as a percentage.

The after-tax cash return rate is the Year 1 cash-flow divided by the initial cash-flow:

[1][2][8][8][5][·][4][1]÷[2][6][0][2][5][0][×][1][0][0][=] (ALG) *or*

[1][2][8][8][5][·][4][1][INPUT][2][6][0][2][5][0]÷[1][0][0][×] (RPN)

Result: **4.95**   The after-tax cash return rate, as a percentage.

<u>Note</u>: If you do many of these lengthy income property analyses, you should consider using the formula on page 384 in Chapter 9.

25. Suppose that $1.00 today will buy a loaf of bread. Then, with 5% inflation, that loaf will cost $1.05 this time next year. So, how many loaves can you buy then if your dollar has increased—by earning interest—to $1.10? It's 1.10÷1.05. Do that arithmetic:

[1][.][1][0][÷][1][.][0][5][=] (ALG) *or* [1][.][1] [INPUT][1][.][0][5][÷] (RPN)

The same value that bought 1 loaf this year will buy 1.0476 loaves next year. So your real buying power has grown by 4.76%.

But that doesn't take taxes into account. If interest is taxable at 27%, then 27% of the $0.10 interest earned by your dollar goes you-know-where. So:

[.][1][−][2][7][%][+][1][÷][1][.][0][5][−][1][×][1][0][0][=] (ALG) *or*
[.][1][INPUT][2][7][%][−][1][+][1][.][0][5][÷][1][−][1][0][0][×] (RPN)

This is the *after-tax* growth rate of your real buying power—as a percentage: **2.19**. This is what you should use as your interest rate in the TVM Menu to grow your $1000 investment:

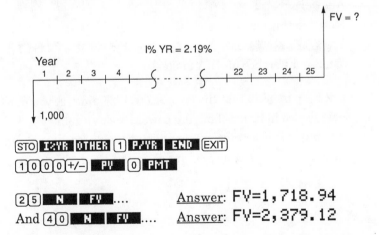

[STO] [I%YR] [OTHER] [1] [P/YR] [END] [EXIT]
[1][0][0][0][+/−] [PV] [0] [PMT]

[2][5] [N] [FV] ....   <u>Answer:</u> FV=1,718.94
And [4][0] [N] [FV] ....   <u>Answer:</u> FV=2,379.12

<u>Note:</u> If you do a lot of after-tax-and-inflation TVM calculations, see the formula on page 398 in Chapter 9.

26. Find the growth rate of the buying power in the taxable account:

⚬ 1 5 − 2 8 % + 1 ÷ 1 ⚬ 0 5 − 1 × 1 0 0 = (ALG) *or*
⚬ 1 5 INPUT 2 8 % − 1 + 1 ⚬ 0 5 ÷ 1 − 1 0 0 × (RPN)

<u>Answer</u>: 5.52

Now use this as your interest rate in the TVM Menu:

STO **I%YR** **OTHER** 1 **P/YR** **END** EXIT
2 0 0 0 +/− **PMT** 0 **PV**
3 0 **N** **FV** ....   <u>Answer</u>: FV=145,472.28

This is the *buying power* (in terms of today's dollars) in your taxable account after 30 years. The actual *face-value* amount of dollars will be higher, but those dollars don't buy as much then.

Repeat this calculation for the IRA—a tax-deferred account (no tax on interest while it's growing):

1 ⚬ 1 5 ÷ 1 ⚬ 0 5 − 1 × 1 0 0 = (ALG) *or*
1 ⚬ 1 5 INPUT 1 ⚬ 0 5 ÷ 1 − 1 0 0 × (RPN)

<u>Answer</u>: 9.52

Now use this as your interest rate in the TVM Menu:

STO **I%YR** **FV** ....   <u>Answer</u>: FV=300,718.13

What a difference an IRA makes!

But keep in mind that the level $2,000 PMT amount you're using here is also in terms of buying power ("today's dollars"). To hold that *buying power* investment amount steady, its *face value* must increase every year by 5%. Inflation is a hard taskmaster.

27. Since you're saving a level *percentage* of your inflation-adjusted income, you're investing a level amount of buying power (today's dollars) each month. So you can just use today's income numbers—if you adjust the growth rate of the account to reflect the true growth rate of its buying power instead of its face value:*

⬚`.`⬚`1`⬚`5`⬚`÷`⬚`1`⬚`2`⬚`+`⬚`1`⬚`÷`⬚`(`⬚`(`⬚`.`⬚`0`⬚`5`⬚`÷`⬚`1`⬚`2`⬚`+`⬚`1`⬚`)`⬚`)`
                                   ⬚`−`⬚`1`⬚`×`⬚`1`⬚`2`⬚`0`⬚`0`⬚`=` (ALG) *or*

⬚`.`⬚`1`⬚`5` `INPUT` ⬚`1`⬚`2`⬚`÷`⬚`1`⬚`+`⬚`.`⬚`0`⬚`5` `INPUT` ⬚`1`⬚`2`⬚`÷`⬚`1`⬚`+`⬚`÷`
                                   ⬚`1`⬚`−`⬚`1`⬚`2`⬚`0`⬚`0`⬚`×` (RPN)

(Result: **9.96**)   Use this as the interest rate in TVM:

`STO` `I%YR` `OTHER` `12` `P/YR` `END` `EXIT`
⬚`3`⬚`3`⬚`3`⬚`3`⬚`.`⬚`2`⬚`×`⬚`5`⬚`%`⬚`=` (ALGebraic) *or* ⬚`3`⬚`3`⬚`3`⬚`3`⬚`.`⬚`2` `INPUT` ⬚`5`⬚`%` (RPN)
`+/−` `PMT` `0` `PV`
⬚`3`⬚`5`⬚`×`⬚`1`⬚`2` (ALGebraic) *or* ⬚`3`⬚`5` `INPUT` ⬚`1`⬚`2`⬚`×` (RPN) `N`
`FV` ....Answer: **FV=626,011.09**   The rollover amount.

Use this as a Present Value to amortize over 30 years of retirement in an account paying 10%: `+/−` `PV` `0` `FV`
⬚`3`⬚`0`⬚`×`⬚`1`⬚`2` (ALGebraic) *or* ⬚`3`⬚`0` `INPUT` ⬚`1`⬚`2`⬚`×` (RPN) `N`
⬚`.`⬚`1`⬚`÷`⬚`1`⬚`2`⬚`+`⬚`1`⬚`÷`⬚`(`⬚`(`⬚`.`⬚`0`⬚`5`⬚`÷`⬚`1`⬚`2`⬚`+`⬚`1`⬚`)`⬚`)`
                                   ⬚`−`⬚`1`⬚`×`⬚`1`⬚`2`⬚`0`⬚`0`⬚`=` (ALG) *or*

⬚`.`⬚`1` `INPUT` ⬚`1`⬚`2`⬚`÷`⬚`1`⬚`+`⬚`.`⬚`0`⬚`5` `INPUT` ⬚`1`⬚`2`⬚`÷`⬚`1`⬚`+`⬚`÷`
                                   ⬚`1`⬚`−`⬚`1`⬚`2`⬚`0`⬚`0`⬚`×` (RPN)

(Result: **4.98**) `I%YR` `PMT` ....Answer: **PMT=3,352.63**
Your monthly retirement income—in today's dollars.

---

*For simplicity here, you may assume that all rates are *nominal* rates that compound monthly (otherwise—if they were *effective* annual rates—you'd need to use the ICONV Menu to find the corresponding nominal rates to use in the TVM Menu).

Repeat for the taxable scenario:*

$\boxed{\cdot}\boxed{1}\boxed{5}\boxed{-}\boxed{2}\boxed{8}\boxed{\%}\boxed{\div}\boxed{1}\boxed{2}\boxed{+}\boxed{1}\boxed{\div}\boxed{(}\boxed{(}\boxed{\cdot}\boxed{0}\boxed{0}\boxed{5}\boxed{\div}\boxed{1}\boxed{2}\boxed{+}\boxed{1}\boxed{)}\boxed{)}$
$\boxed{-}\boxed{1}\boxed{\times}\boxed{1}\boxed{2}\boxed{0}\boxed{0}\boxed{=}$ (ALG) or

$\boxed{\cdot}\boxed{1}\boxed{5}\,\boxed{\text{INPUT}}\,\boxed{2}\boxed{8}\boxed{\%}\boxed{-}\boxed{1}\boxed{2}\boxed{\div}\boxed{1}\boxed{+}\boxed{\cdot}\boxed{0}\boxed{5}\,\boxed{\text{INPUT}}\,\boxed{1}\boxed{2}\boxed{\div}\boxed{1}\boxed{+}\boxed{\div}$
$\boxed{1}\boxed{-}\boxed{1}\boxed{2}\boxed{0}\boxed{0}\boxed{\times}$ (RPN)

(Result: 5.78) **I%YR**

$\boxed{3}\boxed{3}\boxed{3}\boxed{3}\boxed{\cdot}\boxed{2}\boxed{\times}\boxed{5}\boxed{\%}\boxed{=}$ (ALG) or $\boxed{3}\boxed{3}\boxed{3}\boxed{3}\boxed{\cdot}\boxed{2}\,\boxed{\text{INPUT}}\,\boxed{5}\boxed{\%}$ (RPN)
$\boxed{+/-}$ **PMT** $\boxed{0}$ **PV**

$\boxed{3}\boxed{5}\boxed{\times}\boxed{1}\boxed{2}$ (ALGebraic) or $\boxed{3}\boxed{5}\,\boxed{\text{INPUT}}\,\boxed{1}\boxed{2}\boxed{\times}$ (RPN) **N**
FV ....Answer: FV=225,536.96 The rollover amount.

Then: $\boxed{+/-}$ **PV** $\boxed{0}$ **FV**

$\boxed{3}\boxed{0}\boxed{\times}\boxed{1}\boxed{2}$ (ALGebraic) or $\boxed{3}\boxed{0}\,\boxed{\text{INPUT}}\,\boxed{1}\boxed{2}\boxed{\times}$ (RPN) **N**
$\boxed{\cdot}\boxed{1}\boxed{-}\boxed{2}\boxed{8}\boxed{\%}\boxed{\div}\boxed{1}\boxed{2}\boxed{+}\boxed{1}\boxed{\div}\boxed{(}\boxed{(}\boxed{\cdot}\boxed{0}\boxed{0}\boxed{5}\boxed{\div}\boxed{1}\boxed{2}\boxed{+}\boxed{1}\boxed{)}\boxed{)}$
$\boxed{-}\boxed{1}\boxed{\times}\boxed{1}\boxed{2}\boxed{0}\boxed{0}\boxed{=}$ (ALG) or
$\boxed{\cdot}\boxed{1}\,\boxed{\text{INPUT}}\,\boxed{2}\boxed{8}\boxed{\%}\boxed{-}\boxed{1}\boxed{2}\boxed{\div}\boxed{1}\boxed{+}\boxed{\cdot}\boxed{0}\boxed{5}\,\boxed{\text{INPUT}}\,\boxed{1}\boxed{2}\boxed{\div}\boxed{1}\boxed{+}\boxed{\div}$
$\boxed{1}\boxed{-}\boxed{1}\boxed{2}\boxed{0}\boxed{0}\boxed{\times}$ (RPN)

(Result: 2.19) **I%YR** **PMT** ....Answer: PMT=855.32

And what if you could also invest the 7.65% of your income that now goes toward Social Security and Medicare (a total of 12.65% of your income)? Your answers would be *proportionately* higher. So just multiply each answer above by (12.65÷5):

	IRA (tax-deferred) acct.	Taxable acct.
Rollover:	1,583,808.06	570,608.52
Ret. income:	8,482.15	2,163.96

<u>Note</u>: If you do a lot of retirement planning calculations, see the formulas on pages 400 and 402 in Chapter 9.

*Again, for simplicity here, you may assume that you pay monthly taxes on your interest—not generally true, but note that this leads to a slightly more conservative (lower) growth rate, which, if you're going to go wrong with assumptions in retirement planning, is the side on which to err.

Basic Arithmetic...............24

Using Menus.........................60

TVM.............................94

The CFLO Menu..................202

SUM Lists.........................258

TIME, Dates and Appts.....280

The SOLVE Menu...............294

TEXT Lists........................409

Appendix..........................424

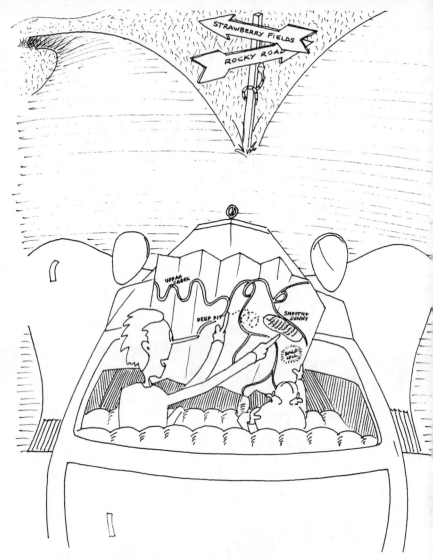

6. Rougher Roads:
The CFLO Menu

Problems with Uneven Payments

So far, all the various finance problems you've been solving have had one thing in common: that smooth, level PMT cash-flow happening once every period. Well, the world isn't always so neat and tidy. Often, you'll run into situations where the periodic cash-flow amounts vary—sometimes quite often—like this:

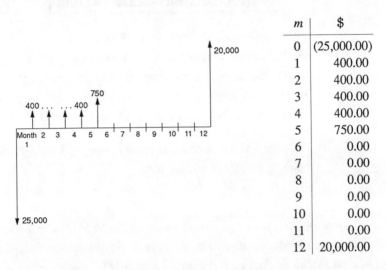

m	$
0	(25,000.00)
1	400.00
2	400.00
3	400.00
4	400.00
5	750.00
6	0.00
7	0.00
8	0.00
9	0.00
10	0.00
11	0.00
12	20,000.00

Notice that there's a cash-flow for every period (zero *is* a cash-flow). But if cash-flows occur at irregular *time* intervals, you're out of luck; the HP 19BII cannot analyze such a situation for you. The HP 19BII can analyze scenarios where the cash-flow *amounts* are uneven, but their *occurrences* must still be regular—once per period.

The above picture does indeed fall within those limitations, but how do you analyze it? Not with the TVM keys—there's no level PMT. You must use the CFLO Menu instead....

Go Find It: From the MAIN Menu, press **FIN**, but instead of **TVM**, hit **CFLO**. You'll see something like this:

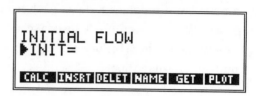

```
INITIAL FLOW
▶INIT=

CALC  INSRT DELET NAME  GET  PLOT
```

This is a CFLO list. The pointer (▶) shows you where you are in the list, and any value you key in will go into the list at that point. To move up and down the list, you use the ⬆ and ⬇ keys. And you can use ⬛⬆ and ⬛⬇ to jump all the way to top or bottom of the list.

This kind of list is just a *specially reserved kind for representing cash-flow diagrams*.

You've already seen how the variables in the TVM Menu "draw the picture" for your calculator. But now you're working under a different set of circumstances, because there's no level PMT value.

Instead, to draw a picture of an *uneven* cash-flow situation, you use the concept of cash-flow *groups*.

Cash-Flow Groups

Here's that uneven cash-flow scenario again:

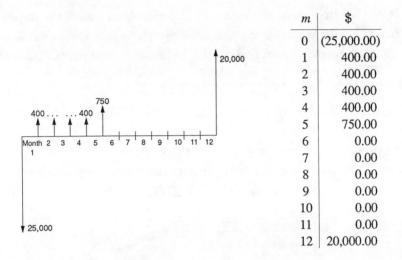

m	$
0	(25,000.00)
1	400.00
2	400.00
3	400.00
4	400.00
5	750.00
6	0.00
7	0.00
8	0.00
9	0.00
10	0.00
11	0.00
12	20,000.00

Notice that you could describe it quite succinctly like this:

> "The initial cash-flow is –25,000.00.
>
> "The amount of the first cash-flow group is 400.00.
> The number of times this occurs in a row is 4.
>
> "The amount of the next cash-flow group is 750.00.
> The number of times it occurs in a row is 1.
>
> "The amount of the next cash-flow group is 0.00.
> The number of times it occurs in a row is 6.
>
> "The amount of the next cash-flow group is 20,000.00.
> The number of time it occurs in a row is 1."

That's the whole idea right there. Notice, however, that you treat the very first cash-flow (the INITIAL FLOW) separately; it usually represents the investment (a negative) cash-flow in the scenario.

But other than that, just read off the groups from your T-bar (top to bottom) or diagram (left to right), note how many times each cash-flow amount occurs in a row, and key this information into your CFLO list.

Do It: Key in the cash-flow scenario from the previous page.

Like So: First, of course, go to the CFLO Menu so that your display looks like that shown on page 204. Now, watch your display as you press ■ CLEAR DATA ▐ YES ▌ and then:

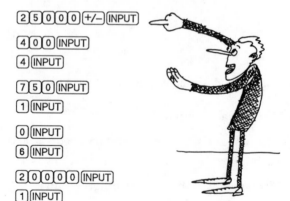

2 5 0 0 0 +/− INPUT

4 0 0 INPUT

4 INPUT

7 5 0 INPUT

1 INPUT

0 INPUT

6 INPUT

2 0 0 0 0 INPUT

1 INPUT

Did you notice your display as you were doing this? The ▶ shows you which item you're currently working on, and the FLOW( )= and #TIMES= tells you what that item is.

Keep in mind that the initial flow is really "**FLOW(0)**," and it always occurs just "1 time in a row." It's the first cash-flow group *after* that which is called **FLOW(1)**.

Also, notice that every time you key in a cash-flow amount, the machine starts out by assuming that this flow occurs only once. That is, it puts a **1** in there for the **#TIMES=** , so that if this *is* the case, you don't need to key in ⑴; you just press (INPUT)—very handy.

Change Values: Go to the top of the list and step down through it to check it. Then change the cash-flow *amounts* (not the number of times each occurs) as follows:

> **INIT=-22,000**
> **FLOW(1): 250.00**
> **FLOW(2): 400.00**
> **FLOW(4): 25,000**

Solution: Press ■ ⑴ (to jump to the top), then ⑴⑴⑴⑴⑴⑴ ⑴, and check the display against your diagram. Then ■ ⑴ once again, and change the numbers:

⑵⑵⓪⓪⓪ (+/−) (INPUT)
⑵⑸⓪ (INPUT)
⑴ ⑷⓪⓪ (INPUT)
⑴⑴⑴⑵⑸⓪⓪⓪ (INPUT)

(You can change the numbers in any order, but it just means more moving around with ⑴ and ⑴.)

With the changed numbers, your situation now looks like this:

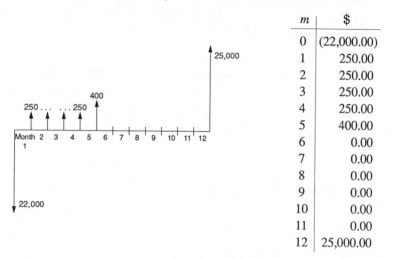

m	$
0	(22,000.00)
1	250.00
2	250.00
3	250.00
4	250.00
5	400.00
6	0.00
7	0.00
8	0.00
9	0.00
10	0.00
11	0.00
12	25,000.00

Now, before you do any calculations, you should NAME your list so that the machine will save it: Press **NAME** (F)(R)(E)(D)(INPUT). Then **CALC** ....

Look: You'll see this menu:

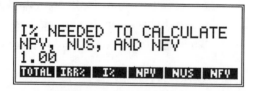

This is the CALCulations Menu, where you "crunch" your answers after drawing the correct picture. Notice the message, telling you that you must key in an interest rate, I%, before you can calculate NPV, NUS, and NFV. Why? What are those calculations anyway?

What Is NPV?

Suppose this cash-flow scenario ("FRED") is a real-life situation—an investment opportunity you're being offered to help your friend, Fred, to get a business started over the course of the next year.

The budding entrepreneur figures that he needs $22,000 up front. He offers to demonstrate his good faith and ability to manage cash by paying a little something back over the first five months ($250 for four months and then one month of $400). Then, if you'll give him until the end of the year with no further payments, he'll pay you off with an even $25,000 at that time.

The pitch: Over the year-long scenario, he claims that you'll be earning an A.P.R. of about 19.175%.

Would you do it? How can you verify his claim?

Go back to the basics: The Time Value of Money is *the interest value that time adds to money*. A little bit now is entirely equivalent to more later, and the equalizer is the interest rate that acts over that time.

Now apply this to the question at hand: Your friend is claiming that your $22,000 given to him now is *entirely equivalent* to his giving you $250/month for 4 months, $400 for 1 month, $0/month for 6 months, and then $25,000, *assuming an interest rate* of 19.175% A.P.R.

Can you prove this equivalence?   Yes—with NPV....

Recall (from pages 109-110) that you can slide cash-flows across a cash-flow diagram (or up and down a T-bar*)—as long as you increase or discount them according to the prevailing interest rate.

What if you were to take each of the cash-flows of this proposal and slide them back to the beginning of the timeline, *discounting* each one of them according to the assumed 19.175% A.P.R.?

Here's the starting situation:

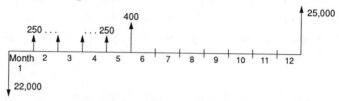

Here it is after you've slid that first $250 back. See how it's reduced? It has been discounted, according to the assumed 19.175% A.P.R.:

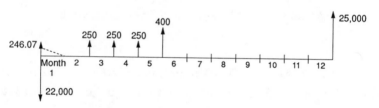

And here it is after the second $250 slides back. It amounts to even less, of course, because it had a longer time to be discounted:

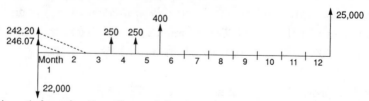

*This particular explanation will use cash-flow diagrams, but you can do it with T-bars, too.

And so on, until the picture looked like this:

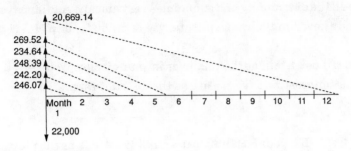

All the cash-flows have been discounted back and stacked up (the zero cash flows would still be zero, right?).

Then, of course, you can add together any simultaneous cash-flows. So one big simplification would be to lump together (sum) all those positive cash-flows:

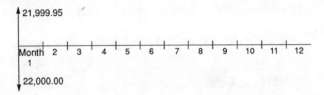

They *balance* the negative cash-flow—to within a nickel! Coincidence? No, this is what your entrepreneur friend, Fred, has said all along: Your $22,000 investment in him *was* equivalent to all his various future repayments, if you discount everything back at 19.175% A.P.R.

That's what NPV is: *A discounting-back-and-summing-up of all cash flows at the beginning of the timeline.*

Of course, the idea here is that your calculator can compute this NPV —do all the discounting and summing—very quickly. And since you've already keyed in the whole picture, you're ready to "crunch," right?

Wrong. Look again at the reminder in your display. You need to tell it what interest rate (I%) to use as the discount rate.

Tell It: Tell your HP 19Bɪɪ to use a 19.175% A.P.R. as the prevailing discount rate in this cash-flow scenario.

Ahem: Do you just key in ⬚1⬚9⬚·⬚1⬚7⬚5 and press ▮ I% ▮? Nope.

The CFLO Menu is not like the TVM Menu, where you don't need to worry about converting the A.P.R. to a D.I.R.—the machine does it for you, once you tell it the P/YR. Here in the CFLO Menu, you must *manually* convert any A.P.R. to its correct form (monthly in this case).

So you must press ⬚1⬚9⬚·⬚1⬚7⬚5⬚÷⬚1⬚2⬚= (ALGebraic) *or* ⬚1⬚9⬚·⬚1⬚7⬚5⬚INPUT⬚1⬚2⬚÷ (RPN), and then ▮ I% ▮.

Now you're ready. If your paper analysis has been correct, then the NPV should be about zero, because it nets together everything at the beginning of the timeline, adding your initial –22,000 to that stack of positive cash-flows that were discounted back from the future. Since these amounts are equal and opposite, they *ought* to net out to be zero—within a nickel or so. So press ▮ NPV ▮ to see: NPV=-0.05

Now, notice the other items on this CALC Menu. Each of them analyzes your CFLO list. For example, press **TOTAL**. You'll get the simple sum of all cash-flows in your list: TOTAL=4,400.00

Silly Question: If you compute an NPV with a discount rate (I%) of zero, what would you get for an answer?

Silly Answer: A zero discount rate means that you're not discounting at all. You're just moving each cash-flow, as is, back to the beginning of the timeline and summing all of them.

So, what should you get? It's the same as taking the TOTAL, which you just did, above: 4,400.00

Make Sure: Do it. Press ⓪ **I%**, then **NPV**....
<u>Answer</u>:   NPV=4,400.00

But what does this 4,400.00 *mean*? And what was the meaning of that leftover nickel (-0.05) from the analysis of Fred's proposal? What *is* the meaning of NPV?

To answer that, look at this simple demonstration....

Problem: If you use a discount rate of 19.175% A.P.R. then the Net Present Value (NPV) of Fred's deal is about zero. That is, after all the discounting-and-summing, *your investments balance your returns.*

But what would be the NPV of Fred's proposal if you were to use a discount rate of 20% A.P.R. instead?

Solution: Press $\boxed{2}\boxed{0}\boxed{\div}\boxed{1}\boxed{2}\boxed{=}$ (ALG) *or* $\boxed{2}\boxed{0}\boxed{\text{INPUT}}\boxed{1}\boxed{2}\boxed{\div}$ (RPN), ▮ I% ▮ NPV .... <u>Answer:</u> NPV=-170.01

Question: What does this number mean?

Answer: It means that *if* the value of your money (i.e. what you could yield with it in some other, similar investment) is really 20% A.P.R., then you would *lose* $170.01 by choosing this deal over that other, similar investment.

That's what you were being told in the 19.175% A.P.R. case also: Under that discount rate, the deal had an NPV of –$0.05, meaning that by helping Fred with his start-up, you were losing just a nickel compared to any other investment that would yield you 19.175% A.P.R..

So NPV is an advisory number that compares the cash-flow scenario you're analyzing with a hypothetical investment that yields exactly the discount rate, I%, that you specify:

- If the resulting NPV is *positive*, this means the cash-flow scenario is earning you *more* than the specified discount rate.

- If the NPV is *negative*, the cash-flow scenario is yielding *less* than the specified discount rate;

- If the NPV is *zero*, then there's no difference—a perfect balance.

Therefore, it's usually wise to use as a discount rate that which you really *could* yield in another investment of similar risk and liquidity. Then the NPV is a very good indicator of any investment's value to you *relative to what else you could reasonably expect to do with that money.*

For another good illustration of the advisory message offered by NPV consider the **4,400.00** NPV value you calculated with a discount rate of 0% (page 213).

$4,400—a *positive* NPV—tells you this: "If the yield on your money in other investments of similar risk and liquidity is *really* 0%, then you come out $4,400 *ahead* by putting your money into Fred's scenario rather than into any of your 0%-yield alternatives."

What Is IRR%?

The other "big" item on your CFLO CALC Menu is IRR%, and now it's time to take a look at what Internal Rate of Return is all about. What exactly does it mean?

In 25 words or less:

> "Internal Rate of Return (IRR%) is the discount rate that produces a Net Present Value (NPV) of *zero* for the given cash-flow situation."

Remember your friend Fred's claim about your 19.175% A.P.R. "yield" on his business startup plan (page 209)? You proved he was right by proving that your returns *balance* your investment if you discount those returns back at a 19.175% discount rate.

This balancing is what IRR% does. It actually performs a set of trial-and-error NPV calculations, varying the discount rate until it finds a rate that gives an NPV of zero.

Indeed, where do you suppose Fred *got* that 19.175 he quoted to you? Lucky guess, maybe? No, he probably did an IRR calculation.

Prove It: Find the IRR% of Fred's proposal (shown again here):

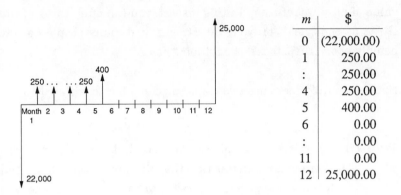

m	$
0	(22,000.00)
1	250.00
:	250.00
4	250.00
5	400.00
6	0.00
:	0.00
11	0.00
12	25,000.00

Solution: This scenario is the list you named FRED, so from the CFLO Menu, GET that list now, by pressing **GET** **FRED**. Then—without any further ado—just go to the CALC Menu and calculate the IRR%: **CALC** **IRR%**....
Answer: <u>IRR%=1.60</u>

Uh... that's not the 19.175 you were expecting, is it? No—remember that all discount rates in the CFLO Menu are *periodic*, not annualized (not true of the I%YR of the TVM Menu). The periods in your friend's scenario are months, so the IRR% is also monthly.

So annualize it: ✕①②= (ALG) *or* ①②✕ (RPN) <u>Result:</u> **19.17**
That's better. And if you see ALL its decimal places (press DISP **ALL**), you'll see that it *was* just about 19.175—but not exactly, which explains why, when you used *exactly* 19.175, you had a nickel or so of difference.

Thus, in many cash-flow scenarios, IRR% is a very convenient way to compute the discount rate that "balances" the situation—the rate that equates the present value of all your investments with the present value of all your returns. In this respect, you can often think of the IRR% as the "yield" on your investment, and many people do rely heavily upon IRR% to tell them their "yields."

But be careful! There are two traps you can fall into with IRR%:

Trap #1: It's entirely possible to have a cash-flow situation where there is no discount rate that will give a zero NPV. And (even worse), it's also possible to have *more than one* rate that zeros out the NPV—*multiple* IRR%'s.

You can often spot such multiple situations because they tend to flip-flop their cash-flows a lot, maybe with some investments first, then some returns, then some more investments, etc., like this:

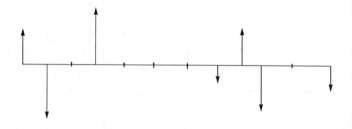

Fortunately, a conventional, one-time investment situation—like FRED—generally has one IRR% at most.

Trap #2: Even when you can find an IRR% that seems reasonable, it's easy to talk yourself right into the land of unreality.

For example, look at this investment:

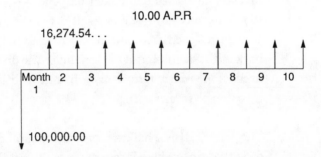

At the beginning, you invested $100,000, and over the next ten years you received steady, even returns on that investment. The IRR% ("yield") for this situation is 10%. So you yielded 10% per year on $100,000 for ten years, right?

Wrong! You *actually* yielded:

10% for *one* year on $14,795.04, then pocketed $16,274.54
10% for *two* years on $13,450.03, then pocketed $16,274.54
10% for *three* years on $12,227.30, then pocketed $16,274.54
...etc. (use TVM to confirm these numbers, if you wish).

In other words, this is the real picture:

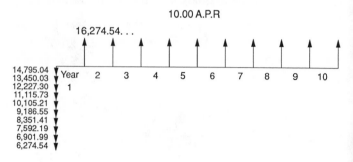

10.00 A.P.R

16,274.54. . .

14,795.04
13,450.03
12,227.30
11,115.73
10,105.21
9,186.55
8,351.41
7,592.19
6,901.99
6,274.54

Year 1 2 3 4 5 6 7 8 9 10

Every multiple cash-flow situation is really made up of investment/return pairs like this. And—as you've seen—this is exactly how NPV looks at it too: It identifies and transforms each cash-flow into its discounted counterpart back at the beginning of the timeline. The discount rate is used as the *rate of return* on each of these little "internal" investment/return pairs.

The point is, IRR% makes no assumptions about what you do with your "pocketed" returns once you get them. It only claims that the growth rate of each of these little investments was 10% per year *while it was invested*. The minute you get your money back, *the growth stops on that money*— who's to say what you do with it after that?

So you actually yield 10% for *ten years* on only $6,274.54. That's a whole lot different than yielding 10% on $100,000 for ten years.

An easy way to illustrate this is to add up all the pocketed returns of your investment: it comes to $162,745.39. This is what you'd have after the entire ten-year term of your cash-flow scenario—assuming that you did nothing but keep those returns in your pocket.

Now compare that with a simple $100,000 note, invested for 10 years at 10% per year. Its maturity value is $259,374.25.

Those are vastly different numbers. But in both cases your yield is 10% per year. The difference arises in the amount of time you let this yield act. Only in the case of the 10-year note can you say that you yielded 10% on your entire $100,000 for the *entire* term.

Never confuse the term of an investment *analysis* with the term(s) of the actual investment(s) *within* that analysis.

CFLO Quiz

(Draw those T-bars or cash-flow diagrams!)

CFLO Review

1. A loan is written at 12% A.P.R., with $450 monthly payments (in arrears), for 30 years. What is the loan amount? As an exercise, find it with an NPV calculation (don't cheat by using the TVM keys!). Do the same for annuity in advance.

2. How much should you deposit now in a bank account that earns 8% A.P.R. (tax deferred), compounded monthly, so that you can withdraw $10,000 at the beginning of every quarter for 20 years, starting 20 years from now? What about $15,000 withdrawals?

3. Suppose that, for one initial $10,000 investment, you could choose between either of these schedules of income: **(i)** $1000 after Years 1 and 2, $2000 after Year 3, $3000 after Year 4, $5000 after Year 5, $8000 after Year 6; *or* **(ii)** $2800 after each of the six years. Which is better? Comparable investments yield you 16%.

4. What even income stream is *equivalent* to the uneven stream in the previous problem? What would be the first year's income in an equivalent stream that increases annually by 4%?

Residential Real Estate

5. You're transferred to a new city for 4 years. You have $10,000 for a down-payment and are considering a $100,000 home. Property values are growing at 8% annually. The 30-year mortgage rate is 10%, and inflation is 5%. A liquid cash fund earns 8%, but a stock mutual fund could earn 15% annually over 4 years.

To buy the home, closing costs are $400; the loan fee is 1%. Insurance starts at $30/month, with $180/month in utilities and maintenance. Property taxes are 1.25% per year. Your tax bracket is 28%; capital gains are 100% taxable. You'll pay a 6% commission to resell the home.

On the other hand, if you rent the home, your security deposit would be $300. Your rent would start at $750, with monthly insurance at $15 and maintenance/utilities at $100.

"To buy or not to buy—that is the question."

6. You have just made the 84th monthly payment (in arrears) on your 30-year mortgage, whose rate is 11.875%. The balance now stands at $64,750, and current rates are at 10.5%. The refinancing fee is 2.5%. Should you refinance? You may pay off the mortgage on time, or in a balloon after 180th month.

Commercial Investment

7. You're considering the purchase of a double mortgage. The first mortgage was written for $90,000 for 30 years, with end-of-the-month payments at 12% A.P.R. After 15 years, a second mortgage for $30,000 was added, at 13.0% for 20 years, again with monthly payments in arrears. The bank now holding both mortgages is willing to discount them to you so that you can earn 16% on your investment. How much should you pay the bank for the right to "inherit" these contracts (begin to receive their payments) at the end of the third year of the second mortgage (i.e. at the end of the 18th year of the first mortgage)? What if you settle instead on a price that yields you 17.5%?

8. What is the monthly payment amount for a 5-year lease with skipped payments (annual schedule shown below) on a $40,000 computer with a 10% residual buy-out? The lessor is asking for 4 advance payments (other than the first normal payment) and wants an 18% yield.

Month	Payment?	Month	Payment?
1	yes	7	no
2	yes	8	no
3	yes	9	no
4	no	10	yes
5	no	11	yes
6	yes	12	yes

9. A manufacturer is relocating and needs a warehouse until its own facilities are completed (2 years). One suitable building is for sale for $100,000, of which 75% is depreciable. The firm has $30,000 in ready cash. The 20-year mortgage rate is 10%, and inflation is 5%. Cash funds earn 7%; stock funds earn 15%. To buy the building, closing costs are $400; the loan fee is 2%. Insurance starts at $60/month, with $250/month in utilities/maintenance. Property taxes are 1.25% per year. The company's tax bracket is 33%, with capital gains 100% taxable. A broker will charge 6% commission to resell the building. Estimated price: $115,000.

Alternatively, to lease the building from the current owner, rent would start at $750/mo. (including property taxes), with 2 payments (in addition to the first regular payment) due immediately, and with annual adjustments for inflation. Insurance would be $85; maintenance/utilities would be $220.

Should the company buy the building or lease it?

10. A home currently has two mortgages: $100,000 at 10% for 30 years (no balloon); and $50,000 at 11.5% for 10 years, with a $10,000 balloon. The second mortgage began after the 15th year of the first. Now, after the 20th year, the owner wishes to consolidate loans and get financing for more remodelling. You offer to "wrap" his current mortgages (cover all their obligations) and loan him $50,000 in new money, in exchange for 120 monthly payments of $2,200 and a $25,000 balloon. What is your yield? And what is the borrower's overall A.P.R.? He paid 1 point up front on the first mortgage, 2 points up front on the second.

11. You are considering an investment in low-income housing. Your cash-flows will look like this:

Year (end)	Cash-Flow
0 (initial flow)	$ -50,000
1	25,000
2	50,000
3	-25,000
4	50,000
5	-25,000
6	-10,000
7	-10,000

What would be your yield on this investment scenario?

12. Find the FMRR for the following cash-flow scenario, assuming that all cash is taken from, and returned to, an account earning 6%. Compare this FMRR with the IRR% for the same situation.

Year	Cash-Flow
0	$ (75,000)
1	15,000
2	15,000
3	(60,000)
4	75,000
5	(35,000)
6	200,000

13. Using a safe rate of 6% and a risk rate of 15%, find the FMRR, $MIN and $MAX of the scenario in Chapter 5, problem 24 (pages 167 and 190-196).

Personal Finance

14. Recall the comparison of IRA's in Chapter 5 (prob. **9**, pages 162 and 175). The idea was that 7 early years of investment were more valuable after 28 years than similar investments made in each of those later 28 years. Prove this again with a CFLO list.

15. After having invested in three no-load mutual funds as shown in the schedule below, you had a sudden, violent attack of prudence on August 31, 1987, and sold everything—for these net amounts:

> A: $34,319
> B: $13,526
> C: $22,410

Fund	Date	Amount Invested
A	9-30-82	$ 3000
B	3-15-83	1000
C	5-31-83	2500
A	6-30-83	2500
B	11-15-83	1000
C	4-15-84	2500
A	5-31-84	3500
B	8-15-84	1000
C	10-15-84	3000
A	12-31-84	3000
B	4-15-85	1500
C	6-30-85	4000

What was your overall annualized yield?

CFLO Quiz Solutions

1. Here's the situation (as the lender would see it):

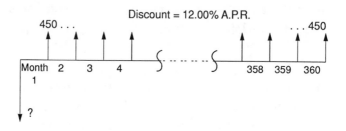

Your unknown is the cash-flow at the beginning of the timeline. Therefore, if you take the NPV of the rest of your list—using the actual rate as the discount rate, the result must exactly balance this unknown flow—equal and opposite (recall Fred's scenario). This makes sense: If the quoted 12% A.P.R. truly represents the interest rate in this mortgage, it *must* be the discount rate for which the entire scenario's NPV is zero. If it produces an NPV either more or less than zero, then the mortgage's yield is either more or less (respectively) than the 12% A.P.R. You use this "incomplete" NPV to deduce what other cash-flow must have happened at the beginning of the timeline to produce a *zero* NPV.

So just key in the cash-flow scenario, ignoring the initial flow: Press **GET** **NEW** at the CFLO Menu. Then:

⓪ INPUT   (no initial cash-flow except the unknown you ignore)

④⑤⓪ INPUT ③⑥⓪ INPUT   (360 months of $450 payments).

To calculate, press **CALC** and ①②÷①②＝ or ①②INPUT①②÷,

then **I%** to specify the monthly discount rate.

Now **NPV**....<u>Answer</u>: NPV=43,748.25

The amount financed (from the lender's viewpoint) was –$43,748.25

Now redraw the picture for the case of annuity in advance:

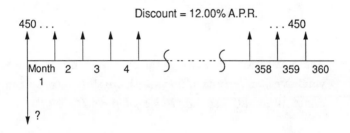

Again, find the unknown flow at the beginning by ignoring it.

EXIT to the CFLO Menu to modify your list now:

■ ↑④⑤⓪ INPUT   (in BEGIN Mode, there's a PMT right away)

↓   (change only the frequency of FLOW(1))

③⑤⑨ INPUT

⓪ INPUT INPUT   (the end of month 360 has no cash-flow)

CALC NPV   <u>Answer</u>: NPV=44,185.73

The initial cash-flow (from the lender's viewpoint) was –$44,185.73.

Verify these values with the TVM Menu, if you wish.

2. The situation:

q	$
0	(?.??)
1	0.00
:	0.00
79	0.00
80	10,000.00
:	10,000.00
159	10,000.00

Discount = 8.00% (compounded monthly)

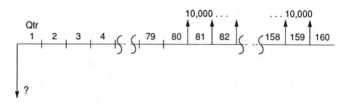

Again, the problem is to find the unknown initial cash-flow. But you have *quarterly* cash-flows with *monthly* interest compounding of interest ("...*sounds like a job for... ICONV!*").

First, draw the picture: At the CFLO Menu: █ CLEAR DATA █ ▐YES▌

⁰ INPUT   (nothing happens initially, except for the
                           unknown flow, which you ignore for now.)

⁰ INPUT ⁷ ⁹ INPUT   (79 quarters of no cash-flows)

¹ ⁰ ⁰ ⁰ ⁰ INPUT ⁸ ⁰ INPUT (80 quarters of withdrawals)

Now convert the interest rate: EXIT ▐ICONV▌ ▐PER▌

⁸ ▐NOM%▌ ¹ ² ▐ P ▌ ▐EFF%▌ ⁴ ▐ P ▌ ▐NOM%▌....

<u>Result</u>: NOM%=8.05

Then EXIT EXIT ▐CFLO▌ ▐CALC▌, then ÷ ⁴ = (ALG) or ⁴ ÷ (RPN),
then ▐I%▌ ▐NPV▌.... <u>Answer</u>: NPV=81,967.88

Change to $15,000 withdrawals: EXIT ↑ ↑ ¹ ⁵ ⁰ ⁰ ⁰ INPUT ▐CALC▌
▐NPV▌.... <u>Answer</u>: NPV=122,951.83

3. The alternatives:

Discount = 16.00% A.P.R.

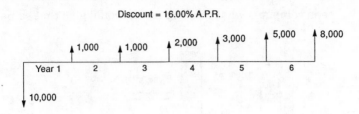

Discount = 16.00% A.P.R.

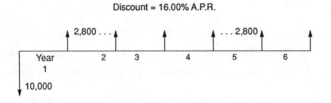

From the CFLO Menu, clear or name the current list, then begin
a new list: ①⓪⓪⓪⓪ +/− INPUT ②⑧⓪⓪ INPUT ⑥ INPUT
CALC ①⑥ **I%** **NPV** .... <u>Answer:</u> NPV=317.26

That's the simple, even cash-flow option. Now EXIT to CFLO, and
name this list: **NAME** E V E N INPUT, and **GET** **%NEW**.

Now for the other case:
①⓪⓪⓪⓪ +/− INPUT   ①⓪⓪⓪ INPUT ② INPUT
②⓪⓪⓪ INPUT INPUT   ③⓪⓪⓪ INPUT INPUT
⑤⓪⓪⓪ INPUT INPUT   ⑧⓪⓪⓪ INPUT INPUT
CALC **NPV** .... <u>Answer:</u> NPV=207.52
(NAME this list UNEVEN: EXIT **NAME** U N E V E N INPUT).

NPV tells you that the EVEN case is worth slightly more to you.

4. This is a question to answer with a NUS ("Net Uniform Series") calculation. NUS takes the NPV of a given set of cash-flows and then computes what uniform series would give that same NPV:

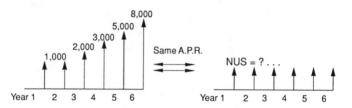

Notice that the initial –$10,000 is not in question; it's assumed in either case. You're analyzing only the positive cash-flows to see what uniform yearly amount could replace each of them.

So just omit the initial investment in your UNEVEN scenario (this should be the current CFLO list if you've just come from the previous problem): [EXIT] ■ [↑] [0] [INPUT] **CALC** and then **NUS** ....
Answer: NUS=2,770.22

So (at a discount rate of 16%), your uneven payment scenario has exactly the same value to you as six level payments of $2,770.22. This seems plausible: it's only slightly less than the $2800 EVEN case of problem **3**, and—as the results of that problem showed—there was only a slight difference between those two NPV's.

Prove the equivalency of your NUS, by using it as the cash-flow amount in the EVEN case; the NPV should then be exactly that of the UNEVEN case: [EXIT] and **GET EVEN**. Then [↓] and simply [INPUT] to replace the $2800 with the NUS (which is still on the Calculator Line). Then **CALC** and **NPV** ....
Answer: NPV=207.52   Sure enough.

The other part of this problem is similar, but it asks you to find a certain *uneven* scenario that satisfies the equivalency:

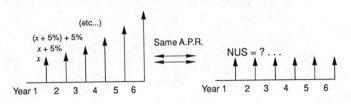

Each cash-flow in the unknown scenario is 4% more than the previous, *and* its NPV must match that of the UNEVEN scenario. First, find that NPV: [EXIT] **GET** **UNEVE**. Then **CALC** **NPV** ....

Answer: $NPV = 10,207.52$

Now, a 4%-increasing scenario that starts with *one dollar* has an NPV that is x times less than that of a 4%-increasing scenario that starts with x. In other words: $NPV_{\$x} = x(NPV_{\$1})$. But you've just calculated that $NPV_{\$x}$ is 10,207.52. So the x in the unknown scenario above is given by: $\quad x = 10,207.52 \div NPV_{\$1}$

So: [EXIT] and **GET** **%NEW**. Then: [0][INPUT]   [1][INPUT][INPUT]

[+][4][%] (ALG) *or* [4][%][+] (RPN)   [INPUT][INPUT][↑][↑][RCL][INPUT][↓][↓]
[+][4][%] (ALG) *or* [4][%][+] (RPN)   [INPUT][INPUT][↑][↑][RCL][INPUT][↓][↓]
[+][4][%] (ALG) *or* [4][%][+] (RPN)   [INPUT][INPUT][↑][↑][RCL][INPUT][↓][↓]
[+][4][%] (ALG) *or* [4][%][+] (RPN)   [INPUT][INPUT][↑][↑][RCL][INPUT][↓][↓]
[+][4][%] (ALG) *or* [4][%][+] (RPN)   [INPUT][INPUT]

CALC **NPV** .... (Result: $NPV = 4.01$)   Then ■[1/x] and
[×][1][0][2][0][7][·][5][2][=] (ALG) *or* [1][0][2][0][7][·][5][2][×] (RPN)

Answer: $2,548.38$

(If you do a lot of calculations with increasing annuities like this, you may find it useful to use the formula on page 368 in Ch. 9.)

5. Which NPV is greater?

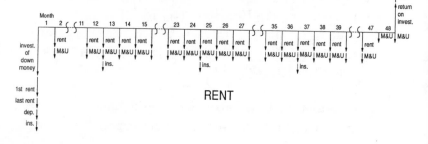

BUY

BUY assumptions: The mortgage payment, utilities and maintenance are due at the END of the month. You pay yearly insurance (in advance) and property taxes (in arrears), and tax relief from deductions comes at the end of the year. When you sell the home and pay off the mortgage, you will owe capital gains tax on your net gain—after any commission to a broker. The property value (and thus its tax) increases annually at the given growth rate.

The RENT assumptions: You owe first and last month's rent, plus a fully-refundable security deposit immediately. Rent is paid at the beginning of each month, maintenance/utilities at the end. Your renter's insurance premium is paid annually, in advance. Also, you pay yearly income tax on the interest accruing on your investment of the down-payment money.

In both cases, insurance, utilities / maintenance (and your rent in the RENT case) increase yearly by the inflation rate.

RENT

The underlined ending balance of the down-payment money invested:

EXIT EXIT [TVM] [OTHER] 1 [P/YR] EXIT, and

4 [N] 1 0 0 0 0 +/- [PV] 0 [PMT]

1 5 – 2 8 % = (ALG) or 1 5 INPUT 2 8 % – (RPN) [I/YR]

[FV] ....   Answer: FV=15,071.59

Monthly rent: 7 5 0 +/-	-750.00	(Year 1)
+ 5 % = (ALG) or INPUT 5 % + (RPN)	-787.50	(Year 2)
+ 5 % = (ALG) or 5 % + (RPN)	-826.88	(Year 3)
+ 5 % = (ALG) or 5 % + (RPN)	-868.22	(Year 4)

Yearly insurance (RENT): 1 5 +/- × 1 2 = (ALG) or		
1 5 +/- INPUT 1 2 × (RPN)	-180.00	(Year 1)
+ 5 % = (ALG) or 5 % + (RPN)	-189.00	(Year 2)
+ 5 % = (ALG) or 5 % + (RPN)	-198.45	(Year 3)
+ 5 % = (ALG) or 5 % + (RPN)	-208.37	(Year 3)

Monthly util./mnt. (RENT): 1 0 0 +/-	-100.00	(Year 1)
+ 5 % = (ALG) or INPUT 5 % + (RPN)	-105.00	(Year 2)
+ 5 % = (ALG) or 5 % + (RPN)	-110.25	(Year 3)
+ 5 % = (ALG) or 5 % + (RPN)	-115.76	(Year 4)

Yearly insurance (BUY): 3 0 +/- × 1 2 = (ALG) or		
3 0 +/- INPUT 1 2 × (RPN)	-360.00	(Year 1)
+ 5 % = (ALG) or 5 % + (RPN)	-378.00	(Year 2)
+ 5 % = (ALG) or 5 % + (RPN)	-396.90	(Year 3)
+ 5 % = (ALG) or 5 % + (RPN)	-416.75	(Year 4)

Monthly util./mnt. (BUY): 1 8 0 +/-	-180.00	(Year 1)
+ 5 % = (ALG) or INPUT 5 % + (RPN)	-189.00	(Year 2)
+ 5 % = (ALG) or 5 % + (RPN)	-198.45	(Year 3)
+ 5 % = (ALG) or 5 % + (RPN)	-208.37	(Year 4)

The <u>net (after-tax) yearly property taxes</u>:

⌨ `1` `0` `0` `0` `0` `0` `+` `8%` `×` `1` `·` `2` `5` `+/-` `%` `-` `2` `8%` `=` (ALG) *or*
⌨ `1` `0` `0` `0` `0` `0` `INPUT` `8%` `+` `1` `·` `2` `5` `+/-` `%` `2` `8%` `-` (RPN)

$$-972.00 \quad \text{(Year 1)}$$

`+` `8%` `=` (ALG) *or* `8%` `+` (RPN) **-1,049.76** (Year 2)

`+` `8%` `=` (ALG) *or* `8%` `+` (RPN) **-1,133.74** (Year 3)

`+` `8%` `=` (ALG) *or* `8%` `+` (RPN) **-1,224.44** (Year 4)

<u>Monthly mortgage pmt</u>: (At TVM—set P/YR to 12) `3` `6` `0` **N**
`1` `0` **I%YR** `9` `0` `0` `0` `0` **PV** `0` **FV** **PMT** ....PMT=**-789.81**

The <u>mortgage balance</u> after 4 years: `4` `8` **N** **FV** ....
FV=-87,662.00

The <u>mortgage interest yearly tax relief</u>: **OTHER** **AMRT**,

`1` `2` **#P** `+/-` `×` `2` `8%` `=` *or* `+/-` `2` `8%` **2,513.70** (Year 1)

NEXT `+/-` `×` `2` `8%` `=` *or* `+/-` `2` `8%` **2,499.03** (Year 2)

NEXT `+/-` `×` `2` `8%` `=` *or* `+/-` `2` `8%` **2,482.83** (Year 3)

NEXT `+/-` `×` `2` `8%` `=` *or* `+/-` `2` `8%` **2,464.93** (Year 4)

The <u>mortgage points tax relief</u>:

`9` `0` `0` `×` `2` `8%` `=` *or* `9` `0` `0` `INPUT` `2` `8%` **252.00** (Year 1)

The <u>proceeds of re-sale</u>:

⌨ `1` `0` `0` `0` `0` `0` `+` `8%` `+` `8%` `+` `8%` `+` `8%` `-` `6%` (ALG) *or*
⌨ `1` `0` `0` `0` `0` `0` `INPUT` `8%` `+` `8%` `+` `8%` `+` `8%` `+` `6%` `-` (RPN)
(<u>result</u>: **127,885.96**). So the gain on the sale is $27,885.96

The <u>net (after-tax) proceeds</u> at resale: `-` `8` `7` `6` `6` `2`
`-` `(` `2` `7` `8` `8` `5` `·` `9` `6` `×` `2` `8%` `=` (ALG) *or* `8` `7` `6` `6` `2` `-`
`2` `7` `8` `8` `5` `·` `9` `6` `INPUT` `·` `2` `8` `×` `-` (RPN) **32,415.89**

The completed RENT diagram:

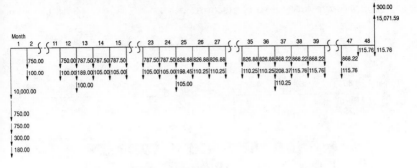

The completed BUY diagram:

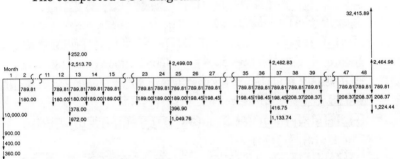

Now find the NPV of each scenario, using your 8% cash fund interest (less taxes) as the discount rate: **MAIN** **FIN** **CFLO**, etc. (you should now know how to key in the above diagrams).

For each scenario, **CALC** and:

⑧⊝②⑧%÷①②⊜(ALG) *or* ⑧INPUT②⑧%⊝①②÷ (RPN)

I% **NPV** .... <u>RENT</u>: NPV=-38,063.48

<u>BUY</u>: NPV=-23,912.24

As you can see, either case is a net *expense* to you—your cost of housing—but it will be less if you buy the house.

<u>Note</u>: If you do a lot of these rent/buy analyses, see the formula on page 356 of chapter 9.

6. Just find the NPV of the refinanced scenario, *using the original mortgage rate* as your discount rate:

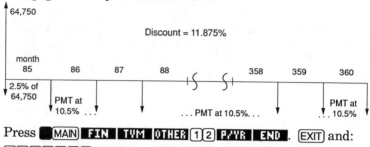

Press ▮ MAIN ▮ FIN ▮ TYM ▮ OTHER ▮ 1 ▮ 2 ▮ P/YR ▮ END ▮. EXIT and:

3 6 0 − 8 4 = (ALG) *or* (RPN) 3 6 0 INPUT 8 4 −

▮ N ▮ 1 0 · 5 I%YR 6 4 7 5 0 ▮ PV ▮ 0 ▮ FV ▮ PMT ▮....

Result: PMT=-622.81   The refinanced payment.

1 8 0 − 8 4 = (ALG) *or* (RPN) 1 8 0 INPUT 8 4 − ▮ N ▮ FV ▮

Result: FV=-56,342.47   The balloon after 180 months.

EXIT CFLO, and then draw the picture for your calculator: ▮ GET ▮

▮#NEW▮. Do the full-term case first: 6 4 7 5 0

− 2 · 5 % = INPUT (ALG) *or* ENTER 2 · 5 % − INPUT (RPN)

Then 6 2 2 · 8 1 +/− INPUT

3 6 0 − 8 4 = INPUT (ALG) *or* 3 6 0 ENTER 8 4 − INPUT (RPN)

▮CALC▮ 1 1 · 8 7 5 ÷ 1 2 = (ALG) *or*

▮CALC▮ 1 1 · 8 7 5 INPUT 1 2 ÷ (RPN)

▮ I% ▮ NPV ▮....   Answer: NPV=4,349.62

If you take the loan to term, you'll save by refinancing now.

If you pay it off in a balloon after the 180th month: EXIT ↑

1 7 9 − 8 4 = INPUT (ALG) *or* 1 7 9 ENTER 8 4 − INPUT (RPN)

5 6 3 4 2 · 4 7 +/− INPUT INPUT ▮CALC▮ ▮ NPV ▮....

Answer: NPV=2,998.81   You save in this case, too, but the savings are *less*; a refinancing fee has a relatively larger effect on a shorter-term scenario (see Ch. 5, prob. **14**, pages 163 and 179). See page 380 in Ch. 9 for a SOLVE formula for such calculations.

7. As the investor, you're the new lender:

Discount = 16.00% A.P.R

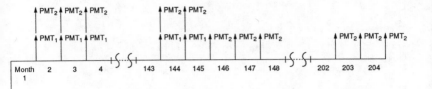

Press $\boxed{\text{MAIN}}$ $\boxed{\text{FIN}}$ $\boxed{\text{TVM}}$ $\boxed{\text{OTHER}}$ $\boxed{1}$$\boxed{2}$ $\boxed{\text{P/YR}}$ $\boxed{\text{END}}$. $\boxed{\text{EXIT}}$ and:
$\boxed{3}$$\boxed{6}$$\boxed{0}$ $\boxed{\text{N}}$ $\boxed{1}$$\boxed{2}$ $\boxed{\text{I/YR}}$ $\boxed{9}$$\boxed{0}$$\boxed{0}$$\boxed{0}$$\boxed{0}$$\boxed{+/-}$ $\boxed{\text{PV}}$ $\boxed{0}$ $\boxed{\text{FV}}$ $\boxed{\text{PMT}}$ ....
<u>Result:</u> PMT=925.75   The payment on the first mortgage.
$\boxed{2}$$\boxed{4}$$\boxed{0}$ $\boxed{\text{N}}$ $\boxed{1}$$\boxed{3}$ $\boxed{\text{I/YR}}$ $\boxed{3}$$\boxed{0}$$\boxed{0}$$\boxed{0}$$\boxed{0}$$\boxed{+/-}$ $\boxed{\text{PV}}$ $\boxed{\text{PMT}}$ ....
<u>Result:</u> PMT=351.47   The payment on the second.

$\boxed{\text{EXIT}}$ $\boxed{\text{CFLO}}$, and enter the scenario, omitting the unknown initial investment, just as in problems **1** and **2**: $\boxed{\text{GET}}$ $\boxed{\text{*NEW}}$, then:
$\boxed{0}$$\boxed{\text{INPUT}}$ (no initial cash-flow besides the unknown)
$\boxed{9}$$\boxed{2}$$\boxed{5}$$\boxed{\cdot}$$\boxed{7}$$\boxed{5}$$\boxed{+}$$\boxed{3}$$\boxed{5}$$\boxed{1}$$\boxed{\cdot}$$\boxed{4}$$\boxed{7}$ (ALG) *or*

                $\boxed{9}$$\boxed{2}$$\boxed{5}$$\boxed{\cdot}$$\boxed{7}$$\boxed{5}$$\boxed{\text{ENTER}}$$\boxed{3}$$\boxed{5}$$\boxed{1}$$\boxed{\cdot}$$\boxed{4}$$\boxed{7}$$\boxed{+}$ (RPN)
$\boxed{\text{INPUT}}$ (your combined payments...) $\boxed{1}$$\boxed{4}$$\boxed{4}$$\boxed{\text{INPUT}}$ (for 12 years...)
$\boxed{3}$$\boxed{5}$$\boxed{1}$$\boxed{\cdot}$$\boxed{4}$$\boxed{7}$$\boxed{\text{INPUT}}$$\boxed{6}$$\boxed{0}$$\boxed{\text{INPUT}}$ (...and 5 more years of the second)
$\boxed{\text{CALC}}$ $\boxed{1}$$\boxed{6}$$\boxed{\div}$$\boxed{1}$$\boxed{2}$$\boxed{=}$ (ALG) *or* (RPN) $\boxed{1}$$\boxed{6}$$\boxed{\text{INPUT}}$$\boxed{1}$$\boxed{2}$$\boxed{\div}$ $\boxed{\text{I%}}$
$\boxed{\text{NPV}}$ ....   <u>Answer:</u> NPV=83,714.46

The price of this double mortgage that will yield you 16%.

To yield 17.5%:
$\boxed{1}$$\boxed{7}$$\boxed{\cdot}$$\boxed{5}$$\boxed{\div}$$\boxed{1}$$\boxed{2}$$\boxed{=}$ (ALG) *or* (RPN) $\boxed{1}$$\boxed{7}$$\boxed{\cdot}$$\boxed{5}$$\boxed{\text{INPUT}}$$\boxed{1}$$\boxed{2}$$\boxed{\div}$ $\boxed{\text{I%}}$
$\boxed{\text{NPV}}$ ....   <u>Answer:</u> NPV=78,431.48

See page 380 in Ch. 9 for a SOLVE formula for such calculations.

8. Here is the proposed scenario:

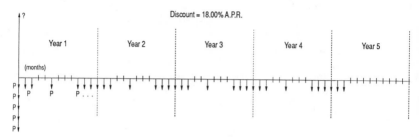

First, find the NPV which the lease payments must "balance:"
At the CFLO Menu: [■ CLEAR DATA] [**YES**] [4][0][0][0][0][INPUT]
[0][INPUT][5][9][INPUT][4][0][0][0][+/−][INPUT][INPUT] [**CALC**]
and [1][8][÷][1][2][=](ALG) or [1][8][INPUT][1][2][÷](RPN) [**I%**] [**NPV**] ....
NPV=38,362.82   The payments must "balance" this.
Now, as in problem **4**, when you don't know the amount of a given
cash-flow—but you do know its NPV—use a $1 cash-flow. That
NPV is *proportionally* less than that of the unknown cash-flow, so
the *ratio* of the NPV's is the amount of the unknown cash-flow:
[EXIT] [■ CLEAR DATA] [**YES**] [5][+/−][INPUT] (4 in advance, plus the first)
[1][+/−][INPUT][2][INPUT]   [0][INPUT][2][INPUT]   [1][+/−][INPUT][INPUT]
[0][INPUT][3][INPUT]   [1][+/−][INPUT][6][INPUT]   [0][INPUT][2][INPUT]
[1][+/−][INPUT][INPUT]   [0][INPUT][3][INPUT]   [1][+/−][INPUT][6][INPUT]
[0][INPUT][2][INPUT]   [1][+/−][INPUT][INPUT]   [0][INPUT][3][INPUT]
[1][+/−][INPUT][6][INPUT]   [0][INPUT][2][INPUT]   [1][+/−][INPUT][INPUT]
[0][INPUT][3][INPUT]   [1][+/−][INPUT][6][INPUT]

(Remember that the final 4 payments were paid in advance)
[**CALC**] [**NPV**] .... NPV=−25.64   Then [■][1/x] and
[×][3][8][3][6][2][.][8][2][=](ALG) *or* [3][8][3][6][2][.][8][2][×](RPN)
<u>Result</u>: −1,496.36 The monthly lease payment amount.
<u>Note</u>: If you do a lot of leasing calculations, see the formula on
page 372 in Chapter 9.

9. This is like #5 (page 234), but all expenses are tax-deductible. Also, there is depreciation (31.5 years, Straight Line); the capital gain is the difference between the re-sale and *depreciated* values.

<u>Ending balance</u> of the down-payment money invested:
[EXIT] [EXIT] **TVM** **OTHER** [1] **P/YR** [EXIT], and
[2] **N** [3] [0] [0] [0] [+/−] **PV** [0] **PMT**
[1] [5] [−] [3] [3] [%] [=] (ALG) *or* [1] [5] [INPUT] [3] [3] [%] [−] (RPN) **I%YR**
FV ....   <u>Answer:</u> FV=36,333.01

<u>Monthly lease payment:</u> [7] [5] [0] [+/−]   −750.00   (Year 1)
[+] [5] [%] [=] (ALG) *or* [INPUT] [5] [%] [+] (RPN)   −787.50   (Year 2)

<u>Yearly insurance</u> (LEASE): [8] [5] [+/−] [×] [1] [2] [=] (ALG)
    or [8] [5] [+/−] [INPUT] [1] [2] [×] (RPN) −1,020.00   (Year 1)
[+] [5] [%] [=] (ALG) *or* [5] [%] [+] (RPN)   −1,071.00   (Year 2)

<u>Monthly util./mnt.</u> (LEASE): [2] [2] [0] [+/−] −220.00   (Year 1)
[+] [5] [%] [=] (ALG) *or* [INPUT] [5] [%] [+] (RPN)   −231.00   (Year 2)

<u>Expenses yearly tax relief (LEASE):</u> [7] [5] [0] [×] [1] [4] [+] [1] [0] [2] [0] [+]
[(] [(] [1] [2] [×] [2] [2] [0] [)] [×] [3] [3] [%] [=] (ALG) *or* [7] [5] [0] [INPUT] [1] [4] [×]
[1] [0] [2] [0] [+] [1] [2] [INPUT] [2] [2] [0] [×] [+] [3] [3] [%] 4,672.80   (Year 1)
[7] [8] [7] [·] [5] [×] [1] [0] [+] [1] [0] [7] [1] [+] [(] [1] [2] [×] [2] [3] [1] [)] [×] [3] [3] [%] [=] *or*
[7] [8] [7] [·] [5] [INPUT] [1] [0] [×] [1] [0] [7] [1] [+] [1] [2] [INPUT] [2] [3] [1] [×] [+] [3] [3] [%]
                            3,866.94   (Year 2)

<u>Yearly insurance</u> (BUY): [6] [0] [+/−] [×] [1] [2] [=] (ALG)
    or [6] [0] [+/−] [INPUT] [1] [2] [×] (RPN)   −720.00   (Year 1)
[+] [5] [%] [=] (ALG) *or* [5] [%] [+] (RPN)   −756.00   (Year 2)

<u>Monthly util./mnt.</u> (BUY): [2] [5] [0] [+/−]   −250.00   (Year 1)
[+] [5] [%] [=] (ALG) *or* [INPUT] [5] [%] [+] (RPN)   −262.50   (Year 2)

Net yearly property taxes: `1` `0` `0` `0` `0` `0` `×` `1` `·` `1` `5` `▮` `√x` `×`
`1` `·` `2` `5` `+/−` `%` `−` `3` `3` `%` `=` (ALG) or `1` `0` `0` `0` `0` `0` `INPUT` `1` `·` `1` `5`
`▮` `√x` `×` `1` `·` `2` `5` `+/−` `%` `3` `3` `%` `−` (RPN)   -898.12   (Year 1)
`×` `1` `·` `1` `5` `▮` `√x` `=` (ALG) or

`1` `·` `1` `5` `▮` `√x` `×` (RPN)   -963.13   (Year 2)

Monthly mortgage payment: (At TVM) **OTHER** `1` `2` **P/YR**
END `EXIT` `2` `4` `0` **N** `1` `0` **I%YR** `7` `0` `0` `0` `0` **PV** `0` **FV**
PMT .... PMT=-675.52

Mortgage balance: `2` `4` **N** **FV** .... FV=-67,562.08

Mortgage interest yearly tax relief: **OTHER** **AMRT** ,
`1` `2` **#P** `+/−` `×` `3` `3` `%` `=` or `+/−` `3` `3` `%` 2,292.80 (Year 1)
NEXT `+/−` `×` `3` `3` `%` `=` or `+/−` `3` `3` `%` 2,252.77 (Year 2)

Mortgage points yearly tax relief: `7` `0` `0` `0` `0` `×` `2` `%` `×` `3` `3` `%` `÷`
`2` `=` (ALG) or `7` `0` `0` `0` `0` `INPUT` `2` `%` `2` `÷` `3` `3` `%` (RPN) 231.00

Depreciation yearly tax relief: `7` `5` `0` `0` `0` `÷` `3` `1` `·` `5` `×` `3` `3` `%` `=`
(ALG) or `7` `5` `0` `0` `0` `INPUT` `3` `1` `·` `5` `÷` `3` `3` `%` (RPN) 785.71

Expenses yearly tax relief (BUY): `4` `0` `0` `+` `7` `2` `0` `+`
`(` `1` `2` `×` `2` `5` `0` `)` `×` `3` `3` `%` `=` (ALG) or `4` `0` `0` `INPUT` `7` `2` `0` `+`
`1` `2` `INPUT` `2` `5` `0` `×` `+` `3` `3` `%` (RPN) 1,359.60 (Year 1)
`1` `2` `×` `2` `6` `2` `·` `5` `+` `7` `5` `6` `×` `3` `3` `%` `=` (ALG) or `1` `2` `INPUT`
`2` `6` `2` `·` `5` `×` `7` `5` `6` `+` `3` `3` `%` (RPN) 1,288.98 (Year 2)

Proceeds at resale: `1` `1` `5` `0` `0` `0` `−` `6` `%` `=` (ALG) or `1` `1` `5` `0` `0` `0`
`INPUT` `6` `%` `−` (RPN) 108,100.00 (Gross proceeds)
`−` `(` `(` `1` `0` `0` `0` `0` `0` `−` `(` `2` `×` `7` `5` `0` `0` `0` `÷` `3` `1` `·` `5` `=` (ALG) or
`1` `0` `0` `0` `0` `0` `INPUT` `7` `5` `0` `0` `0` `INPUT` `3` `1` `·` `5` `÷` `2` `×` `−` `−` (RPN)
12,861.90 (Gain)

⑴⓪⑧①⓪⓪−⑥⑦⑤⑥②•⓪⑧−⟮①②⑧⑥①•⑨×③③%=
(ALG) or ①⓪⑧①⓪⓪ INPUT ⑥⑦⑤⑥②•⓪⑧−①②⑧⑥①•⑨
INPUT •③③ ×−(RPN)   **36,293.49**   (Net proceeds)

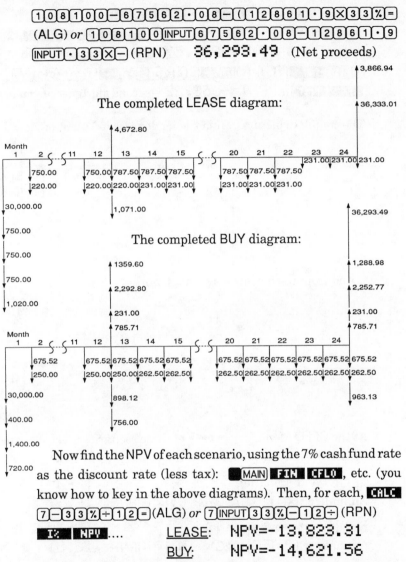

The completed LEASE diagram:

The completed BUY diagram:

Now find the NPV of each scenario, using the 7% cash fund rate as the discount rate (less tax): **MAIN** **FIN** **CFLO**, etc. (you know how to key in the above diagrams). Then, for each, **CALC** ⑦−③③%÷①②=(ALG) or ⑦ INPUT ③③%−①② ÷ (RPN)

I% **NPV** ....   <u>LEASE</u>:   NPV=-13,823.31
                      <u>BUY</u>:   NPV=-14,621.56

The company would be slightly better off leasing the building.
<u>Note:</u> If you do many such lease/buy analyses, see the formula on page 374 of Chapter 9.

10. At the TVM Menu: **OTHER** ①② **P/YR** **END** (EXIT). Then:

③⑥⓪ **N** ①⓪ **I%YR** ①⓪⓪⓪⓪⓪ **PV** ⓪ **FV** **PMT** ....

PMT=-877.57 (first mortgage payment)

①②⓪ **N** ①①·⑤ **I%YR** ⑤⓪⓪⓪⓪ **PV** ①⓪⓪⓪⓪+/-

FV **PMT** .... PMT=-658.22 (second mortgage payment)

The complete pictures, from the lender's (your) point of view...

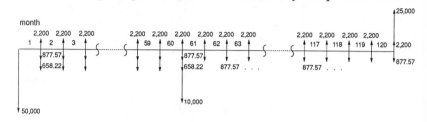

...and from the borrower's point of view:

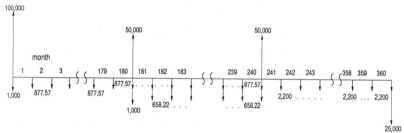

At the CFLO Menu, key in each of these scenarios and calculate their IRR%'s (you should know the keystrokes by now).

<u>Result</u> (your scenario):   IRR%=1.41

Annualize: ✕①②🟰 (ALG) *or* ①②✕ (RPN)   16.97

<u>Result</u> (borrower's scenario):   IRR%=0.88

Annualize: ✕①②🟰 (ALG) *or* ①②✕ (RPN)   10.51

<u>Note</u>: If you do a lot of these calculations, see the formula on page 380 of Chapter 9.

11. Nothing to it—just GET a new CFLO list and key in the numbers:

5 0 0 0 0 +/- INPUT

2 5 0 0 0 INPUT INPUT   5 0 0 0 0 INPUT INPUT

2 5 0 0 0 +/- INPUT INPUT   5 0 0 0 0 INPUT INPUT

2 5 0 0 0 +/- INPUT INPUT   1 0 0 0 0 +/- INPUT INPUT

1 0 0 0 0 +/- INPUT INPUT   **CALC** **IRR%** ....What's this?

```
┌─────────────────────────────────────┐
│                                      │
│ MANY OR NO SOLUTIONS                 │
│ INPUT GUESS [STO]{IRR%}              │
│ TOTAL  IRR%   I%    NPV   NUS   NFV  │
└─────────────────────────────────────┘
```

This is one of those cash-flow scenarios that has *more than one*
IRR%—more than one discount rate that will give an NPV of
zero. The display tells you to key in a guess and press STO **IRR%**.
It will then home in on the *nearest* solution.

What's a good starting guess? Something modest—say, 12%? So
press 1 2 STO **IRR%** .... <u>Result</u>: IRR%=17.77 Not bad.

But you've just been told that there is at least one other solution,
so try to find another—just for comparison. Try a much more
pessimistic guess: 0 STO **IRR%** .... <u>Result</u>: IRR%=-9.49

Which IRR% is right? Will you be losing or making money on this
housing deal?

It's not easy to tell—neither percentage is necessarily "right."
Remember that IRR% is simply a number that, when used as the
discount rate, happens to make the NPV balance at 0. It *doesn't*
always mean that your dollars are actually accruing that much
interest—as this example demonstrates.

So this is one of those times when you cannot simply look to IRR% to tell you your "yield." But, fortunately, there's another very logical way to calculate your "yield," the Financial Management Rate of Return (FMRR). Here's how it works:

When you invest money in any one place, you're choosing *not* to invest it somewhere else. Presumably, you do so because this investment best suits your needs—acceptable levels of risk and liquidity and, within those constraints, a good rate of return. But picture how you would actually make the investment(s) in the required schedule....

Question: Where will you get the money at each of the required dates of the investments?

Answer: From a bank account or another *readily liquid* account that is yielding you at least a little interest in the meantime—say, a money market account.

Question: As you receive returns on these housing investments, what will you do with that money?

Answer: If you have more investments (outflows) left on the schedule, you'll certainly use this money to supply those cash-flows. As for any excess, since you're clearly willing to risk that money to the degree of risk of the housing project, you'll probably put these excess returns into some other equally risky investment—a "risk-rate" account—until the end of the housing venture.

To summarize this strategy:

- You start with a certain amount of cash in a liquid account, earning interest at some "safe rate" until you invest it in the housing project.

- You also use interim returns to supply any subsequent investments in the schedule.

- You let all excess returns "ride" in a higher-yielding ("risk-rate") account until the end of whole investment venture.

Keep in mind that this isn't any big secret formula. It's what any competent financial manager does—just common sense, really—which is exactly why it's used for the FMRR.

Question: Under this strategy, what's the very minimum amount of money ($MIN) you'll actually need to commit at the beginning of the housing deal to get the ball rolling?

Answer: *Just enough* so that it—plus any interim returns—will grow sufficiently in that account to supply all your necessary *investments* (outflows).

Question: What's the maximum amount of money ($MAX) you can expect to hold in your hands at the very end of this whole venture?

Answer: It's the ending balance of your risk-rate account, where you have put all excess returns (those not needed for further investments).

What you're doing, then, is reducing your entire investment scenario to this single-investment/single-return model:

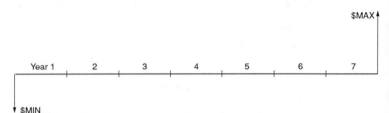

So the only question, really, is how to calculate $MIN and $MAX. The complication is the sharing of returns (positive cash-flows). That is, what portion of these returns must you hold in your safe-rate account to cover investments (outflows) yet to be disbursed; and what portion can you salt away in your risk-rate account? To figure this out, you work *backward* in time—from the last cash-flow to the first—*clearing each flow as you go, by discounting it back or sending it forward:*

- If a cash-flow is *negative*, you discount it back in time—using the *safe rate* as your discount rate—to add to the *previous cash-flow.* Why not just discount this negative flow all the way back to $MIN, just like an NPV calculation? Because it might be covered by a previous positive cash-flow, in which case you don't need to commit any funds for it as part of your minimum up-front commitment, $MIN. Thus, you work back one flow at a time, looking for positive flows to offset negative flows.

- Of course, if a cash-flow is *positive*, you can send it all the way forward—added to $MAX at the end of the scenario—using the *risk rate* as the discount rate. You can salt this flow away, because you don't need any of it to cover future negative cash-flows (working backward, you've already cleared them all).

Watch as you work backward through each of the cash-flows in the housing scenario. Assume a 6% safe rate and a 15% risk rate:

"Discount   –$10,000   *back* 1 period at 6%:"

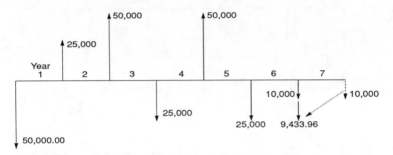

"Discount   –$10,000–$9,433.96   *back* 1 period at 6%:"

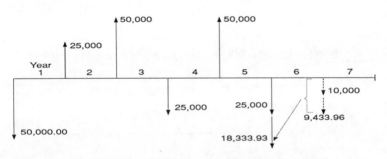

"Discount   –$25,000–$18,333.93   *back* 1 period at 6%:"

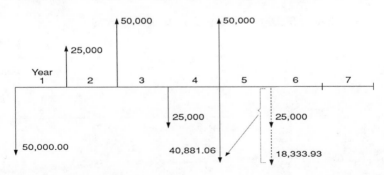

"Send $50,000–$40,881.06   *forward* 3 periods at 15%:"

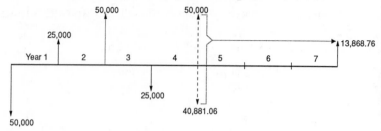

"Discount   –$25,000   *back* 1 period at 6%:"

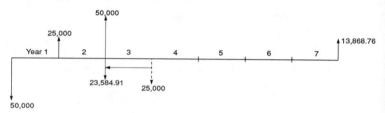

"Send $50,000–$23,584.91   *forward* 5 periods at 15%:"

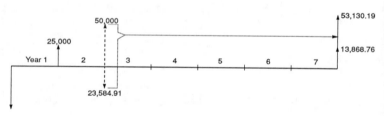

"Send $25,000   *forward* 6 periods at 15%:"

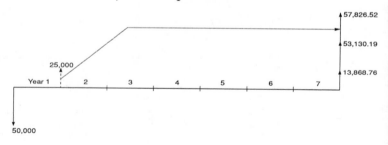

Notice that in this case, $MIN is simply the initial –$50,000.

Now here are the keystrokes for the entire solution—all done at the TVM Menu: ■MAIN FIN TVM OTHER 1 P/YR EXIT. Then:

1 0 0 0 0 FV 0 PMT 1 N 6 I%YR PV ....
PV=-9,433.96

– 1 0 0 0 0 = +/– (ALG) or 1 0 0 0 0 – +/– (RPN) FV
PV ....PV=-18,333.93

– 2 5 0 0 0 = +/– (ALG) or 2 5 0 0 0 – +/– (RPN) FV
PV ....PV=-40,881.06

+ 5 0 0 0 0 = +/– (ALG) or 5 0 0 0 0 + +/– (RPN) PV
3 N 1 5 I%YR FV ....FV=13,868.76

2 5 0 0 0 FV 1 N 6 I%YR PV ....
PV=-23,584.91

+ 5 0 0 0 0 = +/– (ALG) or 5 0 0 0 0 + +/– (RPN) PV
5 N 1 5 I%YR FV ....FV=53,130.19

2 5 0 0 0 = +/– (ALG) or 2 5 0 0 0 +/– (RPN) PV
6 N FV ....FV=57,826.52

Now find the growth rate that transforms $MIN into $MAX:
7 N 5 0 0 0 0 +/– PV , then
1 3 8 6 8 • 7 6 + 5 3 1 3 0 • 1 9 + 5 7 8 2 6 • 5 2 = or
1 3 8 6 8 • 7 6 INPUT 5 3 1 3 0 • 1 9 + 5 7 8 2 6 • 5 2 +
            (Result: 124,825.47   This is $MAX)

Now FV I%YR ....Answer: I%YR=13.96 Your FMRR—
a good estimate of your rate of return in this housing scenario.

Note: See also the FMRR formula on page 388 in Chapter 9.

12. At the TVM Menu, press █OTHER█ ⒈ █P/YR█ [EXIT]. Then:

⒊⒌⓪⓪⓪ █FV█ ⓪ █PMT█ ⒈ █N█ ⒍ █I%YR█ █PV█ ....
PV=-33,018.87

⊞⑦⑤⓪⓪⓪⊜⊞/− (ALG) or ⑦⑤⓪⓪⓪⊞⊞/− (RPN) █PV█
⒉ █N█ █FV█ ....FV=47,170.00

⒍⓪⓪⓪⓪ █FV█ ⒈ █N█ █PV█ ....
PV=-56,603.77

⊞⒈⑤⓪⓪⓪⊜⊞/− (ALG) or ⒈⑤⓪⓪⓪⊞⊞/− (RPN) █FV█
█PV█ ....PV=-39,248.84

⊞⒈⑤⓪⓪⓪⊜⊞/− (ALG) or ⒈⑤⓪⓪⓪⊞⊞/− (RPN) █FV█
█PV█ ....PV=-22,876.27

⊟⑦⑤⓪⓪⓪⊜ (ALG) or ⑦⑤⓪⓪⓪⊟ (RPN)
<u>Result</u>: -97,876.27   This is $MIN.

Now █PV█ ⒍ █N█ , then
⒉⓪⓪⓪⓪⓪⊞⒋⑦⒈⑦⓪⊜ *or* ⒉⓪⓪⓪⓪⓪[INPUT]⒋⑦⒈⑦⓪⊞
          (<u>Result</u>: 247,170.00   This is $MAX)
█FV█ █I%YR█ .... <u>Answer</u>: I%YR=16.70   The FMRR.

To compare this to the IRR%, key in the scenario as a CFLO list
(you know the keystrokes by now, right?), then █CALC█ █IRR%█ ....
<u>Result</u>: IRR%=20.69

Which is more accurate? Look at it this way: IRR% is the rate
at which your money appears to grow *only while it is invested*,
and it doesn't account at all for what happens to the returns—the
positive flows—after you receive them (recall pages 219-221). On
the other hand, your FMRR assumes that you reinvest excess
returns at a rate of 6%. Which is closer to reality?

13. Here's the T-bar of the situation:

y	$
0	(260,250.00)
1	12,896.21
2	14,497.94
3	16,834.26
4	19,244.19
5	414,242.63

Now, you *could* just grind out the FMRR at the TVM Menu, as in problems **11** and **12**. Or, you could observe that all the cash-flows except the initial flow are positive. So $MIN *is* the initial flow.

And notice therefore, that, to find $MAX, you'll just be sending all the positive values forward, using the risk rate, summing the results. That's an NFV (Net *Future* Value) calculation—and it's available on the CFLO Menu. Similar to NPV, NFV sends all cash-flows *forward* (rather than back), summing the results at the *end* of the timeline (instead of the beginning).

So use NFV to find $MAX: At the CFLO Menu, GET a new list (or clear the current one). Then: ⓪INPUT (just the *positive* flows) ①②⑧⑨⑥•②①INPUT INPUT   ①④④⑨⑦•⑨④INPUT INPUT ①⑥⑧③④•②⑥INPUT INPUT   ①⑨②④④•①⑨INPUT INPUT ④①④②④②•⑥③INPUT INPUT   **CALC** ①⑤ **I%** **NFV** ....
Result: **NFV=503,241.86**   This is $MAX.

Now go to the TVM Menu for the final calculation:
EXIT EXIT **TVM** STO **FV** **OTHER** ① **P/YR** EXIT ②⑥⓪②⑤⓪+/– **PV** ⑤ **N** **I%YR** ....   Answer: **I%YR=14.10**   The FMRR.

14. The two alternatives:

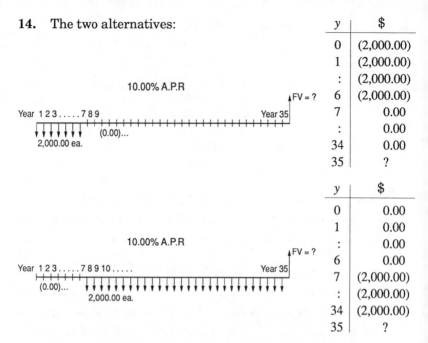

y	$
0	(2,000.00)
1	(2,000.00)
:	(2,000.00)
6	(2,000.00)
7	0.00
:	0.00
34	0.00
35	?

y	$
0	0.00
1	0.00
:	0.00
6	0.00
7	(2,000.00)
:	(2,000.00)
34	(2,000.00)
35	?

Your strategy: Find the Net Future Value (NFV) of each scenario.
The save-early plan: At the CFLO Menu, clear the current list
(■CLEAR DATA) or NAME it and GET a *NEW list. Then:

2 0 0 0 INPUT

2 0 0 0 INPUT 6 INPUT

0 INPUT 2 9 INPUT

CALC 1 0 **I%** **NFV** .... <u>Answer:</u> NFV=300,991.75

The save-later plan: EXIT to the CFLO Menu, ■↑, then:

0 INPUT

0 INPUT

↑ 2 0 0 0 INPUT 2 8 INPUT

0 INPUT INPUT

CALC **NFV** .... <u>Answer:</u> NFV=295,261.86

15. To find an *overall* rate of return, ignore the fund names (A-B-C). Notice, however, that the time periods between cash-flows are *uneven* (the machine can't handle this). Stymied? Not totally. Look at the dates of those investments. Why not designate the period in the analysis to be a *half-month* (24 per year)? It's a little imprecise, but the error is only a day or two in any given case, and the analysis spans about 5 years, so it's a decent approximation:

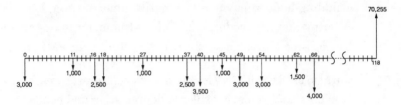

At the CFLO Menu, clear the current list or get a new one. Then:

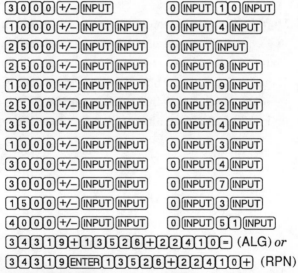

$3419 + 13526 + 22410 =$ (ALG) *or*
3419 ENTER $13526 + 22410 +$ (RPN)

INPUT INPUT **CALC IRR%**   Answer: IRR%=1.09

Annualize: ×24= (ALG) *or* 24× (RPN)....   **26.22**

Rest Area

Need a break? It's probably time to stop, stretch your legs, and look at your map.

- In Chapter 5, you saw several variations on amortized loans, including balloon payments, negative amortization, loan fees, differing annuity modes, etc. TVM is the menu to use on such "smooth-road" problems—they all involve a steady PMT amount.

  You also used the ICONV Menu to convert interest rates for these problems, and you also explored depreciation and bonds.

- Here in Chapter 6, you saw how to represent and then build *uneven* cash-flow solutions—the "rougher roads"—with the CFLO Menu. You then learned what NPV does and what it means. Next came IRR%. You saw how IRR% *can* represent your yield in an investment scenario—but not necessarily! So you learned when and how to obtain an alternative investment measure: FMRR.

Next Destination?

Time to check the map again, because here's another junction. Check the signs now and choose your route....

Basic Arithmetic...............24

Using Menus........................60

TVM.....................................94

The CFLO Menu..................202

SUM Lists...........................258

TIME, Dates and Appts.....280

The SOLVE Menu................294

TEXT Lists.........................409

Appendix.............................424

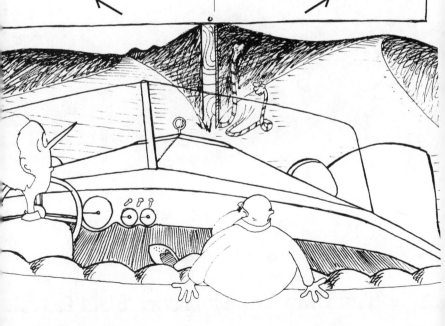

Next Destination?

7. THE DATA YOU COLLECT: SUM LISTS

Saving Numbers

Of course, the whole point of "navigating" through the menus of your HP 19BⅡ is to get to places where you can do calculations.

But what about afterwards? What do you do with the results of these calculations? What if you need to use the results from one menu in some other menu—"way across town?"

How do you store your answers for later use? And how do you retrieve this information, edit it, erase it, view it, use it, etc.?

With its continuous memory, the HP 19BⅡ doesn't forget numbers, and you should know how to take advantage of this. Up to this point in the Course, although you kept a few results in the Stack while changing menus, that's about the only place you've really stored anything. It's time to learn about other places (the best places) to save numbers—in *registers* and in *lists*.

The Numbered Registers

The simplest way to save the result of any calculation is in a *numbered* storage register, so called because that's how you refer to it—by number—when you want to store into it or recall from it.

Try This: Store the result of 789÷5 into register 4.

Solution: Press ⎗7⎖⎗8⎖⎗9⎖⎗÷⎖⎗5⎖⎗=⎖(ALG), or ⎗7⎖⎗8⎖⎗9⎖⎗ENTER⎖⎗5⎖⎗÷⎖ (RPN),
                  to get **157.80**, then press ⎗STO⎖⎗4⎖.... Simple, right?

Now Do This: Clear the Stack (by pressing ⎗■⎖⎗CLEAR⎖). Then *recall* the number you just stored.

Nothing To It: Press ⎗RCL⎖⎗4⎖.

See how these numbered registers can act as convenient holding bins? And there are ten such registers, numbered 0-9.

Notice that the ⎗STO⎖ and ⎗RCL⎖ keys both *copy* values. That is, after you pressed ⎗STO⎖⎗4⎖, the value **157.80** was still in the Stack, too; a *copy* was sent to register 4.

Likewise, when you pressed ⎗RCL⎖⎗4⎖ to bring that value back, you were bringing back a *copy* of the contents of register 4. Right now, there's still a 157.80 in register 4 (clear the Stack and do another ⎗RCL⎖⎗4⎖, if you want to prove this to yourself).

Lists of Numbers

So the ten numbered storage registers give you one option for saving results—the quickest, simplest way. But there's another, far more sophisticated way you may need, too.

For example, what if you have a set of numbers that represent, say, your income levels for the past 11 years? You can't store these in the numbered registers because there are only ten registers. Besides, it would be very handy to keep all of these figures in one list, so you can compare them and analyze them, right?

Well, you *can* do this—and here's how: Suppose that you're an income property owner, and that the numbers below show the gross annual rental incomes for 11 different buildings:

Building	Gross Rental Income
1	17,000.00
2	22,000.00
3	21,500.00
4	24,000.00
5	14,500.00
6	19,000.00
7	23,000.00
8	24,000.00
9	24,500.00
10	18,000.00
11	27,000.00

Starting from the MAIN Menu, press the **SUM** key. You'll see something like this:

The SUM Menu is for *lists*—and you're about to start building one.

Question: How do you start a new list?

Answer: First you GET a *NEW (blank) list—so press **GET**.

The machine then asks you which list you want to get, and it gives you a choice of list names on the Menu Line. If you had already saved some lists of your own, their names would now appear alongside ***NEW**.

But right now, ***NEW** is probably the only game in town, so choose it (actually, therefore, you didn't need to GET it at all, since a *NEW list was already in your display, above. But now you know how to GET any list, new or named).

That takes you back to the SUM Menu display (above)— and you're ready to enter numbers.

What you see there on Line 2 is the list *pointer* (▶). It tells you which item in the list you're dealing with at the moment.

And down below it, you'll see the running total of all the numbers in your list (of course, it's 𝟢.𝟢𝟢 right now—because you haven't put any numbers in yet).

Fill in the Numbers: Put all eleven items of your rental income data into this list.

Solution: (Watch your display as you do these keystrokes. That will tell you a lot about how to lists work in the HP 19Bɪɪ.):

1 7 0 0 0 INPUT
2 2 0 0 0 INPUT
2 1 5 0 0 INPUT
2 4 0 0 0 INPUT
1 4 5 0 0 INPUT
1 9 0 0 0 INPUT
2 3 0 0 0 INPUT
2 4 0 0 0 INPUT
2 4 5 0 0 INPUT
1 8 0 0 0 INPUT
2 7 0 0 0 INPUT

Not too tough, right?

But here are some important things to notice:

1. Items in a list are *numbered*. In this particular list, each *building* is identified by its number, **1**-**11**.

2. You tell to the calculator to "accept" a number by pressing INPUT.

3. Each time you press INPUT, the machine accepts the number *and* recomputes the TOTAL of all items.

4. After you've keyed in all eleven of your numbers, the machine still sits there and waits for the twelfth item....

Now what? How do you say, *"I'm finished!"* ?

(Read on)

Editing Your List

First of all, just ignore your machine's prompting for another item. It's *always* going to allow you to add one more to the bottom of your list.

But are you sure all your numbers are keyed in correctly? How about a quick review?

Do It: Jump to the beginning of your list and step down through it to check each entry.

How? First, you must move the pointer back up to the top. Remember the two keys, ⊤ and ⊥ that roll your Stack around? Those two keys are good for *all sorts* of lists and stacks—including this kind of storage list.

So you could press ⊤ eleven times to move the pointer back to item 1. *Or* you could press ■⊤. That's a quick way to *jump* to the beginning of the list, all in one motion (and no prizes for guessing how to jump to the *end* of the list again).

So "go first class"—use the ■⊤ method. Then use ⊥ to "walk" down the list and check your numbers…. If you find a mistake, simply position the pointer to the erroneous number, key in the correct value and press [INPUT].

A good indicator that your numbers are all right is that your **TOTAL** is **234,500.00**.

Problem: Suppose that you've numbered your income properties according to the time you have owned them—oldest to newest. But now you sell building 1, which you've held longer than any of the others—and buy a new building, which produces $34,000 in rental income. How do you change the list?

Solution: You delete the first building's income and then tack on the new building's income at the end of the list:

First, press ■ ⬆ to jump to the top of the list, if you're not there now. Then press the **DELET** selection from the SUM Menu. This deletes the item the pointer is currently indicating—**17,000.00**—the first value in the list. Remember: the pointer determines which item is affected when you do anything to a single item in your list.

So now the *new* first item in your list is **22,000.00**, and there should be *ten* items altogether. Jump to the end of the list (press ■ ⬇), to check this ....Sure enough— **ITEM(11)** is now blank, and the pointer is pointing to it. So key in ③④⓪⓪⓪ and press [INPUT] to store it there. Voilá! You've just updated your 11-building income list. And notice that your running **TOTAL=251,500.00** is now up-to-date, too.

Notice that this same method works for any fixed-length list intended to keep a chronological record (for moving averages, etc.): Delete the oldest value (at the top) and add the newest value to the bottom.

Analyzing Your List

Of course, you can do much more analysis on your list data than simply to sum the TOTAL. Notice the **CALC** item on the menu. Press **CALC** now and experiment with some of the calculations available:

TOTAL...(you've already seen this).... $TOTAL=251,500.00$
MEAN...the *average* data item value.... $MEAN=22,863.64$
MEDN...the *median* value, the value that is less than half the values but greater than the other half.... $MEDIAN=23,000.00$
STDEV...the *standard deviation* is a measure of how consistent (closely grouped around the mean) your data is.... $STDEV=5,074.89$
RANG...the difference between the greatest item value and the least... $RANGE=19,500.00$

(press **MORE**)

MIN...the least value in your data set... $MIN=14,500.00$
MAX...the greatest value in your data set... $MAX=34,000.00$
(*Don't* press **SORT** or **FRCST** right now; you'll see them a little later.)

But now press **HIST**....

Pretty slick, eh? This is a *histogram* of your data's distribution—a bar graph of the data's frequencies, divided into ten sub-ranges, or *cells*.

Use the ⬅ and ➡ keys to move the little cell pointer to any given cell. Then you can press INPUT to get more specific information on that cell. And EXIT returns you to the CALC Menu.

Naming Your List

Before you go any farther into analyzing the data in your rental income list, you should [EXIT] back to the SUM Menu and *name* it—so that you can build other lists and do other calculations and yet be able to GET this list back again whenever you need it.

Problem: Name your list INCOME.

Solution: Press **NAME**; then type [I][N][C][O][M][E][INPUT], as you're told to do by the display. Your list is now named, and you can [EXIT] to the MAIN Menu.

Later: First, GET a *NEW list (press **SUM** **GET** **#NEW**)—to pretend that you've been working with other lists.

Now go GET your INCOme list (**GET** **INCO**).... As you see, all *named* lists appear on the GET Menu, too. But notice that not all the letters of INCOME will fit into a menu box. There's room only for four or five letters, so choose short names.

FoReCaSTing with Your List

One of the most common kinds of analysis you'll probably want to do with a list of data is to use it to forecast—to *predict*—something.

Example: Suppose you're considering the construction of another income property—a twelfth building in your list—similar to the other eleven in quality and location. How can you predict the annual rental income it might generate?

Answer: Use the pattern of rents from the existing buildings to help you forecast this.

Problem: Your existing buildings all have different rents because they are of different sizes (floor square footage). So a simple average of those rents won't tell you very much—especially for your new building, which will have quite a bit more space (5000 ft²).

Solution: Create a second list, composed of each building's rental floor area, to *correlate* with its rental income. Use that correlation (rental income per square foot), to predict the rental income for your new building.

Take it step-by-step....

Here are the rental floor areas of your current 11 buildings, alongside their annual rents (which you've already built into your INCOme list):

Building	Rental Floor Area (ft²)	Gross Rental Income
1	2,650	$ 22,000.00
2	2,500	21,500.00
3	2,700	24,000.00
4	1,500	14,500.00
5	2,100	19,000.00
6	2,600	23,000.00
7	2,650	24,000.00
8	2,700	24,500.00
9	2,000	18,000.00
10	2,900	27,000.00
11	3,750	34,000.00

So: GET and NAME a new list: `GET` `%NEW` `NAME` A R E A S `INPUT`

Then fill in the data:

2 6 5 0 `INPUT` 2 5 0 0 `INPUT` 2 7 0 0 `INPUT`

1 5 0 0 `INPUT` 2 1 0 0 `INPUT` 2 6 0 0 `INPUT`

2 6 5 0 `INPUT` 2 7 0 0 `INPUT` 2 0 0 0 `INPUT`

2 9 0 0 `INPUT` 3 7 5 0 `INPUT`

(Quick accuracy check: Your **TOTAL** should be **28,050.00**)

Now you can use this list of floor areas to forecast the *income* of your new building. To do so, you must GET the list of the *income* data.

Do It: Press **GET INCO**, then **CALC MORE**, then **FRCST**....

Question: What does SELECT X VARIABLE mean?

Answer: To forecast, you need to decide "what to graph against what." So the question your machine is really asking you is, "Which list is your X-variable data—your *area* list (AREAS) or your *income* list (INCOme)?"

Think about it like this: You're looking for a trend that shows that the income level *depends* on the floor area. So your income must be the *dependent* variable (along the Y-axis), and therefore area must be the *independent* variable (along the X-axis) on your graph:

So, answer your calculator's question by pressing **AREAS**.

Question: What does SELECT A MODEL mean?

Answer: Your machine is asking: "What mathematical model—
what shape curve—do you want to fit to your data?" Your
choices are LINear, LOGarithmic, EXPonential or POWer.
You're looking for the linear relationship between floor
area and rent per square foot. So press **LIN** to see the
FoReCaSTing Menu itself.

Watch: Press **MORE** and **PLOT**.... See your data points—and the
straight line your HP 19BII has tried to fit to them? And
notice that you can use the arrow keys to move those little
crosshairs around, to see approximate coordinates of any
point (the coordinates show in the display).

The plot is all well and good for a general picture, but what you want
is a number. You want to be able to key in any X-value (a floor area)
and have the machine tell you the Y-value of that point on the curve.

Easy: Key in your X-value—that's the area of your new building:
(EXIT) 5 0 0 0, then **MORE** **MORE** **XLIST**. Now press **YLIST** to
find the corresponding income: YLIST=44,433.47

And now you can play "What-If?" all day like this—with
any building size you wish: Just enter the floor space, and
press **XLIST**, then **YLIST**. What could be simpler?

Quiz

1. Fill up the Stack with $1.00, 2.00, 3.00$, and 4.00. Now use the numbered storage registers to reverse their order.

2. GET your INCOME list. Make a copy of it, called 11RNTS. Make another copy, TMP. Now *erase* TMP—data first, then the name.

3. Still in your INCOME list, label each list item as a BLDG (instead of ITEM). Then change only BLDG(4) back to ITEM(4).

4. Use the menu items START and SUBT (SUBTotal) keys to compute the total income generated by buildings 6 through 10.

5. Is there a strong *non*-linear correlation between your building rents and floor areas? Is it stronger than the linear correlation?

6. Use the following values of your current 11 properties to estimate the value of your 5000 ft² building now under construction:

1. $ 160,000	2. $ 162,500	3. $ 180,000
4. $ 105,000	5. $ 144,000	6. $ 175,000
7. $ 175,000	8. $ 190,000	9. $ 140,000
10. $ 210,000	11. $ 250,000	

Quiz Solutions

1. (First, [EXIT] from the SUM Menu, to see more of the Stack.)
   Fill up the History Stack: press [1][INPUT], [2][INPUT], [3][INPUT], [4].

   Then extract its four values, storing the numbers into four corresponding storage registers: [STO][1][↓][STO][2][↓][STO][3][↓][STO][4]

   Now recall them back to the Stack: [RCL][1][RCL][2][RCL][3][RCL][4]....

   Voilá! And notice that you don't need to clear the previous Stack before beginning your recall process. Those previous values simply get "popped off the top" as you recall more values to the Stack.

2. Press **SUM** **GET** **INCO**, if necessary, then **MORE** **COPY**. Then follow the display's instructions and type [1][1][R][N][T][S][INPUT].

   You've now made a copy of the INCOME list, and the copy's name is 11RNTS. But now that you've made the copy, you're still working in the original—the INCOME list.

   So make another copy: **COPY** [T][M][P][INPUT]....and then go GET this TMP list: **MORE** **GET** **TMP**.

   Now erase it: Press **CLEAR DATA** and answer **YES** to both of the questions it asks you. This is how to clear both the data and the name—in that order (to clear the data but save the name, you would answer **NO** to the second question).

3. On the second page of the SUM Menu, notice the item called **LABEL**. Press that now.... This feature allows you to give your own customized label to any or all items in the list.

   To change *all* item labels at once (that is, make a *global* change), simply type in the new label ($\boxed{B}\boxed{L}\boxed{D}\boxed{G}$) and then **GLOBL**. You'll see the results immediately in your list....

   Now change **BLDG(4)** back to **ITEM(4)**: Press $\boxed{\blacksquare}\boxed{\uparrow}$ (if you're not already at the top of the list), then $\boxed{\downarrow}\boxed{\downarrow}\boxed{\downarrow}$ to move the ▶ to **BLDG(4)**. Then press **LABEL**, type $\boxed{I}\boxed{T}\boxed{E}\boxed{M}$, and choose **CURR**, which changes only the *current* item's label.

4. Here's the idea: Move the pointer to the *first* item to be included in your subtotal and press **START**. Then move to the *last* item in the subtotal and press **SUBT**.

   So, assuming you're at **ITEM(4)** from the previous problem, press $\boxed{\downarrow}\boxed{\downarrow}$ to get to **BLDG(6)**. Then press **START**. Next, press $\boxed{\downarrow}\boxed{\downarrow}\boxed{\downarrow}\boxed{\downarrow}$ to move the pointer down to the last item in your subtotal, **BLDG(10)**, and press **SUBT**....

   <u>Answer:</u> **SUBTOTAL=116,500.00**

   SUBT tells you the SUBTotal of all items from the STARTing item to the pointer's position.

5. When you use the FoReCaSTing feature in the SUM Menu, it asks you to SELECT A MODEL. To estimate the income likely from your new building, you selected LIN to find the best *straight-line* correlation between floor space and rent. But what about the other three types of correlations the HP 19BII can compute— LOGarithmic, EXPonential and POWer curves?

How do you know which curve will best fit your data? You don't —not without trying each type. You could get a *general* feel by plotting each type, to see which curve stays closest to the points. But often it's hard to tell by looking at plots, so on the FoReCaSTing Menu, there's an item called **CORR**, that finds the *CORRelation coefficient* (r) for the current curve type. This r is a measure of the "goodness" of the fit of the curve to the data points. The better the fit, the closer r approaches 1 or -1. A poorer fit gives an r nearer to 0. So to find the best-fitting curve, (EXIT) the plotter and simply compute r for each type of curve:

(EXIT) **LIN** **CORR** Result: CORR=0.99 (.987475213604)
(EXIT) **LOG** **CORR** Result: CORR=0.96 (.959580918724)
(EXIT) **EXP** **CORR** Result: CORR=0.99 (.988251144624)
(EXIT) **PWR** **CORR** Result: CORR=0.99 (.986513832084)

All the fits are quite good (close to 1), but the EXPonential fit is the best of the four. So, what does it predict for the income of your 5000 ft² building? Find out: (EXIT) **EXP** (5)(0)(0)(0) **XLIST** **YLIST** ....

Result: YLIST=57,517.50. That's quite a bit higher than the LINear estimate, so the more conservative amount to figure on as income from your new building is still the linear estimate —about $44,500.

6. This is just another practice problem in forecasting.

First, GET and NAME a new list: `GET` `※NEW` `NAME` $\boxed{V}\boxed{A}\boxed{L}\boxed{S}$
`INPUT`. Then fill in the data:

$\boxed{1}\boxed{6}\boxed{0}\boxed{0}\boxed{0}$ `INPUT` $\boxed{1}\boxed{6}\boxed{2}\boxed{5}\boxed{0}\boxed{0}$ `INPUT` $\boxed{1}\boxed{8}\boxed{0}\boxed{0}\boxed{0}$ `INPUT`
$\boxed{1}\boxed{0}\boxed{5}\boxed{0}\boxed{0}\boxed{0}$ `INPUT` $\boxed{1}\boxed{4}\boxed{4}\boxed{0}\boxed{0}\boxed{0}$ `INPUT` $\boxed{1}\boxed{7}\boxed{5}\boxed{0}\boxed{0}\boxed{0}$ `INPUT`
$\boxed{1}\boxed{7}\boxed{5}\boxed{0}\boxed{0}\boxed{0}$ `INPUT` $\boxed{1}\boxed{9}\boxed{0}\boxed{0}\boxed{0}$ `INPUT` $\boxed{1}\boxed{4}\boxed{0}\boxed{0}\boxed{0}\boxed{0}$ `INPUT`
$\boxed{2}\boxed{1}\boxed{0}\boxed{0}\boxed{0}\boxed{0}$ `INPUT` $\boxed{2}\boxed{5}\boxed{0}\boxed{0}\boxed{0}$ `INPUT`

(Accuracy check: Your TOTAL should be 1,891,500.00)

Press `CALC` `MORE`, then `FRCST`. To forecast the value of your new building based upon its floor area, use `AREAS` as your X-variable list. Try a linear correlation: Press `LIN` $\boxed{5}\boxed{0}\boxed{0}\boxed{0}$ `X:LIST`, then `Y:LIST` to find the predicted value: YLIST=331,563.73

But is linear the best type of correlation? Find out:*

`CORR`	Result: CORR=0.97 (.974993369088)
`EXIT` `LOG` `CORR`	Result: CORR=0.96 (.956276883471)
`EXIT` `EXP` `CORR`	Result: CORR=0.97 (.970082365602)
`EXIT` `PWR` `CORR`	Result: CORR=0.98 (.97768675078)

All the fits are quite good (close to 1), but the POWer fit is the best of the four. And what does it predict for the income of your 5000 ft² building? Find out: $\boxed{5}\boxed{0}\boxed{0}\boxed{0}$ `X:LIST` `Y:LIST`....

Result: YLIST=325,030.20. That's a bit lower than the LINear estimate, and since the fit *is* slightly better, maybe this is the better—more conservative—value to assume for your new building: about $325,000.

---

*If you find yourself needing to do a lot of these comparisons—trying to find the best correlation coefficient (r)—you might study the SOLVE equation on pages 392-393.

Which Way Now?

Here's another fork in the road.

As you've heard, the best choice is probably to keep going straight on through the book. Each topic will teach you a lot about the calculator. But if you want to, you can "skip around."

So read the sign now, and make another choice....

Basic Arithmetic.............24

Using Menus.......................60

TVM..................................94

The CFLO Menu.................202

SUM Lists.........................258

TIME, Dates and Appts.....280

The SOLVE Menu................294

TEXT Lists........................409

Appendix..........................424

Which Way Now?

8. TIME Travelling

Using the Clock

Hold your place here and flip back for a minute to page 62.... Remember that big diagram of the TIME Menu "highway and suburbs?" You didn't get to explore those "routes" then, so now here's your chance.

Basics First: What time is it? What's today's date? Is it Friday yet?

One Key: To find out *all* of this from your HP 19Bɪɪ, go to the MAIN Menu (█MAIN) and press **TIME** . You'll see a display similar to this (but of course, yours will probably show a different date and time):

```
02/27/1991   02:57:12 PM
WEDNESDAY
34,805.00
 CALC  APPT  ADJST  SET
```

One key tells you all that; anytime you want to check the clock or the calendar, press █MAIN **TIME** .

But what if your HP 19Bɪɪ clock/calendar is wrong? How do you *set* it or *adjust* it?*

---

*You've had one quiz problem (Chapter 4, problem 2, page 76) that showed you briefly how to set the time and date, but there's a lot more to that story.

SETting the TIME

Suppose that today is actually March 29, 1990, and that it's about 1:30:36 in the afternoon. To set your HP 19BII to show this, from the TIME Menu, press ■■■. You'll see a display similar to this:

```
┌─────────────────────────────────────┐
│ 02/27/1991   02:59:22 PM            │
│ WEDNESDAY                            │
│                                      │
│ DATE │TIME │A/PM │ M/D │ 12/24 │ HELP │
└─────────────────────────────────────┘
```

The idea is to *key in a number* that represents the date or the time, then press ■■■ or ■■■.

Like So: Press ③·②⑨①⑨⑨⓪ **DATE** ; ①·③⓪③⑥ **TIME** ....

See how this works? You mimic the order of the time and date numbers as you see them in the display, using the · to separate months/days and hours/minutes.

If you ever forget how this works, you can press **HELP** for a reminder (do it now, just to see)....

The other selections on this menu (**A/PM**, **M/D** and **12/24**) are all *format* options for the time and date. Try them now and observe how your display changes....

And simply press them again to undo the changes.

ADJuSTing the TIME

When the time and date are just plain wrong—"_way_ off"—as they were on the previous page, the easiest thing to do is to use **SET**, as you did.

But what if the time is only slightly off—and you want to improve the accuracy? Use **ADJST**....

Ah, Spring: On the first Sunday in April, most parts of the U.S. go to Daylight Savings Time, setting all clocks ahead by an hour. So before you step out to get the Sunday paper, you open your HP 19Bɪɪ and...

Do This: [EXIT] the SET Menu (if you're still there), then press **ADJST**. Now, with _one keystroke,_ you can advance or delay the clock by exactly one hour, one minute, or one second. So just press **+HR**, and voilá!—you've Saved some Daylight.

Anytime you want, you can adjust the clock for more accuracy. As another example, suppose you notice that your HP 19Bɪɪ is, say, 4 seconds fast, according to The Official Time. No big problem: Just press **-SEC** **-SEC** **-SEC** **-SEC**, and that's all there is to it.

CALCulating with Dates

How do you calculate the number of days between two given dates? For example, how would you calculate how many days in 1990 will be on Daylight Savings Time, which runs from April 1 to October 28 (the first Sunday in April to the last Sunday in October)?

Easy: ⌷EXIT⌷ the ADJuST Menu, if necessary, and press **CALC**. Now, the idea here is to *key in any two dates* (using the current date format, as the display reminds you now), then press **DAYS** to calculate the actual number of calendar days between those two dates. Try it:

⌷4⌷⌷•⌷⌷0⌷⌷1⌷⌷1⌷⌷9⌷⌷9⌷⌷0⌷ **DATE1** ⌷1⌷⌷0⌷⌷•⌷⌷2⌷⌷8⌷⌷1⌷⌷9⌷⌷9⌷⌷0⌷ **DATE2**
DAYS .... Result: ACTUAL DAYS=210.00

And you can go the other way, too—knowing the number of days and one of the dates, then calculating the other date.

Like So: What date was 45 days after March 22, 1988? How about 45 days *before* March 22, 1988?

⌷3⌷⌷•⌷⌷2⌷⌷2⌷⌷1⌷⌷9⌷⌷8⌷⌷8⌷ **DATE1** ⌷4⌷⌷5⌷ **DAYS** **DATE2** ....
Result: DATE2=05/06/1988   FRI

⌷4⌷⌷5⌷⌷+/−⌷ **DAYS** **DATE2** ....
Result: DATE2=02/06/1988   SAT

As you can see, a *negative* number of DAYS means simply that you go backward into the past—instead of ahead into the future. And *notice* that the calculator assumes that DATE1 is earlier than DATE2: if you give a DATE1 *later* than a DATE2, the number of DAYS will be *negative*.

Now, what about those other three items on the CALC Menu: **3600**, **3650** and **TODAY**? What do they do?

Well **TODAY** is easy—it's just a convenient way to see and/or key in the current date. Try it.... As for the other two items,...

Find Out: How many days are there from February 1st to March 1st, in the year 1992?

> ②・⓪①①⑨⑨②**DATE1** ③・⓪①①⑨⑨②**DATE2**
> **DAYS** .... Result: ACTUAL DAYS=29.00

Ah, but *what if you ignore leap-year considerations* and simply assume that every year has 365 days?
Press **3650** .... Result: 365 DAYS=28.00

And *what if you assume that every month has 30 days*—making for a nice, tidy 360-day year?
Press **3600** .... Result: 360 DAYS=30.00

These *alternative calendar assumptions* help you calculate days between dates on the "simplified calendars" commonly used for interest calculations with bonds and other financial instruments.

Making APPoinTments

Probably the best thing about the TIME Menu in your HP 19BII is that it can store appointments for you (up to six of them, in fact)—and then beep to remind you at the right times.

[EXIT] from the CALC Menu, if you're still there now. Then press **APPT**. You'll probably see the following messages in the display:

PENDING: NONE   (currently, you have no appointments set for any time in the future.)*

PAST DUE: NONE   (currently, there are no appointments that have come due *that you haven't already acknowledged.*)*

Fine. Now, to set up a demonstration appointment, choose one of the appointments from the menu (say, **APPT1**). Then press **[CLEAR DATA]** to clear everything so that you're ready to begin.

To set an appointment, the idea is to key in (in any order):

- the **date** and **time** you want to be reminded of the appointment;
- the **message** you want to see at that time;
- the **repeat** interval (if any), so that the machine will automatically reset itself to go off again after that interval (handy for daily or weekly schedules.

---

*Don't worry if your machine has one or more appointments showing as pending or past due. These won't interfere.

OK, suppose you want to set an appointment that repeats every 2 minutes, starting about 2 minutes from now, with a message that says, **THIS IS ONLY A TEST.**

Easy: Press **MSG**, then follow the display's instructions, typing a message and pressing (INPUT) when you finish:

(T)(H)(I)(S)(SPACE)(I)(S)(SPACE)(O)(N)(L)(Y)(SPACE)(A)(SPACE)(T)(E)(S)(T)(.)
(INPUT)....The display will come back to the APPT Menu and echo the information you've given it so far.

Now set the repeat interval: Press **RPT**, then key in (2) and press **MIN** ....Again, the display returns to the APPT Menu, echoing all the known information.

Next, key in a time that reflects *your* current time, plus about two minutes, then press **TIME** (the date should automatically default to your current date). Be sure that the am/pm setting is correct (adjust it with **A/PM** if necessary).

Now (EXIT) the APPT Menu. You should see:

PENDING: 1   (appointment #1 is now pending.)
PAST DUE: NONE

So, press **■**(MAIN), then turn the page and wait for your appointment to come due....

When Your Appointment Comes Due

Even if your calculator is off, an appointment that comes due will cause it to turn on, beep at you, and show the message for about 20 seconds. Here are your options:

- If you press any key ($\boxed{\text{ON}}$ is a good one) *during* that time, this automatically acknowledges the appointment, and allows the machine to reset it for the next repeat interval, if there is one.

- If you don't press any key until after the beeping stops, the (•) annunciator will stay on, to tell you—no matter where you are in the machine's menu system—that you have a past due appointment. To acknowledge it, you must simply go into that appointment's menu (press **APPT1** or **APPT2**, etc.—whichever one it was). *Only after you acknowledge it* will it reset itself for any repeat.

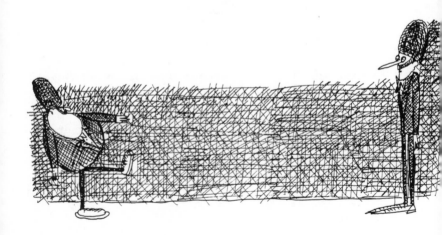

Quiz TIME

1. When it's 2:00 p.m. in Arch Cape, Oregon, it's 7:00 a.m. *the following day* in Okinawa. How do you cure your calculator's "jet lag" when travelling back and forth across the International Date Line like this?

2. According to your HP 19Bɪɪ, how many (actual) days are in the years 2000 and 2100?

3. Set the following appointments in your HP 19Bɪɪ:

   APPT1: Today, 15 minutes from now
   TAKE A BREAK (repeat: 2 hours)

   APPT2: September 9, 1999   9:09 a.m.
   CATCH PLANE (repeat: 10 days)

   APPT3: February 29, 2040   10:30 a.m.
   SEE DENTIST (no repeat)

4. How do you stop an appointment from repeating? How do you clear any given appointment? How about *all* appointments?

5. Can an appointment come due without beeping at you?

Answers TIME

1. Okinawa is 17 hours *ahead* of Oregon. Or, you can think about this as being 7 hours *less* than one *day* ahead. So, when going west (to Okinawa), and assuming your HP 19Bɪɪ is set to Oregon time, you could do one of the following:

   Starting from the MAIN Menu (■MAIN)), press **TIME** **ADJST**, then press **+HR** *seventeen* times (just don't lose count);

   Or, starting from the MAIN Menu (■MAIN)), press **TIME** **ADJST**. Then press **+HR** *seven* times, then (EXIT) **SET** and set the date to tomorrow (whatever your current date happens to be, just key in the date for the next day).

   Of course, when going east (to Oregon), you'd do the reverse of one of those two procedures: Use **-HR** seventeen times; or use **-HR** seven times and SET the date to yesterday.

2. From the MAIN Menu (press ■MAIN)), press **TIME** **CALC**.
   Then ①·⓪①②⓪⓪⓪ **DATE1** ①·⓪①②⓪⓪① **DATE2** **DAYS** ....
   <u>Answer:</u> ACTUAL DAYS=366.00

   ①·⓪①②①⓪⓪ **DATE1** ①·⓪①②①⓪① **DATE2** **DAYS** ....
   <u>Answer:</u> ACTUAL DAYS=365.00

   The year 2000 is a leap year, but the year 2100 is not (you might want to read up on the rules of leap years to find out why this is the case).

3. Starting from the MAIN Menu (■ MAIN), press **TIME** **APPT**, then select **APPT1**. Now key in some time about 15 minutes from now (using the format HH.MM), then press **TIME** (the current date will automatically be entered at this point).

    Then: **MSG** [T][A][K][E][SPACE][A][SPACE][B][R][E][A][K][INPUT];
    then **RPT** [2] **HR** and [EXIT].

    Next: Press **APPT2**, and [9][·][0][9][1][9][9][9] **DATE**, [9][·][0][9] **TIME**;
    then **MSG** [C][A][T][C][H][SPACE][P][L][A][N][E][INPUT];
    then **RPT** [1][0] **DAY** and [EXIT].

    Next: **APPT3**, then [2][·][2][9][2][0][4][0] **DATE** *[1][0][·][3] **TIME**;
    then **MSG** [S][E][E][SPACE][D][E][N][T][I][S][T][INPUT], then **RPT** **NONE**, and [EXIT].

4. To stop an appointment from repeating, from the MAIN Menu (■ MAIN) press **TIME** **APPT**, then select the appointment you're interested in—say, APPT1 (press **APPT1**), for example. Then select **RPT** **NONE**, to specify no repeat.

    To clear an appointment altogether, from the MAIN Menu (■ MAIN) press **TIME** **APPT**, then select the appointment you want to clear —say, APPT1 (press **APPT1**). Then ■ CLEAR DATA.

    To clear all appointments at once, from the MAIN Menu (■ MAIN) press **TIME** **APPT**, then ■ CLEAR DATA and respond with **YES** to the machine's request for confirmation of this "sweeping purge."

---

*"Whoops—say! That's a Wednesday! Guess we'll have to reschedule! How about…next year…?"

5. Well, the machine will always *try* to beep when an appointment comes due, *but you won't hear it if the beeper is turned off.* Press ■⟨MODES⟩ and notice the messages in the display. One of those messages probably says: BEEPER: ON

This means, of course, that when the beeper is "beeped," you'll hear it. But notice the menu item called **BEEP**. Press it *once*.... The beeper message changes: BEEPER: APPTS ONLY

This is just like having the beeper turned off—i.e. anytime the beeper would normally sound, it will be silenced—*except* for appointments, so that you won't miss them.

Now press **BEEP** once more.... BEEPER: OFF
In this mode, you *never* hear a beep—not even for appointments.

Now press **BEEP** again to set the beeper to ON again.... As you can see, **BEEP** is a *three*-way switch that controls the beeper.

Whither Now?

Time to check the map again, because here's another junction.

As usual, it's best to simply keep on going, straight through the book. But check the signs now and choose your route....

Basic Arithmetic................24

Using Menus.......................60

TVM.....................................94

The CFLO Menu..................202

SUM Lists...........................258

TIME, Dates and Appts.....280

The SOLVE Menu................294

TEXT Lists.........................409

Appendix...........................424

Whither Now?

9. BUILDING YOUR OWN ROADS: THE SOLVE MENU

Memory Space: The Final Frontier

So much for civilization. Now you're on your own.

Now you need to learn how to solve problems for which there are no calculations already built into your HP 19BII. That is, you need to learn how to go to places that just aren't on the map.

"How?"

You literally add to your calculator's "map"—invent your own solutions. And once you've invented these formulas, you can *store* them in a list in the machine, where they'll reside until you need them again. Of course, you can erase them, too, when you don't need them anymore.

But since your customized formulas will take up space in the memory of your HP 19BII, you need to know a little more about that memory before you start building your formulas....

First of all, recall (from Chapter 7) what the numbered registers are all about: There are ten of them, called 0-9, and each stores just one number at a time—usually some value you want to keep "on the side" for awhile.

But you've discovered some other registers, too: As you recall (from Chapter 4), the names that appear on a calculations menu are really names of *built-in registers* used by that menu. And because you vary their values when playing "What-If," these are called "variable registers," or just "variables."

The point is, every variable uses space in your calculator's memory. Sometimes, the same variable is used in more than one formula. For example, you saw how the variables COST and PRICE are actually shared between the MU%C and MU%P formulas. When you stored a value into the variable PRICE at the MU%C Menu, *that value was still there* when you moved over to the MU%P Menu and pressed [RCL] **PRICE**.

A Picture of Memory

The variable registers used by the built-in formulas are indeed built into the machine. You can reset their values to zero, but you can't erase their formulas. But that's not the case for your "user memory." There you can create (and delete) new lists, formulas and registers of your own.

For example, here's a picture of how your HP 19BII's memory probably looks right now:

Numbered Registers

0
1
2
3
4
5
6
7
8
9

Built-In Variables

| OLD | NEW | %CH | COST | PRICE | M% | M%P |

| DATE | TIME | MIN | HR | DAY | WEEK | (APPT1) |

| DATE | TIME | MIN | HR | DAY | WEEK | (APPT2) |

.
.
.

| DATE | TIME | MIN | HR | DAY | WEEK | (APPT6) |

| N | I%YR | PV | PMT | FV |

.
.
.

(And so on, for all the variables of the built-in menus)

CFLO Lists	SUM Lists	Appointment Messages
FRED	INCOME	(APPT1:) TAKE A BREAK
EVEN	AREAS	(APPT2:) CATCH PLANE
UNEVEN	11RNTS	(APPT3:) SEE DENTIST
	VALS	

SOLVE Formulas	SOLVE Variables	TEXT Lists

◄――――――――――― (Nothing here so far) ―――――――――――►

Of course, you'll notice that you haven't created any formulas or formula variables yet—which is what this chapter is all about:

Full Speed Ahead: From the MAIN Menu, press the **SOLVE** key, and enter the world of HP SOLVE:

```
            α
TYPE AN EQUATION:
PRESS {CALC} OR [INPUT]
▶
 CALC  EDIT  DELET
```

This is the SOLVE Menu, where you go to create or use a formula of your own.

Notice the little α ("alpha") annunciator up in the Annunciator Area (you may have seen this before, when naming lists). It means that the machine is now expecting you to type in alphabetical characters from the left-hand keyboard.

So here you are, ready to type in an equation—a useful formula that creates its own menu for you....

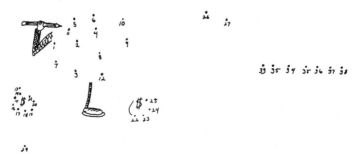

Creating Formulas

For openers, since you're "driving" through this Easy Course, how about a simple little formula to help you figure your gas mileage?

Do It: Create an equation for gas mileage. Then compute your mileage for a trip of 350 miles, which used 12 gallons of gasoline. If the car has a 15 gallon tank, how far could you have gone before the last "fumes" ran out?

Solution: From the SOLVE Menu, $\boxed{M}\boxed{P}\boxed{G}\boxed{=}\boxed{M}\boxed{I}\boxed{L}\boxed{E}\boxed{\div}\boxed{G}\boxed{A}\boxed{L}$.

Then press **CALC** ....The machine verifies your formula, to make sure that it understands everything you typed.

```
MPG=MILE÷GAL
14.15
 MPG  MILE  GAL
```

And then you know what to do:
$\boxed{3}\boxed{5}\boxed{0}$ **MILE**
$\boxed{1}\boxed{2}$ **GAL**
MPG   Answer: MPG=29.17

Now for that old familiar "What-Iffing:" Change the number of gallons to the maximum: $\boxed{1}\boxed{5}$ **GAL**.

And calculate how many miles you could have gone:
MILE ....   Answer: MILE=437.50

All right, you're happy with the way your formula works, but suppose you'd like to rename the variables in it. What do you do?

Edit It: Instead of **MILE**, you want **MILS**; and instead of **GAL**, you want **GALS**.

Solution: [EXIT] to the SOLVE Menu. Notice that the α comes on again and that the pointer is pointing to your formula. Now press **EDIT** and see the blinking cursor return.

Next, look on the left-hand keyboard down at the bottom, and find these keys: [INS] [DEL] [←] [→]. Try one—press [→].... Now press [■] [→]. See? The [■] key does the same for the cursor as it does for the list pointer. And now, since you're there, type [S] to change GAL to GALS.

Next, press [←] [←] [←] [←] [←] [←] and [S] again. Not much to this editing business, is there? Notice how the cursor simply replaces the character currently under it.

Finally, press **CALC** to let the machine verify the formula again, and then you'll see your modified variable names come up in the menu.

Problem: Some service stations sell gasoline by the liter. Write yourself an equation to help you convert between liters and gallons so that you can still use your mileage formula (there are about 3.785 liters in a U.S. gallon).

Solution: From the SOLVE Menu, type this equation into your list of equations (notice that when you begin typing, your mileage formula "bumps up" a notch and the pointer now indicates the new formulas you're now starting):

⬚L⬚T⬚R⬚S⬚=⬚G⬚A⬚L⬚S⬚×⬚3⬚·⬚7⬚8⬚5

Now **CALC** ...and there it is—a conversion formula.

Try It: On another trip, you used 40.7 liters to cover 306 miles. What was your mileage?

Solution: Press ⬚4⬚0⬚·⬚7 **LTRS**, then **GALS**.
Answer: GALS=10.75

Now EXIT to the SOLVE Menu, move the pointer up to the mileage equation (press ⬚↑), and press **CALC**.

Then press RCL **GALS**, and notice that GALS is already set to 10.75. Simply by spelling its name the same in each equation, you have created a *shared variable*.

Now key in what you need to finish the calculation:
⬚3⬚0⬚6 **MILS** and **MPG** .... Answer: MPG=28.46

Take a look at the memory diagram of your machine now:

Numbered Registers	Built-In Variables

Numbered Registers:
0
1
2
3
4
5
6
7
8
9

Built-In Variables:

OLD NEW %CH COST PRICE M% M%P

DATE TIME MIN HR DAY WEEK   (APPT1)

DATE TIME MIN HR DAY WEEK   (APPT2)

·
·
·

DATE TIME MIN HR DAY WEEK   (APPT6)

N I%YR PV PMT FV

·
·
·

(And so on, for all the variables of the built-in menus)

CFLO Lists	SUM Lists	Appointment Messages
FRED	INCOME	(APPT1:) TAKE A BREAK
EVEN	AREAS	(APPT2:) CATCH PLANE
UNEVEN	11RNTS	(APPT3:) SEE DENTIST
	VALS	

SOLVE Formulas	SOLVE Variables	TEXT Lists
MPG = MILS ÷ GALS	MPG	(Nothing here so far)
LTRS = GALS x 3.785	MILS	
	GALS	
	LTRS	

How much more room do you have? If you're curious, just press ▮MEM▮ to see the percentage of the total memory still available.... Now try another problem, to become more familiar with the rules of SOLVE....

A contractor often quotes the square-footage area of the rectangular concrete slabs he lays and then figures the cubic yards of mixed concrete necessary for the job. He knows the length and width (in feet) of the slab, and its depth in inches—and he orders ready-to-pour concrete only in whole cubic yards (no extra fractions of yards).

First: Devise a SOLVE formula to help him compute the area of a slab, in square feet.

Easy: You get area by multiplying length by width. So an area formula isn't too much of a problem:

$$\mathtt{AREA=LONG \times WIDE}$$

Next: Devise a SOLVE formula to help the contractor find the volume of concrete required for a given slab.

OK: You get volume when you multiply length by width by depth—or, multiply *area* by depth. So here's a formula:

$$\mathtt{VOL=AREA \times DEEP}$$

That's about all there is to the logic of the formulas—but you must take care to keep your units consistent! You can't expect to get a volume in cubic yards by multiplying a length and width in feet and a depth in inches. After all, what kind of unit is a "foot·foot·inch?" It's neither a cubic foot, nor a cubic inch, nor a cubic yard.

To use your formulas meaningfully, therefore, you must key in all your dimensions *in the same unit.* Things work fine as is for your area formula, but—as you just observed—your *input* units aren't consistent with one another, nor do they match the *output* units you need in your volume formula. To get the right result, you would have to *convert* the inputs to other units at the time you key them in—not too convenient.

Suggestion: Let the calculator do these conversions for you. That is, build the conversion into the formulas, thus allowing the inputs to be keyed in in the conventional-but-inconsistent units that the contractor would be likely to use—depth in inches; length and width in feet.

How?   How do you modify your formulas to do this?

Hmm: The area formula doesn't need to change at all; multiplying feet × feet gives area in square feet:

$$\text{FTAR}=\text{FTLG}\times\text{FTWD}$$

The *names* of the variables should probably be improved like this, though, to tell you which units they assume. This is a good habit—making the name of a variable tell you as much as possible about it.

The volume formula needs some work: First, you convert the depth in inches to depth in feet by dividing the number of inches by 12: $\text{VOL}=\text{FTLG}\times\text{FTWD}\times(\text{INDP}\div12)$

But that's cubic *feet*, so now divide by 27 (because 27 cu. ft = 1 cu. yd.): $\text{VLYD}=(\text{FTLG}\times\text{FTWD}\times(\text{INDP}\div12))\div27$

About those parentheses: You don't really need them here. They're included simply to remind you of the reasons for the 12 and the 27. If you omit them, the result will be the same, because ✕ and ÷ have the same *priority of evaluation* in a formula.

The HP 19Bɪɪ doesn't evaluate a SOLVE formula in quite the same way as it evaluates an ALGebraic* arithmetic problem. For instance, to compute 2+(3×5) via ALGebraic arithmetic, you press ②⊞①③✕⑤⊜, because the machine just works left-to-right if you don't use parentheses. But the SOLVE formula A=2+3×5 will produce the same result *without* parentheses, because the ✕ has a higher priority of evaluation than does the ✛. So keep in mind that the HP 19Bɪɪ does not simply proceed left-to-right when evaluating a SOLVE formula; it evaluates according to the following list of different operations:

- First are the *functions*, such as SQRT(A+B), which is "the square root of A+B."

- Next comes *exponentiation*, such as A^5, i.e. "A raised to the fifth power."

- Next in line are multiplication (✕) and division (÷).

- Last of all come addition (✛) and subtraction (−).

Note, however, that whenever there are two or more operations of the *same* priority, then the calculator does indeed work left-to-right.

---

*With SOLVE formulas, you don't have the choice of arithmetic methods: The syntax for SOLVE formulas is only algebraic—parentheses and all—no RPN.

Those are the rules that tell you if you need parentheses in your formulas. Of course, if it's too much to remember, you can just go ahead and use parentheses anyway—to be on the safe side.

Back to the problem of those concrete slabs. Here are the two formulas you've developed—without unnecessary parentheses:

$$FTAR=FTLG\times FTWD$$

$$VLYD=FTLG\times FTWD\times INDP\div 12\div 27$$

Notice: Dividing by 12 and then by 27 is really dividing by 324:

$$FTAR=FTLG\times FTWD$$

$$VLYD=FTLG\times FTWD\times INDP\div 324$$

And notice that you could *share* the variable **FTAR** between the two formulas:

$$FTAR=FTLG\times FTWD$$

$$VLYD=FTAR\times INDP\div 324$$

Now you can use the first equation to compute the area of a slab, then use the second equation to compute the yards of concrete necessary—simply by keying in the inches of depth—since the area (**FTAR**) will already be calculated and sitting there!

So that's it then....except...the problem stated that the contractor could order concrete loads only in whole cubic yards.

Oh: You need to round your volume calculation *up* to the next whole cubic yard. How do you adjust the equation for this?

Ah: Suppose you take your actual cubic yards requirement, add 1 yard, and then keep just the whole-yards portion of the result. Thus, if your real concrete needs were 3.4 yards, you'd calculate it to be IP(3.4+1), where IP stands for the *Integer Portion*. The IP of (3.4+1) is just 4. So the formula would correctly recommend an order of 4 cubic yards when a slab needs 3.4.

How about 1.9 yards?   IP(1.9+1) = 2.   That checks, too.

How about 2.0 yards?   IP(2.0 +1) = 3.

Hmmm... if a slab needs exactly 2 yards, then you *don't* want to order and waste an entire extra yard—the formula isn't perfect yet. To fix it, just use some common sense: If the real needs were 2.01 yards, would you order 3? Probably not. But if the requirement were 2.1 yards? Probably so.

So change your formula to reflect this judgement—adding a tenth *less* than a whole yard, like this: IP(2.0+.9). Therefore:

$$FTAR = FTLG \times FTWD$$

$$VLYD = IP(FTAR \times INDP \div 324 + .9)$$

Ready: Key in those versions of the formulas and test them.

Solution: From the SOLVE Menu, press ■⬇ to position the ▶ to the bottom of your growing list of formulas. Then:

Ⓕ Ⓣ Ⓐ Ⓡ ⊟ Ⓕ Ⓣ Ⓛ Ⓖ ⓧ Ⓕ Ⓣ Ⓦ Ⓓ **CALC**
Looks OK on the menu.

Try it: ④⓪ **FTLG** ③⓪ **FTWD** **FTAR**
<u>Answer</u>: FTAR=1,200.00   OK.

Now ⓔⓍⓘⓣ and ⬇ and do the other one:
Ⓥ Ⓛ Ⓨ Ⓓ ⊟ ⓘ Ⓟ ⓘ Ⓕ Ⓣ Ⓐ Ⓡ ⓧ ⓘ Ⓝ Ⓓ Ⓟ ⓘ ③②④
⊞ ⓘ ⼁ ⑨ ⓘ), and **CALC** to verify it and create its menu.

Now press ⓡⒸⓛ **FTAR**, to see if your shared FTAR variable works correctly: FTAR=1,200.00   Yep.

So this slab is 30 feet × 40 feet. If it's 6 inches deep, how many cubic yards of concrete should you order?

Press ⑥ **INDP** and **VLYD** ....
<u>Answer</u>: VLYD=23.00   Right on!

Combining Formulas

So there you have it— a set of equations to help the contractor. What could be more convenient?

Well...actually, it *would* be more convenient to have just a single equation—one menu—offer both calculations, no? *Could you* put both of these calculations into the same formula?

Stop and think for a minute: Isn't every formula an *equation* (i.e. "something *equals* something else")? Right now, for example, you've developed these two separate equations:

$$FTAR=FTLG\times FTWD$$

$$VLYD=IP(FTAR\times INDP\div 324+.9)$$

And when you CALCulate with either of these, it builds its own separate menu, of course. But, more importantly, notice that you always solve for one of the variables by using the given values of *all* the others.

It seems, therefore, that you can have only one "unknown;" the rest must all be "knowns." So it seems that you can't have a single formula for both FTAR or VLYD— because that would be two unknowns in the same equation.

But this is where the HP 19BII "cheats" a bit—to make such things possible. There *is* a way to write two separate, unrelated formulas into one, so that all the variables of both formulas appear on one menu....

To use this method, first you must hearken back to those happy, golden days of algebra class, and *rewrite* both formulas so that everything is on one side of the $=$ and a 0 is on the other (you "add the negative to both sides of the equation"—remember?):

$$FTAR-FTLG \times FTWD=0$$

$$VLYD-IP(FTAR \times INDP \div 324+.9)=0$$

Now, notice that if you keep FTAR as a shared variable, it would be the *unknown* in the first equation but a *known* in the second one. There's nothing wrong with this, but it would mean that you would always have to solve for the FTAR before solving for the VLYD, which would defeat your purpose here—to use a single menu to solve for either unknown, *in any order you want*.

Therefore, you should probably use **FTLG×FTWD** in the VLYD formula, since FTLG and FTWD are always *knowns* that you key in anyway.*

Thus, here is your set of equations, properly written in ...=0 form, so that they're ready to be combined:

$$FTAR-FTLG \times FTWD=0$$

$$VLYD-IP(FTLG \times FTWD \times INDP \div 324+.9)=0$$

---

*This is a good point in general: If a set of equations uses a shared variable that is treated as the *unknown* in one equation but as a known in another, then combining them will limit the order of your calculation.

Now to do the combining itself, you need to use the proper "phrase" in the SOLVE language, which is IF(S)....* Here's how:

```
IF(S(FTAR)
  :FTAR-FTLG×FTWD
  :VLYD-IP(FTLG×FTWD×INDP÷324+.9))=0
```

(The line breaks and indentations appear for clarity only. When you key this in—don't do it yet—simply ignore this formatting. The result will appear in your display as follows:)

```
              α
▶IF(S(FTAR):FTAR-FTLG×F
TWD:VLYD-IP(FTLG×FTWD×I
NDP÷324+.9))=0
 CALC   EDIT  DELET
```

Here's what that formula says:

"**IF** you're Solving for **FTAR**
then [the first **:** means *"then"*] *solve* **FTAR-FTLG×FTWD=0**
otherwise [the second **:** means *"otherwise,"* i.e., **IF** you're Solving for something *other* than **FTAR**], *solve* **VLYD-IP(FTLG×FTWD×INDP÷324+.9)=0**"

You rewrote the two separate equations set equal to **0** so that you could also implicitly equate them with the **0** at the end of the **IF(S**... combined-equation structure.

---

*In fact, for the rest of this chapter, keep your Owner's Manual opened to Table 12-1, to get an idea of the various handy "phrases" in your HP 19BII's SOLVE "vocabulary."

Test It: Key in and use this combined, two-in-one formula.

Solution: First delete your FTAR equation: At the SOLVE Menu, use the ⏶ key to move the ▶ to your FTAR formula. Then press **DELET**. You then have the option to delete both the formula and its variables or just the variables. If you delete just the variables, the formula will remain in your list, but none of its variables will exist in the machine's memory until the next time you CALCulate with it (an option to save memory). But you want to delete both the formula and its variables, so press **BOTH**.

Now, since your new combined formula is rather long, why not create it by EDITing VLYD? Press **EDIT**, and use [INS] to insert space in your formula for the new part (26 [INS]'s should do it). Then type: [⋅][F][(][S][(][F][T][A][R][)] [:][F][T][A][R][−][F][T][L][G][×][F][T][W][D][:].

Now move four places: [→][→][→][→] and replace = with − (press[−]). Then replace the **FTAR** with **FTLG×FTWD**: [→][→][→][→][→][INS][INS][INS][INS][INS][L][G][×][F][T][W][D]. Then finish the formula: ■[→][)][=][0].

Now **CALC** and check this with your 30×40 slab: [3][0] **FTWD** [4][0] **FTLG** [6] **INDP** and **VLYD** .... Answer: VLYD=23.00

Now find the **FTAR** .... Answer: FTAR=1,200.00 Voilá!

Take a moment now to review the steps you take to use the $IF(S...$ syntax to combine separate formulas onto a single menu:

1. Rewrite the separate formulas so that nothing but 0 appears to the right of the $=$. For example, you would rewrite

$$25\times(A+B)=11\div C+D$$

   as $\quad (25\times(A+B)-D)\times C-11=0$

   and $\quad\quad\quad\quad E=M\times C^2$

   as $\quad\quad\quad\quad E-M\times C^2=0$

2. To avoid being forced to solve in a certain order for the unknowns in the combined formula, be sure that any variable shared between the equations will always be a *known* value. Thus, the above formulas will best combine as long as the shared variable C is always a known. If C is an unknown in one formula, you'll always be forced to solve for C before you can use it in the other part of the combined formula.

3. Use the $IF(S...$ syntax to tell the HP 19BII when to use each part* of the combined formula:

   $IF(S(E)$ ("*IF you're Solving for* E
   $:E-M\times C^2$ *...then solve this*
   $:(25\times(A+B)-D)\times C-11)=0$ *...otherwise solve this*")

*You're not limited to just two parts. You can combine many formulas with a *nested* arrangement of $IF(S...$:

$IF(S(A)$	("*IF you're Solving for* A
$:...$	*...then solve this*
$:IF(S(B)$	*...otherwise,* IF *you're Solving for* B
$:...$	*...then solve this*
$:IF(S(C)$	*...otherwise,* IF *you're Solving for* C
$:...$	*...then solve this*"), etc.

To see if you're getting the hang of **IF‹S›**, try one more...

For the Road: Remember your gas mileage and your liters-gallons conversion formulas (pages 299-301)? Combine them now into a single formula that will allow you to compute your mileage (in miles per gallon) no matter whether you buy fuel in liters or gallons.

A Good Route: Here are the two formulas as they exist now in your HP 19BⅡ's memory:

$$\mathrm{MPG=MILS \div GALS}$$

$$\mathrm{LTRS=GALS \times 3.785}$$

Of course, you could re-write the latter as

$$\mathrm{GALS=LTRS \div 3.785}$$

And so your two formulas for mileage would be:

$$\mathrm{MPG=MILS \div GALS}$$

$$\mathrm{MPGL=MILS \div (LTRS \div 3.785)}$$

Now you have two formulas with two separate unknowns. So you're ready to rearrange them to get zero on the right sides and then scoop them both into a single formula with **IF‹S**....

Rearranging to isolate 0 on the right:

MPG-MILS÷GALS=0

MPGL-MILS÷LTRS×3.785=0

Now combine these, using the IF(S... structure:

IF(S(MPG)
  :MPG-MILS÷GALS
  :MPGL-MILS÷LTRS×3.785)=0

Or, in the format you'll see it when editing:

▶IF(S(MPG):MPG-MILS÷GAL
S:MPGL-MILS÷LTRS×3.785)
=0

Key this in: At the SOLVE Menu, press ▨↓ to begin a new formula (and delete the two separate formulas shown on page 302, also).* Then type the above formula and press **CALC** and test it—try that first mileage problem you did on page 299:

③⑤⓪ **MILS** ①② **GALS** **MPG**
Answer: MPG=29.17

And if you went the same distance on 50 liters?
⑤⓪ **LTRS** **MPGL**   Answer: MPGL=26.50

---

*To delete a formula, position the ▶ to it and select **DELET**. You will then be asked whether you want to delete just the variables (**VARS**) for that formula or **BOTH** the formula and its variables. Select **BOTH** (you'll soon see the reason for the **VARS** option).

Naming Formulas

Question: As you begin to build your list of SOLVE formulas, what with the **IF(S**...and all that), how will you remember which formula does what, as you move the ▶ up and down the list, looking for the proper one to select?

Answer: Just put a *name* in front of any formula whose purpose you might otherwise forget. A name is separated from the start of the formula itself by a colon (**:**).

Thus, you could give your combined gas mileage formula the name **GAS**, like this:*

```
GAS:IF(S(MPG):MPG-MILS÷GALS:MPGL
    -MILS÷LTRS×3.785)=0
```

Or, give your combined concrete slab formula the name **SLAB**, like this:

```
SLAB:IF(S(FTAR):FTAR-FTLG×FTWD
    :VLYD-IP(FTLG×FTWD×INDP÷324
    +.9))=0
```

Exercise: Do it—name your two formulas as shown: Just ▐EDIT▌ each and insert the name and a colon at the beginning of each formula. Now they're stored in your HP 19Bᴨ.

---

*Again, remember that the line breaks and indents are shown here simply to emphasize the parts of the formula under discussion. Such formatting will never appear in your calculator's display.

Question: How many formulas can you store in your HP 19Bɪɪ?

Answer: That depends on how long or complex they are and how many variables they use. Of course, it takes memory to store the typed formula itself, but each *variable* created by the formula needs space when you use the formula.

Prove It: Select your GAS formula and press **CALC** as if you were going to use it.... Now **EXIT** (as if you've finished using it) and check the available free memory (press **■**MEM). Make a note of the result.

Now press **DELET** and then **VARS**, to delete the *variables* of the GAS formula—without deleting the formula itself. Since you're through using GAS for the moment, why take up memory space for its variables (MPG, MILS, GALS, MPGL and LTRS)? After all, you'll just create them again anyway, whenever you next **CALC** with GAS.

Press **■**MEM again.... <u>Result</u>: There's more memory available, now that you've deleted the GAS variables.

<u>Moral of the Story</u>: To maximize the amount of memory available to you, delete the variables of SOLVE formulas that you're *not currently using.*

Of course, you can do a lot more with SOLVE than just gas mileage. As Table 12-1 of the HP Owner's Manual shows, you have many "formula-building-blocks," including sophisticated financial calculations....

Optimizing Formulas

Problem: How would you devise a SOLVE formula to compute the true A.P.R. of a loan with loan fees ("points up front"), as you computed manually back on pages 136-137?

Solution: You would build a *simulated TVM* solution, using the TVM equation shown in Appendix B (page 297) of your HP Owner's Manual.

In Appendix B, HP lists most of the mathematical formulas it has used for the built-in menus, including these two TVM formulas:

$$i\% = \frac{I\%YR}{P/YR}$$

and

$$0 = PV + \left(1 + \frac{i\% \times S}{100}\right) \times PMT \times \text{USPV}(i\%{:}n) + FV \times \text{SPPV}(i\%{:}n)$$

Now, if you substitute the smaller, top expression for $i\%$ into the longer, main formula, here's how that main formula would look:

$$0 = PV + \left(1 + \frac{\dfrac{I\%YR}{P/YR} \times S}{100}\right) \times PMT \times \text{USPV}\left(\frac{I\%YR}{P/YR}{:}n\right) + FV \times \text{SPPV}\left(\frac{I\%YR}{P/YR}{:}n\right)$$

Or, in SOLVE notation, it would look like this:

```
0=PV+(1+I%YR÷P/YR×S÷100)×PMT
    ×USPV(I%YR÷P/YR:N)+FV×SPPV(I%YR÷P/YR:N)
```

This is the one equation that correctly relates all seven TVM variables.

"But aren't there just five TVM variables?"

No! Don't forget about the OTHER Menu, where you establish the values of two other variables: the number of payments per year (P/YR) and the annuity mode (BEGIN or END—represented in the formula by the value of the variable, S). Even if you don't usually vary these when playing "What-If?", they are still used—and essential—for TVM computations. And there's no OTHER Menu for SOLVE formulas, so you must include all relevant values in one equation like this.

Question: What are those two SOLVE functions, USPV and SPPV?

Answer: They are "Uniform-Stream Present Value" and "Single-Payment Present Value."

USPV(i%:n) is the Present Value of a Uniform Stream of n periodic $1 cash-flows, discounted at $i\%$ per period.

SPPV(i%:n) is the Present Value of a *single* $1 cash-flow discounted n periods at $i\%$ per period.

These are useful for all sorts of TVM calculations; indeed, HP even used them in their built-in formulas.

Here again is the "TVM-mimicking" formula you've developed so far:

```
0=PV+(1+I%YR÷P/YR×S÷100)×PMT
    ×USPV(I%YR÷P/YR:N)+FV×SPPV(I%YR÷P/YR:N)
```

Question: If they're named the same, are SOLVE variables then *shared* with those of the built-in TVM Menu?

Answer: No! A SOLVE variable may be shared only with another SOLVE variable. And variables for the *built-in* menus are shared only with those of other *built-in* menus. So you can give your SOLVE variables names such as the PV, PMT, FV, etc., as above, and *they will have absolutely no connection* to the built-in TVM variables of the same names. The SOLVE variable names may *mean* similar things to you (that's why you use similar names*). But the actual, built-in TVM Menus (and BUS Menus, etc.) are in a separate world from your SOLVE formulas.

---

*After all, you could use other, less meaningful names in your formula, like this:

```
0=A+(1+B÷C×D÷100)×E×USPV(B÷C:F)+G×SPPV(B÷C:N)
```

But then, how would you remember that A is the variable name for your Present Value, and F is the name for the number of periods, etc.? A SOLVE formula without meaningful variable names is almost worse than useless.

Now, back to the problem: to develop a formula that mimics TVM *and* accounts for a loan's prepaid finance charge ("points up front"). Right now you have just a simple TVM simulator: If you were to **CALC** with it now, you'd key the number of payments into **N**, the amount financed (using the sign convention) into **PV**, etc.* It would look and feel much like the built-in TVM—but it wouldn't be any more convenient for handling a finance charge—so what would be the point?

Problem: Modify your formula to account for "points up front."

Solution: Looking back at your keystroked solution for a mortgage with loan fees (pages 136-137), you'll see that there's no difference in the way you treated any TVM quantity except PV. So there's no need to change the way you're using the N, PMT, FV, P/YR and S variables in your formula here. But in calculating the true A.P.R. on page 137, the idea was to *reduce* the actual amount financed (i.e. the original PV) by the amount of the finance charges, then put *that* into the PV register and recompute I%YR. So use PV+FC** instead of PV (thus FC becomes another variable on the menu):

$$0=PV+FC+(1+I\%YR\div P/YR\times S\div 100)\times PMT$$
$$\times USPV(I\%YR\div P/YR:N)+FV$$
$$\times SPPV(I\%YR\div P/YR:N)$$

---

*For the **S** variable, you would key in a 1 for BEGIN mode or a 0 for END mode.

**You might think this would increase PV, but remember that the TVM equation you're mimicking assumes the cash-flow sign conventions: FC will always be of the *opposite sign* from PV.

Test It: Try a 30-year, 10.3935% mortgage for $100,000, monthly payments (in arrears) of $906.79 and a 2% loan fee.

Solution: At the SOLVE Menu, press ■ ↓ and ⓪═ⓅⓋ╋ⒻⒸ╋
⦅①╋Ⓘ%ⓎⓇ÷Ⓟ╱ⓎⓇ╳Ⓢ÷①⓪⓪⦆╳ⓅⓂⓉ
╳ⓊⓈⓅⓋ⦅Ⓘ%ⓎⓇ÷Ⓟ╱ⓎⓇ꞉Ⓝ⦆
╋ⒻⓋ╳ⓈⓅⓅⓋ⦅Ⓘ%ⓎⓇ÷Ⓟ╱ⓎⓇ꞉Ⓝ⦆ (INPUT).
Then **CALC** and test: ①⓪⓪⓪⓪⓪ **PV**
②⓪⓪⓪╋╱─ **FC** (remember the sign convention!)
①② **P/YR** ⓪ **S** (for END mode)
MORE ⑨⓪⑥∙⑦⑨╋╱─ **PMT** ③⑥⓪ **N** ⓪ **FV**
MORE **I%YR** .... Result: I%YR=10.64   Correct!

Question: Wouldn't it be more convenient to key in the loan fee as percentage points rather than as a dollar amount?

Answer: Probably. So instead of PV+FC, you could use

PV×(1-PTS÷100)

Your formula would then become:

0=PV×(1-PTS÷100)+(1+I%YR÷P/YR×S÷
100)×PMT×USPV(I%YR÷P/YR:N)+FV×
SPPV(I%YR÷P/YR:N)

So **EXIT** and **EDIT** your formula, then **CALC** to test it:
①⓪⓪⓪⓪⓪ **PV** ② **PTS** ①② **P/YR** ⓪ **S**
MORE ⑨⓪⑥∙⑦⑨╋╱─ **PMT** ③⑥⓪ **N** ⓪ **FV**
MORE **I%YR** .... Result: I%YR=10.64   Still OK.

Hm: The order of menu items in your formula doesn't really match the order on the built-in TVM Menu—disconcerting if you're used to finding things in certain places. Can you somehow adjust your formula to get its menu to more closely match the built-in TVM Menu? █ **N** █ **I%YR** █ **PV** █ **PMT** █ **FV** █**MORE**

Yes: The order of menu items is the order in which each variable first appears in the formula. To rig this order, just use a phony set of "first appearances"—in the order you want—*multiplying them by zero so as not to affect the math*:

```
0×(N+I%YR+PV+PMT+FV+P/YR+S+PTS)
+PV×(1-PTS÷100)
+(1+I%YR÷P/YR×S÷100)×PMT
                        ×USPV(I%YR÷P/YR:N)
+FV×SPPV(I%YR÷P/YR:N)=0
```

This is a good, simple trick to remember. Re-edit your formula into the above version and **CALC** to test this as before:

[3][6][0] █ **N** █ [1][0][0][0][0][0] █ **PV** █
[9][0][6][•][7][9][+/−] █ **PMT** █ [0] █ **FV** █
█**MORE**█ [1][2] █**P/YR**█ [0] █ **S** █ [2] █ **PTS** █
█**MORE**█**I%YR**█ .... <u>Result</u>: I%YR=10.64

That's an easier menu to use, don't you think?

Problem: Your formula now computes the true A.P.R. of a mortgage with "points up front"—as long as you've already used the real, built-in TVM Menu to compute the PMT and/or FV and then copied all values to the corresponding variables on the formula's menu. But wouldn't it be nice to be able to do all the computation in one place?

You Can: Use your formula to perform the other calculations *first*, using the original mortgage rate as your I%YR *and ignoring the finance charge.* Watch:

⓷⓺⓪ **N** ①⓪·⓷⓽⓷⓹ **I%YR**
①⓪⓪⓪⓪⓪ **PV** ⓪ **FV**
MORE ①② **P/YR** ⓪ **S** ⓪ **PTS**
MORE PMT .... <u>Result</u>: PMT=-906.79
Then **MORE** ② **PTS**
and **MORE I%YR** .... <u>Result</u>: I%YR=10.64

Comment: This can still be confusing: Sometimes **I%YR** will contain the mortgage rate; sometimes the true A.P.R. Isn't there some way to further simplify things?

Idea: Create two formulas and combine them with **IF(S**...: In one formula, use the loan amount less points to allow you to solve for the true A.P.R. In the other formula, use the nominal mortgage rate and the real loan amount in a true "TVM-mimicking" manner to allow you to solve for (and play "What-If?" with) *any* of the TVM parameters.

Do It: First—to solve for the true A.P.R. (this should look familiar, except for the name of the interest rate, `APR`)—this formula:

```
PV×(1-PTS÷100)+(1+APR÷P/YR×S÷100)×PMT
×USPV(APR÷P/YR:N)+FV×SPPV(APR÷P/YR:N)
=0
```

And the second formula—the simple "TVM-mimicker"—is this:

```
PV+(1+I%YR÷P/YR×S÷100)×PMT×USPV
(I%YR÷P/YR:N)+FV×SPPV(I%YR÷P/YR:N)=0
```

Notice that both are already conveniently arranged into the proper "=0" format required by `IF(S`.... So, combine them:

```
IF(S(APR)
:PV×(1-PTS÷100)+(1+APR÷P/YR×S÷100)×PMT
 ×USPV(APR÷P/YR:N)+FV×SPPV(APR÷P/YR:N)
:PV+(1+I%YR÷P/YR×S÷100)×PMT×USPV
 (I%YR÷P/YR:N)+FV×SPPV(I%YR÷P/YR:N))=0
```

Add "opening appearances"—for the menu order—and a name:

```
POINTS:0×(N+I%YR+PV+PMT+FV+P/YR+S+PTS)
+IF(S(APR)
:PV×(1-PTS÷100)+(1+APR÷P/YR×S÷100)×PMT
 ×USPV(APR÷P/YR:N)+FV×SPPV(APR÷P/YR:N)
:PV+(1+I%YR÷P/YR×S÷100)×PMT×USPV
 (I%YR÷P/YR:N)+FV×SPPV(I%YR÷P/YR:N))=0
```

Now key in and test this.... The menu will behave like the built-in TVM Menu except for the last items, **PTS** and **APR**.

Question: Can you imitate the built-in TVM Menu's **BEG** and
END items on your menu—instead of using **5** ?

Answer: Yes, to a great extent, you can.

Consider how the **BEG** and **END** items operate on the built-in TVM
Menu: They are always *knowns* (you never solve for the annuity mode
as your unknown). But you don't key in any values before pressing
them, either; they're just "yes-or-no" *mode* items. You simply select one
item or the other and that selects the annuity mode.

But in a SOLVE formula, whenever you press a variable's menu key
without first keying in a value, the HP 19BII will solve for that variable.
You can't stop it from doing this solving, but you can tell it to do
something else—*set another value*—in the process.

Look: These simple formulas will always give you the same result
for the variable BEG: 1=BEG   *or*   1+0=BEG

So will this: 1+L(END:0)=BEG   You are still
saying "BEG=0+1," but *at the same time* ("in passing," so to
speak) you are also saying "Let END be set to: 0."

Does this give you any ideas on the **BEG** and **END** problem?

??: Write three formulas that, respectively: set BEG to 1 and END to Ø; set BEG to Ø and END to 1; and use BEG as the annuity mode variable in a "TVM-mimicking" formula. Then use IF(S... to combine the three formulas into one.

!!: To set BEG to 1 and END to Ø: 1+L(END:0)=BEG

To set BEG to Ø and END to 1:   1+L(BEG:0)=END

To use BEG as the annuity mode in a "TVM-mimicker":

```
PV+(1+I%YR÷P/YR×BEG÷100)×PMT×USPV
  (I%YR÷P/YR:N)+FV×SPPV(I%YR÷P/YR:N)=0
```

Now two of them need to be rearranged into ...=Ø format:

```
            1+L(END:0)-BEG=0
            1+L(BEG:0)-BEG=0
```

Then combine them all:*

```
IF(S(BEG)
 :1+L(END:0)-BEG
 :IF(S(END)
   :1+L(BEG:0)-END
   :PV+(1+I%YR÷P/YR×BEG÷100)×PMT×USPV
    (I%YR÷P/YR:N)+FV×SPPV(I%YR÷P/YR:N)
))=0
```

---

*This is an example of a combination of *more* than two formulas—as in the footnote on page 313. The parentheses that end the two *nested* IF(S... statements are isolated here for clarity (as always, line breaks and indents are for clarity only; the calculator doesn't display this way).

Note: Don't confuse the S in the SOLVE-phrase IF(S... with the *variable* name S for the annuity mode here. You could have chosen any name for that variable (you were simply using the names shown in HP-s equation in Appendix B of their Owner's Manual).

OK: Using what you've just learned, see if you can modify the formula from page 325 to include BEG and END items that behave a little more like their TVM counterparts.

Go: It's going to be a nested set of **IF(S**...'s, for sure. Your existing formula already has one **IF(S**..., and now you're going to add a couple more....   Here goes nothing:

```
POINTS:                          (The formula's name)
0×(N+I%YR+PV+PMT+FV              (Set up
    +P/YR+BEG+END+PTS+APR)+       the menu order)
IF(S(BEG)                        ("IF you're Solving for BEG
  :1+L(END:0)-BEG               ...then solve this formula
  :IF(S(END)        ...otherwise, IF you're Solving for END
    :1+L(BEG:0)-END             ...then solve this formula
    :IF(S(APR)     ...otherwise, IF you're Solving for APR
      :PV×(1-PTS÷100)+(1+APR÷P/YR×BEG
       ÷100)×PMT×USPV(APR÷P/YR:N)+FV×
       SPPV(APR÷P/YR:N)  ...then solve this formula
      :PV+(1+I%YR÷P/YR×BEG÷100)×PMT
       ×USPV(I%YR÷P/YR:N)+FV×
       SPPV(I%YR÷P/YR:N)  ...otherwise solve this")
)))=0
```

Notice how you work through each *specific* case first—where you tell the machine what to do when solving for one specific variable. That leaves the final *"otherwise"* formula to include all the other possible variables you might solve for.

Exercise: Key in and test this formula (EDIT the previous version).

Solution: Press **EDIT** and modify the formula. Then **CALC** to test
it: ③⑥⓪ **N** ①⓪·③⑨③⑤ **I%YR**
①⓪⓪⓪⓪ **PV** ⓪ **FV** **MORE** ①② **P/YR**
END (the display will show END=1.00)
MORE **PMT** .... Result: PMT=-906.79
Then **MORE** ② **PTS** **APR** Result: APR=10.64

Question: The formula uses I%YR÷P/YR and APR÷P/YR three
times each. Could you avoid this repetition?

Answer: Yes. For example, use L(I: I%YR÷P/YR) the first
time you need I%YR÷P/YR—to also assign that value
to another variable I. Then, to use that value again, just
use G(I), which means: "Get the value of I without
showing I on the menu." Thus:

```
▶POINTS:0×(N+I%YR+PV+PM
T+FV+P/YR+BEG+END+PTS+A
PR)+IF(S(BEG):1+L(END:0
)-BEG:IF(S(END):1+L(BEG
:0)-END:IF(S(APR):PV×(1
-PTS÷100)+(1+L(A:APR÷P/
YR)×BEG÷100)×PMT×USPV(G
(A):N)+FV×SPPV(G(A):N):
PV+(1+L(I:I%YR÷P/YR)×BE
G÷100)×PMT×USPV(G(I):N)
+FV×SPPV(G(I):N))))=0
```

(defining A)

(using A)

(defining I)

(using I)

Question: Using L⟨:⟩ and G⟨⟩, you saved yourself some typing—but did you save the machine any memory space?

Find Out: A formula uses more memory when you use it (when its menu is in the display). So, with your current version of POINTS, run the test calculations on page 329. Then press ■ MEM to see how much memory is available.... Note this number.

Now edit your formula back to the "longer" form shown below (i.e. as it was on page 328) and repeat the above calculations and memory test....

```
▶POINTS:0×(N+I%YR+PV+PM
T+FV+P/YR+BEG+END+PTS+A
PR)+IF(S(BEG):1+L(END:0
)-BEG:IF(S(END):1+L(BEG
:0)-END:IF(S(APR):PV×(1
-PTS÷100)+(1+APR÷P/YR×B
EG÷100)×PMT×USPV(APR÷P/
YR:N)+FV×SPPV(APR÷P/YR:
N):PV+(1+I%YR÷P/YR×BEG÷
100)×PMT×USPV(I%YR÷P/YR
:N)+FV×SPPV(I%YR÷P/YR:N
))))=0
```

This "longer" formula uses about 28 *fewer* bytes during calculation—*because it uses fewer variables*. Recall (from page 296) that each variable uses memory space. With the additional variables A and I, you bought some typing convenience by using a little more memory.

One other comment: Notice that in your POINTS formula, you must always solve for PMT first—so that the APR portion of the formula has that value to use when solving for APR. In the POINTS formula, that assumption isn't a big problem; you're probably in the habit of solving for the PMT first, anyway. But you *can* make these unknowns entirely independent—just as you did with your SLAB formula (page 311). As usual, you trade memory for convenience. Here's the modification:*

```
▶POINTS:0×(N+I%YR+PV+PM
T+FV+IF(P/YR=0:L(P/YR:1
2):0)+BEG+END+PTS)+IF(S
(BEG):1+L(END:0)-BEG :IF
(S(END):1+L(BEG:0)-END:
IF(S(APR):PV×(1-PTS÷100
)+(1+APR÷P/YR×BEG÷100)×
(-PV-FV×SPPV(I%YR÷P/YR:
N))÷USPV(I%YR÷P/YR:N)÷(
1+BEG÷100×I%YR÷P/YR)×US
PV(APR÷P/YR:N)+FV×SPPV(
APR÷P/YR:N):PV+(1+I%YR÷
P/YR×BEG÷100)×PMT×USPV(
I%YR÷P/YR:N)+FV×SPPV(I%
YR÷P/YR:N))))
```

Is this capability worth the extra typing and/or memory, just to be able to solve for APR first, if you wish? Maybe not. But you'll see formulas where such *unknown independence* is indeed advisable—where, instead of just two unknowns, you may have nine or ten. Then it's *really* inconvenient to dictate the order in which you must solve for them.

---

*Notice some other modification in this version, too: It sets the value of P/YR to 12, as a *default*, if you neglect to give it a value (i.e. leave it at 0). Also, in the menu-ordering portion (0×(...)), there's really no need to include APR, since it's the last variable in the menu anyway. Finally, notice that there's no =0 at the end. Anytime a formula ends in =0, you may omit it.

SOLVE Review

"Set the brake and idle" for a moment, and review all the things you now know about the SOLVE Menu of your HP 19Bıı:

- You know how to use the SOLVE Menu to select or type a formula, and how to EDIT a formula—use [INS], [DEL], [←], [→], [↑] and [↓]—to create space, delete characters and move the cursor;

- You know that ■[MEM] shows the memory remaining, and you can maximize this by deleting the *variables* of formulas not in use;

- You know that a SOLVE formula is basically just an algebraic equation—variables and numbers equated by an = and evaluated according to *operator priorities* (not just right-to-left).

- You know how the machine creates the menu of variables that appear in a formula—in the order of the first appearance of each variable. So you choose a short but *meaningful* name for each variable, to describe it and its units or other assumptions;

- You know that SOLVE formulas may share variables (i.e. use the same variable name and value) with other SOLVE formulas, and built-in menus may share with other built-in menus—but a SOLVE variable is never shared with a built-in variable;

- You've worked through the logic of some practical calculations, including unit conversions and rounding (recall the IP function); you've worked quite a lot with the IF(S... notation, which allows you to combine two or more separate formulas (so long as each formula has been written into the form "*something* =Ø");

- You've seen how to use L(∶) to assign a value to a variable "in passing;" and you've seen how to use G( ) to get the *value* of a variable without causing its name appear on the menu.

Formulas For Practical Use (and More Study)

Of course, there are many more SOLVE functions to discover—and much more practicing to do. So the rest of this chapter is simply an extensive and useful collection of formulas—listed in EDIT format, for easy entry.

Note: These formulas will *not* all fit into your HP 19Bɪɪ at once. With some of the longer ones, you may be able to fit only one or two. Designed for real-world situations, they use a lot of memory (recall the memory/convenience trade-off); some may take 20-25 minutes to key in. Although not handy for the odd occasion, each can easily pay for itself (and this book), saving you hours of time, if you need such a calculation regularly.

Browse the formula descriptions on the next few pages (they are grouped by category). For any that interest you, study their solutions, sample problem(s) and memory requirements. If you wish to have several large formulas in the machine at once, note that it takes a lot more memory to *verify* a formula than to *use* it (the extra amount needed is unpredictable). So leave at least 25% of memory free at all times, for verification space, and (after deleting the variables of all other formulas), key in the formulas *by size*—largest to smallest.

Although you needn't understand the logic of the formulas to employ them fruitfully in your work, they are posed as problems, so you can treat them as a quiz, if you wish. They use the techniques you've seen here, plus many others. Polish your SOLVE skills by studying them. <u>Very Helpful Study Tip</u>: To learn about the design of a formula, a good first step is to *rewrite it in expanded, indented, commented format*— like that used on page 328—to help identify each part and its function.

SOLVE Problems

Misc. SOLVE Functions

1. Your company does a lot of direct-mail advertising. The response
    on mailings varies, depending on the list you rent and the time
    of year. Develop a formula to calculate the net profit from a
    mailing. (The solution is on page 342.)

2. An obstetrician friend has a new HP 19Bɪɪ, and she has asked you
    to write a combination of two formulas for her work: One formula
    uses the estimated starting date for a woman's pregnancy and
    calculates her delivery date (280 days later). The other formula
    uses today's date and the starting date to calculate the number
    of weeks and days in the pregnancy progress. (Page 343)

3. You are a lineman for the county, and you drive the main road,
    but the county reimburses you monthly for using your own car
    and gas on the job. Write a SOLVE formula to do the monthly
    mileage and reimbursement calculations. (Page 344)

4. Write a set of formulas to compute, from an employee's weekly
    time card, the gross pay (hourly wage plus overtime), the proper
    amounts to withhold for FICA and Medicare, federal and state
    income taxes, and then the net paycheck amount. (Page 346)

5. Suppose that all payroll deduction taxes were combined into one tax on *gross* income. Although tax rates would still be progressively structured (higher earners would still be paying a higher percentage of gross income as tax), nobody would be allowed to take any deductions before computing his/her tax.

Suppose further that this tax structure had *no discrete brackets*. That is, the percentage of gross income paid by each taxpayer would be given by a *continuous function*, like this:

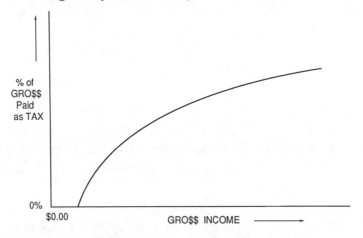

The formula for the tax itself might be something like this:

$$TAX = .01 \times GRO\$\$ \times \text{LOG}(GRO\$\$)$$

(the LOGarithm function produces a curve of the above shape).

Of course, a payroll clerk would still need a SOLVE formula to process an employee's weekly timecard into a paycheck. Write the formula to do so, and compare this solution with that for the previous problem. (Page 350)

6. Write one formula to compute the maximum home price and principal-and-interest payment for which a borrower could qualify for financing under these rules:

    a. Conventional
    b. FNMA
    c. GNMA
    d. FHA
    e. VA   (Page 352)

7. Write a formula to help a prospective home buyer determine whether it is more advantageous to rent or buy a home during a given period of time. Include considerations for taxes, inflation, and alternative investments over this time period. (Page 356)

8. A mortgage borrower can significantly reduce the term of the mortgage by paying _a portion_ of the normal monthly payment _more often_ than once a month (e.g. 24 or 26 "half-payments" per year). Write a TVM formula, including AMRT, for this. (Page 360)

9. Write a kind of TVM formula for an Adjustable Rate Mortgage (ARM). (Page 362)

10. In a conventional amortizing loan (i.e. with a shrinking balance), the periodic payment usually pays that period's entire interest, plus some principal: Payment = Interest + Principal

As the unpaid balance shrinks, so the interest amount in each payment shrinks. But in a conventional mortgage, the *total* payment amount is nevertheless held constant, so as the interest portion of each payment shrinks, the principal portion grows. Thus, over the life of the loan, the pay-down rate accelerates (see the diagram on page 181). Write a TVM-like formula (including AMRT) that calculates when a conventional mortgage balance will reach a given percentage of the original loan. (Page 364)

11. Occasionally, an amortizing loan is written to specify a *constant* payment to principal, so that the payoff rate is indeed steady over the entire term of the loan. But a constant principal amount requires a *non-constant payment* amount. Write a kind of TVM formula, including AMRT, for this situation. (Page 366)

12. Write a TVM-like formula (excluding AMRT) to compute present and future values of a cash-flow stream that periodically changes by either a set *percentage* (%CH) or by a set *amount* ($CH). Such terms are often built into contracts to adjust for inflation. (Page 368)

Commercial Investment

13. Write a combined formula to compute price and yield on a bond, *after* income taxes, capital gains taxes and broker commissions, otherwise mimicking the HP 19Bɪɪ's built-in BOND Menu as much as possible. (Page 370)

14. Write a TVM-like formula to compute a lease's value, payment amount, residual (as a percentage of the value), or rate. Allow for an annual pattern of skipped payments and/or advanced payments. (Page 372)

15. Write a formula to help analyze the relative merits of steady leasing or outright buying a commercial asset, including the cost of money, property, depreciation, capital gains and income tax rates, and resale value. (Page 374).

16. Write a formula to estimate an income property's value to an investor, based upon its operating income and expenses, current market rates for mortgage and equity performance, investment risk, etc. (Page 378)

17. Write a kind of TVM formula to compute wraparound mortgages and second mortgages, either from the borrower's or the lender's point of view. (Page 380)

18. Write a formula to compute these values for an income property:

- the initial after-tax cash-flow at purchase;
- the after-tax cash-flow for any operating year;
- the after-tax cash-flow at sale (after any operating year);
- the ratio of the purchase price to the potential gross income (often called the Gross Rent Multiplier);
- the Capitalization rate (ratio of the first year's Net Operating Income to the purchase price), in percentage form;
- the rate of return on *equity* in year 1 (in percentage form);
- the rate of return on *cash* in year 1 (in percentage form)— both before and after taxes.

(Page 384)

19. Write a formula to compute the following values for a single CFLO list, under the assumptions of a risk rate and a safe rate for alternative investments:

- the IRR;
- the Financial Management Rate of Return (FMRR);
- the minimum initial investment required under FMRR assumptions;
- the final net lump-sum return expected under FMRR assumptions (also called the Future Wealth).

(Page 388)

Business Management

20. Write a formula for the maximum depreciation allowed and the remaining depreciable value under 1990 rules for regular MACRS depreciation of an asset, given its class life (3, 5, 7, 10, 15, 20, 27.5 or 31.5 years) and the current year in that life. (Page 390)

21. Often an inventory item's unit cost depends on the volume of the order. Write a combination formula to help an inventory manager estimate the unit cost of any order size, and the *best* order size for an inventory item, given the following values:

    a. An estimate of the total number of this item that will be used—at a steady rate—over a given period

    b. The unit cost of holding the item in inventory over that period (warehousing, financing, insurance, etc.).

    c. A set of quotes from the manufacturer—aggregate prices for orders of various sizes.

(Page 392)

22. Write a formula to evaluate the return on investment and the minimum cash commitment for a manufacturer to develop a new product. Include time and cost-of-money considerations, and assume a linearly increasing sales pattern. (Page 396)

Personal Finance

23. Write a TVM-like formula to do compound interest calculations in terms of *buying power* (i.e. "today's dollars")—after inflation and taxes. (Page 398)

24. Assume that at the beginning of your career, you begin to invest a set percentage of your gross monthly paycheck in a taxable, interest-bearing account. Assume steady employment—with yearly salary raises to keep pace with inflation—and the same tax bracket for all your working years. Write a combined formula to compute how much (in terms of today's dollars or "purchasing power") would be in the account at the time you retire, *and* the monthly annuity you could draw from this (earning a different interest rate, if desired) for a given number of years thereafter. (Page 400)

25. Write a combined formula that will project retirement income— in terms of today's dollars—for a married couple, in a given tax bracket, who may have IRA's and Social Security incomes to draw upon, in addition to a taxable savings account. (Page 402)

SOLVE Solutions

1. This is a straightforward problem, but it's a good reminder of how
    useful a simple SOLVE formula can make the "What-If" game:

    > `►DIRMAIL:-TOTL×$CST+$PR`
    > `F×TOTL×RET%÷100=$NET`

    <u>Approximate Memory Required</u>: 5% to use, 1% to store.
    <u>Required Knowns</u>: None (i.e. any value may be the unknown).

    <u>Example</u>: If you send out 130,000 flyers, costing $0.30 apiece, and
    the average profit per response is $19.00, what is the
    break-even response percentage? How much will a
    4% response net you?

    <u>Solution</u>: Key in the above formula and press **CALC**. Then:
    ⑴③⓪⓪⓪⓪ **TOTL** ·③ **$CST** ①⑨ **$PRF**
    ⓪ **$NET** **RET%**.... <u>Answer</u>: `RET%=1.58`
    ④ **RET%** **$NET**.... <u>Answer</u>: `$NET=59,800.00`

<u>Notice</u>:

*   The variables are named with $ or % wherever possible, to
    remind you of the assumptions of the formula;

*   The order of the formula's arithmetic is a little "unnatural,"
    but this makes the menu more convenient, left-to-right.

2. This uses some of the calendar functions in the HP 19BⅡ's SOLVE vocabulary (DATE, DDAYS and CDATE):

```
▶BABY:0×L(D:DATE(START:
280))+IF(S(DUE):DUE-G(D
):IDIV(L(P:280-DDAYS(CD
ATE:G(D):1)):7)+MOD(G(P
):7)÷10-WW.D)
```

<u>Approximate Memory Required</u>: 7% to use, 2% to store.
<u>Required Knowns</u>: The starting date (START) of the pregnancy.

<u>Example</u>:   If today is 9/9/91, and a pregnancy began on 2/27/91, what is its due date and progress as of today?

<u>Solution</u>:   First, set the clock to the "correct" date (of course, the date is usually correct already): ■(MAIN) **TIME** **SET**
(DISP) **ALL** (9)·(0)(9)(1)(9)(9)(1) **DATE** . Next, go to the SOLVE Menu, enter the formula and **CALC** .
Then give the starting date: (2)·(2)(7)(1)(9)(9)(1) **START**
DUE   <u>Answer</u>: DUE=12.041991   (12/4/91)
WW.D   <u>Answer</u>: WW.D=27.5 (27 weeks, 5 days)

<u>Notice</u>:

- The formula uses one number, WW.D, to give two pieces of information—just as the calculator uses a single number of the form MM.DDYYY to show all three parts of a date.

- Thanks to the formula's hidden variable, D, you need not solve for **DUE** before solving for **WW.D**.

- There's no =0 at the end of the formula. Anytime a formula would normally end with =0, you may omit it.

3. A SOLVE formula can use (but not alter) any value in a SUM list. Also, the SOLVE language has a summation tool: $\Sigma(\quad)$. So if you record your starting and ending odometer readings (one pair after another) in a SUM list named TRIPS, here's the formula:

```
▶MILE$REIMB:0×L(M:Σ(N:2
:SIZES(TRIPS):2:ITEM(TR
IPS:N)-ITEM(TRIPS:N-1))
)+IF(S(MILS):MILS-G(M):
$/MI×G(M)-$RMB)
```

Approximate Memory Required: 7% to use, 2% to store, not including the TRIPS list.

Required Knowns: A list named TRIPS, containing sequential pairs of odometer readings.

Example: Below are odometer readings for last month's trips. Find your mileage and reimbursement @ $.21/mile.

Trip	Start Reading	End Reading
1	45,678.9	46,111.0
2	47,142.8	47,376.5
3	48,123.4	48,571.4
4	49,012.3	50,987.6

Solution: First, build your TRIPS list (in actual use, of course, you would do this during the month, as you record the odometer readings for each trip):

```
[MAIN] SUM GET ≥NEW NAME [T][R][I][P][S] [INPUT]
[4][5][6][7][8][·][9] [INPUT]   [4][6][1][1][1] [INPUT]
[4][7][1][4][2][·][8] [INPUT]   [4][7][3][7][6][·][5] [INPUT]
[4][8][1][2][3][·][4] [INPUT]   [4][8][5][7][1][·][4] [INPUT]
[4][9][0][1][2][·][3] [INPUT]   [5][0][9][8][7][·][6] [INPUT]
```

Next, press (DISP) **FIX** (2) (INPUT).

Then **(MAIN) SOLVE**, key in the formula, press **CALC**,
MILS (maybe twice) <u>Answer:</u> MILS=3,089.10

(·)(2)(1) **\$/MI** **\$RMB** .... <u>Answer:</u> \$RMB=648.71

<u>Notice:</u>

- The SIZES( ) and ITEM(:) functions are defined "phrases" in the SOLVE language. In the formula, the term SIZES(TRIPS) means "the SIZE of the SUM list named TRIPS." And ITEM(TRIPS:N) means "the value of ITEM number N in the SUM list named TRIPS."

- The meaning of the summation formula, Σ( ), is this:

  Σ(N   *(A sum, using N, a tempor-*
                               ary counter variable...
  :2   *...starting at N = 2...*
  :SIZES(TRIPS)   *...ending when N is equal to*
                               the size of the TRIPS list...
  :2   *...counting by twos...*
  :ITEM(TRIPS:N)-ITEM(TRIPS:N-1)
                               ...summing this expression
                               for each value of N.)
)

The Σ(: : : :) function is yet another defined "phrase" in the SOLVE language.

4. The only hard part is to compute the withholding amounts from the formulas provided by the various tax agencies. This solution assumes actual 1991 formulas for withholding Social Security, Medicare and Federal income tax, and (as an example) a hypothetical state income tax structure, all summarized as follows:

<u>Social Security</u>: 6.20% of first $53,400 of annual gross income
<u>Medicare</u>: 1.45% of first $125,000 of annual gross income

Federal tax (weekly payroll):

The portion of (Gross Pay − 39.42×W4 Allowances)

for single <u>or</u> married, falling between			is taxed at
0	and	23 <u>or</u> 65	0%
23 <u>or</u> 65	and	397 <u>or</u> 689	15%
397 <u>or</u> 689	and	928 <u>or</u> 1,573	28%
928 <u>or</u> 1,573	and	2,121 <u>or</u> 3,858	33%
2,121 <u>or</u> 3,858	and	∞	28%

State tax (weekly payroll):

The portion of (Gross Pay − Federal Tax − 33×W4 Allowances)

for single <u>or</u> married, falling between			is taxed at
0	and	21 <u>or</u> 55	0%
21 <u>or</u> 55	and	131 <u>or</u> 250	5.0%
131 <u>or</u> 250	and	∞	7.5%

```
▶PAY:0×(W4+L(F1:SNGL×23
+MARR×65)+L(F2:SNGL×397
+MARR×689)+L(F3:SNGL×92
8+MARR×1573)+L(F4:SNGL×
2121+MARR×3858)+L(S1:SN
GL×21+MARR×55)+L(S2:SNG
L×131+MARR×250)+L(H:Σ(I
```

```
:2:SIZES(TCARD):2:MOD(2
4+HRS(ITEM(TCARD:I))-HR
S(ITEM(TCARD:I-1)):24))
)+L(G:$/HR×(MIN(40:G(H)
)+OT×MAX(0:G(H)-40)))+L
(A:G(G)-39.42×W4)+L(SS:
.062×IF($YTD<53400:MIN(
G(G):53400-$YTD):0))+L(
M:.0145×IF($YTD<125000:
MIN(G(G):125000-$YTD):0
))+L(F:.15×MIN(MAX(G(A)
:G(F1))-G(F1):G(F2)-G(F
1))+.28×MIN(MAX(G(A):G(
F2))-G(F2):G(F3)-G(F2))
+.33×MIN(MAX(G(A):G(F3)
)-G(F3):G(F4)-G(F3))+.2
8×(MAX(G(A):G(F4))-G(F4
)))+L(B:G(G)-G(F)-W4×33
)+L(S:.05×MIN(MAX(G(B):
G(S1))-G(S1):G(S2)-G(S1
))+.075×(MAX(G(B):G(S2)
)-G(S2))))+IF(S(SNGL):L
(MARR:0)+1-SNGL:IF(S(MA
RR):L(SNGL:0)+1-MARR:IF
(S(HOURS):HOURS-G(H):IF
(S($GR):$GR-G(G):IF(S($
SS):$SS-G(SS):IF(S($MC)
:$MC-G(M):IF(S($FED):$F
ED-G(F):IF(S($ST):$ST-G
(S):IF(S($NET):G(G)-G(S
S)-G(M)-G(F)-G(S)-$NET:
$NYG-G(G)-$YTD))))))))))
```

Approximate Memory Required: 54% to use, 14% to store, not
                                          including the TCARD list.

Required Knowns: The employee's W4 withholding allowances; marital status (SNGL or MARR); hourly wage ($/HR); overtime factor (OT); Year-To-Date gross pay ($YTD) before this paycheck; a SUM list, TCARD, containing his work-time log for the week.

Example: Shown below is an employee's work log for last week. Calculate his hours, gross pay, tax, net pay and new year-to-date gross. He is single, with 3 withholding allowances claimed on form W4. His previous year-to-date gross was $10,000; his wage is $10/hour, and his overtime factor (for hours over 40 per week) is 1.5.

Period	In	Out
1	6:00 a.m.	12:45 p.m.
2	11:00 p.m.	1:00 a.m.
3	8:00 a.m.	4:00 p.m.
4	9:00 a.m.	5:15 p.m.
5	9:00 a.m.	5:00 p.m.
6	8:00 a.m.	5:00 p.m.

Solution: First, build the TCARD list (in actual use, of course, you would do this during the week, as the employee "clocks in and out" of work each day):

■ (MAIN) **SUM** **GET** **※NEW** **NAME** (T)(C)(A)(R)(D) (INPUT)
(6) (INPUT) (1)(2)(·)(4)(5) (INPUT) (2)(3) (INPUT) (1) (INPUT)
(8) (INPUT) (1)(6) (INPUT) (9) (INPUT) (1)(7)(·)(1)(5) (INPUT)
(9) (INPUT) (1)(7) (INPUT) (8) (INPUT) (1)(7) (INPUT)

Now ▊ `[MAIN]` `SOLVE`, key in the formula and `CALC`.

Now `[3]` `W4` `SNGL`.... (result: SNGL=1.00).

Then `[1][0]` `$/HR` `[1][.][5]` `OT` `MORE` `[1][0][0][0]` `$YTD`

`HOURS`....	Answer: HOURS=42.00
`$GR`....	Answer: \$GR=430.00
`$SS`....	Answer: \$SS=26.66
`$MC`....	Answer: \$MC=6.24
`MORE` `$FED`....	Answer: \$FED=43.31
`$ST`....	Answer: \$ST=17.25
`$NET`....	Answer: \$NET=336.54
`$NYG`....	Answer: \$NYG=10,430.00

Notice:

- In the formula, the use of a hidden variable to actually calculate each of the unknowns—and then the extensive set of nested IF(S... statements—allows you to solve for those unknowns in any order.

- The expression MOD(24+HRS(ITEM(TCARD:I))
                    -HRS(ITEM(TCARD:I-1))
                    :24)

   in the TCARD summation is just a simple subtraction (i.e. "time out minus time in"), but with the necessary conversions to decimal hours and a mathematical adjustment to allow for the case where the employee works past midnight.

- The `SNGL` and `MARR` items on this formula's menu have been constructed to allow you to use them as mode keys (no numerical input necessary)—similar to the way you devised `BEG` and `END` in your modified-TVM formula (POINTS) on pages 326-328.

5. After the previous problem, this should seem quite simple:

```
▶NEWTAX:0×(IF($YTD=0:L(
$YTD:1):0)+L(H:Σ(I:2:SI
ZES(TCARD):2:MOD(24+HRS
(ITEM(TCARD:I))-HRS(ITE
M(TCARD:I-1)):24)))+L(G
:$/HR×(MIN(40:G(H))+OT×
MAX(0:G(H)-40)))+L(T:.0
1×(L(N:$YTD+G(G))×LOG(G
(N))-$YTD×LOG($YTD))))+
IF(S(HOURS):HOURS-G(H):
IF(S($GR):$GR-G(G):IF(S
($TAX):$TAX-G(T):IF(S($
NET):G(G)-G(T)-$NET:$NY
G-G(N)))))
```

Approximate Memory Required: 19% to use, 5% to store, not
                               including the TCARD list.

Required Knowns: The employee's Year-To-Date gross ($YTD)
                   before this paycheck; hourly wage ($/HR)
                   and overtime factor (OT); and the SUM
                   list, TCARD (see previous solution)

Example: Shown below is an employee's work log for last week.

Period	In	Out
1	6:00 a.m.	12:45 p.m.
2	11:00 p.m.	1:00 a.m.
3	8:00 a.m.	4:00 p.m.
4	9:00 a.m.	5:15 p.m.
5	9:00 a.m.	5:00 p.m.
6	8:00 a.m.	5:00 p.m.

Calculate his hours, gross pay, tax, net pay and new year-to-date gross. His previous year-to-date gross was \$10,000; his wage is \$10/hour, and his overtime factor (for hours over 40 per week) is 1.5.

Solution: First, build the TCARD list (if it doesn't exist already —in actual use, you'd do this during the week, as the employee "clocks in and out" of work each day):

■(MAIN) SUM | GET |※NEW| NAME (T)(C)(A)(R)(D) (INPUT) (6)(INPUT)(1)(2)(·)(4)(5)(INPUT)(2)(3)(INPUT)(1)(INPUT) (8)(INPUT)(1)(6)(INPUT)(9)(INPUT)(1)(7)(·)(1)(5)(INPUT) (9)(INPUT)(1)(7)(INPUT)(8)(INPUT)(1)(7)(INPUT)

Now ■(MAIN)SOLVE, key in the formula and CALC. Then (1)(0)(0)(0)(0) $YTD (1)(0) $/HR (1)(·)(5) OT

HOURS....	Answer: HOURS=42.00
$GR....	Answer: $GR=430.00
MORE $TAX....	Answer: $TAX=19.11
$NET...	Answer: $NET=410.89
$NYG....	Answer: $NYG=10,430.00

Notice:

- A hidden variable calculates each of the unknowns—to let you solve for them in any order.

- The expression $MOD(24+HRS(ITEM(TCARD:I)) -HRS(ITEM(TCARD:I-1)) :24)$

in the TCARD summation is just a simple subtraction (i.e. "time out minus time in"), but with conversions to decimal hours and adjustments to allow for an employee working through midnight.

6. This solution assumes the following rules for the five qualifying methods (*note:* your applicable rules may now be different):

<u>Conventional</u>: Maximum PITI (Principal, Interest, Property Taxes and Insurance, plus mortgage insurance/association dues, if any) is the *lesser* of
- 28% of Gross Income ($GI)   *or*
- 36% of $GI, less long-term debt pmt. ($LTD).

Use 25% of $GI and 33% of $GI, respectively, if the down-payment is less than 10%.

<u>FNMA</u>: Maximum PITI is 28% of $GI.

<u>GNMA</u>: Maximum PITI is 36% of $GI, less $LTD.

<u>FHA</u>: Maximum PITI is the *lesser* of
- 29% of Gross Income ($GI)   *or*
- 41% of $GI, less long-term debt pmt. ($LTD).

<u>VA</u>: Maximum PITI is *lesser* of
- 41% of $GI, less long-term debt pmt. ($LTD).
- $GI less $FED, $ST, Social Security, $LTD, less family support, maintenance/utilities, from this table:

| Fl. Area | Total Family Members | | | | | | |
(Sq. Ft)	1	2	3	4	5	6	7
< 1101	457	704	834	930	968	1044	1122
1100-1500	472	720	851	948	988	1065	1143
> 1500	487	736	867	966	1007	1086	1164
plus:	53	88	105	120	122	127	132

if the loan amount > $69999, *plus* $6 for a house older than 20 years, *plus* $40 if it's not heated by gas.

The formula:

```
▶QUAL:0×(L(S:.062×MIN($
GI:4450)+.0145×MIN($GI:
10416.67))+$LTD+L(T:T%Y
R÷1200)+$INS+$DUS+L(Z:U
SPV(I%YR÷12:#YRS×12)))+
IF(S(CV):(-DN+CV)÷G(Z)-
MIN($GI×IF(CV>DN×10:.25
:.28):$GI×IF(CV>DN×10:.
33:.36)-$LTD)+$INS+$DUS
+G(T)×CV:IF(S($C):$C-(C
V-DN)÷G(Z):IF(S(FMV):(F
MV-DN)÷G(Z)-$GI×.28+$IN
S+$DUS+G(T)×FMV:IF(S($F
M):$FM-(FMV-DN)÷G(Z):IF
(S(GMV):(GMV-DN)÷G(Z)-$
GI×.36+$INS+$DUS+G(T)×G
MV+$LTD:IF(S($GM):$GM-(
GMV-DN)÷G(Z):IF(S(FHAV)
:(FHAV-DN)÷G(Z)-MIN($GI
×.29:$GI×.41-$LTD)+$INS
+$DUS+G(T)×FHAV:IF(S($F
HA):$FHA-(FHAV-DN)÷G(Z)
:IF(S(GAS?):GAS?-ABS(G(
GAS?)-1):IF(S(VAV):MIN(
$GI×.41:$GI-IF(AGE>20:6
:0×SQFT)-40×(1-GAS?)-RN
D(ITEM(VA:L(N:MIN(#FAM:
7)))+(14+1.1×MIN(G(N):6
))×IF(SQFT<1101:0:IF(SQ
FT<1500:1:2)):0)-IF(G(V
AV)-DN>69999:ITEM(VA:G(
N)+7):0)-$FED-$ST-G(S))
-$LTD-$INS-$DUS-G(T)×VA
V-(VAV-DN)÷G(Z):$VA-(VA
V-DN)÷G(Z)))))))))))
```

Also, you'll need this SUM list, named VA:

```
ITEM(1)=456.50        ITEM(8)=53.00
ITEM(2)=703.50        ITEM(9)=88.00
ITEM(3)=833.50        ITEM(10)=105.00
ITEM(4)=929.50        ITEM(11)=120.00
ITEM(5)=968.00        ITEM(12)=122.00
ITEM(6)=1,044.40      ITEM(13)=127.00
ITEM(7)=1,122.00      ITEM(14)=132.00
```

<u>Approximate Memory Required</u>: 53% to use, 14% to store—
including the VA list.

<u>Required Knowns</u>: <u>All</u>: $GI, $LTD, T%YR, $INS, $DUS, I%YR, #YRS, $DN.

<u>VA</u>: GAS?, AGE, SQFT, #FAM, $FED, $ST.

<u>Example</u>: A couple with four children and $10,000 for a down-payment finds a 25-year-old, 3000-ft² home (gas heat).

Their gross monthly income is $3500, less $319 and $209 for federal and state taxes, respectively. In addition, they pay $200 per month toward other long-term debt. Insurance on the home will be about $30/month; taxes are 1.25% annually.

With a 30-year mortgage at a fixed rate of 10%, what price could they offer and still qualify for financing? Use each of the five sets of qualifying rules.* Find the corresponding principal-and-interest payments, also.

*Assume no mortgage insurance or other association dues in this example.

<u>Solution</u>:   Key in the VA list, then the formula, then **CALC**.

Then ③⑤⓪⓪ **%GI** ②⓪⓪ **%LTD** ①•②⑤ **T%YR**
③⓪ **%INS** ⓪ **%DUS**, then **MORE**
①⓪ **I%YR** ③⓪ **#YRS** ①⓪⓪⓪⓪ **%DN**

CV ....   <u>Answer</u>: CV=100,000.00
%C ....   <u>Answer</u>: $C=789.81
MORE **FMV** ...<u>Answer</u>: FMV=105,706.10
%FM ....   <u>Answer</u>: $FM=839.89
GMV ....   <u>Answer</u>: GMV=113,854.91
%GM ....   <u>Answer</u>: $GM=911.40
FHAV ....   <u>Answer</u>: FHAV=109,271.20
MORE **%FHA** .. <u>Answer</u>: $FHA=871.18

Then **GAS?** ...(toggle until GAS?=1.00)
And ②⑤ **AGE** ③⓪⓪⓪ **SQFT** ⑥ **#FAM**
MORE ③①⑨ **%FED** ②⓪⑨ **%ST**
VAV ....   <u>Answer</u>: VAV=131,680.43
%FHA ....   <u>Answer</u>: $VA=1,067.83

<u>Notice</u>:

- The formula requires that, for each qualifying method, you solve for the maximum home value *before* calculating the corresponding monthly payment.

- The menu has been ordered so that you can work left-to-right and reach an unknown item immediately after having keyed in all its required knowns.

- The **GAS?** item on the menu is a mode *toggle*: Press it once for "yes" (1.00); again for "no" (0.00).

7. Which scenario has a greater Net Present Value?

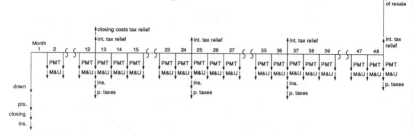

BUY assumptions: You own the home for a whole number of years. The mortgage payment (amortized over a whole number of years) and utilities/maintenance are paid at the END of each month. Insurance premiums (in advance) and property taxes (in arrears) are paid yearly. Tax relief from interest deductions is realized at the end of the year. When you sell the home and repay the mortgage, you'll owe capital gains tax on your gain—after any commission to a broker. The property value and taxes are increased annually by the property growth rate.

RENT assumptions: You owe first and last month's rent, plus a fully-refundable security deposit immediately. Rent is paid at the beginning of each month; maintenance/utilities at the end. Your renter's insurance premium is paid annually, in advance. Also, you pay yearly income tax on the interest accruing on your investment of the down-payment money. *In both scenarios, insurance, utilities and maintenance (and your rent in the RENT case) increase yearly by the inflation rate.* All percentage rates are annual but are compounded monthly.

9. Building Your Own Roads: The SOLVE Menu

The formula:

```
▶B~RNT:0×(L(P:($PR-$DN+
0×NY)÷USPV(I%YR÷12:NY×1
2))+PTS+$CL.B+PTX%+B$IN
+B$UM+G%.IT+$DEP+$RNT+R
$IN+R$UM+INF%+YRS+INV%)
+($PR÷100×IP(G%.IT)×L(T
:FP(G%.IT))+$PR×SPFV(PG
R%÷12:YRS×12)×(1-FP($CL
.B))×(1-IP(G%.IT)÷100×G
(T)))×L(Z:SPPV(L(C:((((
1+DSC%÷1200)^12-1)×(1-G
(T))+1)^(1÷12)-1)×100):
YRS×12))-Σ(K:12:YRS×12:
12:SPPV(G(C):K)×((1-G(T
))×PTX%÷100×$PR×SPFV(PG
R%÷12:K)-G(T)×(12×G(P)-
(($PR-$DN-G(P)×USPV(I%Y
R÷12:K-12))÷SPPV(I%YR÷1
2:K-12)-($PR-$DN-G(P)×U
SPV(I%YR÷12:K))÷SPPV(I%
YR÷12:K))))-G(P)×USPV(
G(C):YRS×12)-G(Z)×($PR-
$DN-G(P)×USPV(I%YR÷12:Y
RS×12)÷SPPV(I%YR÷12:YR
S×12)-PTS÷100×($PR-$DN)
×(1-G(T)×SPPV(G(C):12))
-IP($CL.B)-(((B$UM-R$UM
-$RNT×(1+G(C)÷100))×USP
V(G(C):12)+12×(B$IN-R$I
N))×USFV((((1+INF%÷1200
)÷(1+G(C)÷100))^12-1)×1
00:YRS)+$RNT×(1+INF%÷12
00)^(12×(YRS-1))÷(1+G(C
)÷100)^(YRS×12-1)+G(Z)×
```

```
($DEP+$DN×SPFV((SPFV(IN
V%÷12:12)-1)×100×(1-G(T
)):YRS))-$DEP-$RNT)=B~R
```

Approximate Memory Required: 50% to use, 13% to store.

Required Knowns: NY (the mortgage term); I%YR (mortgage rate); $CL.B (composite value: the costs of closing at purchase and the sales commission % upon resale); G%.IT (a composite value: the capital gains taxability and the normal income tax bracket).

Example: You're transferred to a new city for 4 years (YRS). You have $10,000 for a down-payment and are considering a $100,000 home. Property values are growing at 8% annually (PGR%), and the mortgage rate (I%YR) is 10%. Inflation (INF%) is 5%, and a liquid taxable fund earns 8% (DSC%), but a taxable stock mutual fund earns 15% (INV%). To buy the home, closing costs are $400; the loan fee is 1%. Insurance start at $30/month, with $180/month in utilities and maintenance. Property taxes are 1.25% per year. Your tax bracket is 28%, and capital gains are 100% taxable. You'll pay a 6% commission to resell the home.

On the other hand, if you rent the home, your security deposit would be $300. Your rent would start at $750, with monthly insurance and maintenance/utilities at $15 and $100, respectively. So, should you buy the home or rent it (investing the down payment in the stock mutual fund) instead?

<u>Solution:</u> Key in the formula, and `CALC` . Then:

`1` `0` `0` `0` `0` `0` `$PR` `1` `0` `0` `0` `0` `$DN`
`3` `0` `NY` `1` `0` `I%YR`
`1` `PTS`

`MORE`

`4` `0` `0` `.` `0` `6` `$CL.B` (closing costs. broker com%)
`1` `.` `2` `5` `PTK%` `3` `0` `B%IN`
`1` `8` `0` `B$UM`
`1` `0` `0` `.` `2` `8` `G%.IT` (CG taxability%. income tax %)

`MORE`

`3` `0` `0` `$DEP` `7` `5` `0` `$RNT`
`1` `5` `R%IN` `1` `0` `0` `R$UM` `5` `INF%`

`MORE`

`4` `YRS` `1` `5` `INV%`
`8` `PGR%` `8` `DSC%`
`B~R` ....   <u>Answer:</u> B~R=14,616.60

<u>Notice:</u>

- B~R represents the *difference* between the Net Present Value of the BUY scenario and that of the RENT. If B~R is positive, it's better to buy than to rent.

- The analysis is *after-taxes*; both the discount (DSC%) and alternative investment rates (INV%) are assumed taxable.

- The property growth rate is assumed to include wear-and-tear depreciation in the value of the house.

- The menu has been ordered so that the five variables you might be most likely to play "What-If?" with are all located on the last "page" of the menu.

8. P.% specifies any principal (P) paid *in addition to* a P&I payment that is a percentage (%) of the conventional monthly payment:

```
▶TVM~ACCPYDN:0×(M+I%YR+
PV+PMT+FV+L(I:I%YR÷IF(P
/YR=0:L(P/YR:12):P/YR))
+L(P:L(F:IF(FP(G(P.%))=
0:1:FP(G(P.%))))×(-PV-F
V×SPPV(L(R:I%YR÷12):M))
÷USPV(G(R):M)÷(1+G(BEG)
×G(R)÷100)-L(D:IP(G(P.%
))×SGN(PV))))+IF(S(BEG)
:ABS(G(BEG)-1)-BEG+0×P.
%:IF(S(Y):PV+(1+BEG×G(I
)÷100)×G(P)×USPV(G(I):Y
×P/YR)+FV×SPPV(G(I):Y×P
/YR):IF(S(AMRT):L(Z:BEG
)×L(BAL:RND(PV:2))×L(NE
XT:L(INT:L(PRIN:0)))-AM
RT:IF(S(NEXT):1E3+#P+10
01E3×FP(G(NEXT)÷1E3)-NE
XT+0×L(B:BAL):IF(S(BAL)
:RND((RND(PMT:2)×USPV(G
(I):#P-G(Z))+G(B)+G(Z)×
RND(PMT:2))÷SPPV(G(I):#
P-G(Z)):2)-BAL:IF(S(PRI
N):PRIN+G(B)-BAL:IF(S(I
NT):#P×RND(PMT:2)-PRIN-
INT+L(Z:0):PV+(1+BEG×G(
R)÷100)×(2×PMT-G(P)+G(D
))÷G(F)×USPV(G(R):M)+FV
×SPPV(I%YR÷12:M)))))))))
```

Approximate Memory Required: 39% to use, 10% to store.
Required Knowns: #P.

Example: In how many years can you pay off a 30-year, $100,000 mortgage at 10%, with 26 payments/year, each *half* the conventional monthly amount, plus $20? What is this payment? Amortize the first 2 years' payments.

Solution: 3 0 $\times$ 1 2 $=$ (ALG) *or* 3 0 INPUT 1 2 $\times$ (RPN) **M**
1 0 **I%YR** 1 0 0 0 0 0 **PV** 0 **FV** , **MORE**
2 6 **P/YR** **BEG** (toggle this until BEG=0.00)
2 0 $\cdot$ 5 **P%** **Y** .... Result: $Y=18.26$
MORE **MORE** **PMT** .... Result: $PMT=-458.79$
Next, **MORE** **AMRT** (display: AMRT=0.00), to begin the amortization, then **MORE** and 2 6 **#P** to amortize 26 payments at once. Now, *in this order*, press:
NEXT to identify the payments in the group:
   $NEXT=1,026.00$ (that is, payments 1-26)
BAL $BAL=97,975.82$
PRIN $PRIN=-2,024.18$
INT $INT=-9,904.36$
NEXT $NEXT=27,052.00$ (pmts 27-52)
BAL $BAL=95,739.19$
PRIN $PRIN=-2,236.63$
INT $INT=-9,691.91$

Notice:

- P/YR defaults to 12 if you forget and leave it as zero.

- PMT and YRS are entirely independent as unknowns; you may calculate them in any order. M is the loan's conventional term (in Months); Y is "Years until actual pay-down."

- As with the built-in AMRT, you may change #P between groups or use **AMRT** to start over completely.

9. In this formula, the interest rate may change yearly until Year 5. After specifying those rates, you solve for payment, balance, and APR% as of any month. Payments are monthly, in arrears.

```
▶ARM: 0×(NT+L(A: I1%÷12)+
L(Q: (PV+P1×USPV(G(A): 12
))÷-SPPV(G(A): 12))+FV+P
TS+L(B: I2%÷12)+L(C: I3%÷
12)+L(D: I4%÷12)+L(E: I5%
÷12)+N+PMT+BAL+APR%+***
**+L(R: (Q-FV×SPPV(B: NT-
12))÷USPV(B: NT-12))+L(S
: (Q-R×USPV(B: 12))÷SPPV(
B: 12))+L(T: (S-FV×SPPV(C
: NT-24))÷USPV(C: NT-24))
+L(U: (S-T×USPV(C: 12))÷S
PPV(C: 12))+L(V: (U-FV×SP
PV(D: NT-36))÷USPV(D: NT-
36))+L(W: (U-V×USPV(D: 12
))÷SPPV(D: 12))+L(Y: (W-F
V×SPPV(E: NT-48))÷USPV(E
: NT-48))+L(F: IF(N<13: (P
V+L(P: P1)×USPV(A: N))÷-S
PPV(A: N): IF(N<25: (Q-L(P
: R)×USPV(B: N-12))÷SPPV(
B: N-12): IF(N<37: (S-L(P:
T)×USPV(C: N-24))÷SPPV(C
: N-24): IF(N<49: (U-L(P: V
)×USPV(D: N-36))÷SPPV(D:
N-36): (W-L(P: Y)×USPV(E:
N-48))÷SPPV(E: N-48)))))
))+IF(S(PMT): PMT-G(P): I
F(S(BAL): BAL-F: IF(S(APR
%): PV×(1-PTS÷100)+F×SPP
V(L(Z: APR%÷12): N)+P1×US
```

```
PV(Z:MIN(12:N))+R×USPV(
Z:MIN(12:MAX(0:N-12)))×
SPPV(Z:12)+T×USPV(Z:MIN
(12:MAX(0:N-24)))×SPPV(
Z:24)+V×USPV(Z:MIN(12:M
AX(0:N-36)))×SPPV(Z:36)
+Y×USPV(Z:MAX(0:N-48))×
SPPV(Z:48):PV+P1×USPV(A
:NT)+FV×SPPV(A:NT))))
```

<u>Approximate Memory Required</u>:   56% to use, 14% to store.

<u>Required Knowns</u>:   PTS, I2%, I3%, I4%, I5% and N.

<u>Example</u>: The interest rates for a 30-year ARM of \$100,000 are:
Year 1=9.0%; Year 2=9.5%; Year 3=10.0%; Year 4=10.5%;
Year 5 (and beyond) =11.0%. Find the starting payment, and for Year 5, the payment amount and the
year-end balance and APR. The loan fee is 1.5%.

<u>Solution</u>: Key in the formula, and `CALC`. Then:

⑶⑹⓪ `NT` ⑼ `I%` ①⓪⓪⓪⓪ `PV` ⓪ `FV`
`P1` ....   <u>Result</u>: P1=-804.62
`MORE` ①•⑤ `PTS` ⑼•⑤ `I2%` ①⓪ `I3%`
①⓪•⑤ `I4%` ①① `I5%` `MORE`
⑹⓪ `N` `PMT` ...<u>Result</u>: PMT=-946.66
`BAL` ....   <u>Result</u>: BAL=-96,586.63
`APR%` ....   <u>Result</u>: APR%=10.28

<u>Notice</u>:

- You must solve for P1 (the starting monthly payment) first.

- Memory doesn't permit concealment of intermediate variables, but the variable ***** pushes them onto later pages.

10. You specify a *percentage* of the principal as a remaining balance (RB%) and then find the number of years (YRS) it will take to amortize the loan down to that point:

```
▶TVM~RB%:0×(N+I%YR+PV+P
MT+FV+L(I:I%YR÷IF(P/YR=
0:L(P/YR:12):P/YR)))+IF
(S(BEG?):ABS(G(BEG?)-1)
-BEG?:IF(S(YRS):PV+(FV-
(PV+FV)×RB%÷100)×SPPV(G
(I):YRS×P/YR)+(1+BEG?×G
(I)÷100)×L(PMT:(-PV-FV×
SPPV(G(I):N))÷USPV(G(I)
:N)÷(1+BEG?×G(I)÷100))×
USPV(G(I):YRS×P/YR):IF(
S(AMRT):L(Z:BEG?)×L(BAL
:RND(PV:2))×L(NEXT:L(IN
T:L(PRIN:0)))-AMRT:IF(S
(NEXT):1E3+#P+1001E3×FP
(G(NEXT)÷1E3)-NEXT+0×L(
B:BAL):IF(S(BAL):RND((R
ND(PMT:2)×USPV(G(I):#P-
G(Z))+G(B)+G(Z)×RND(PMT
:2))÷SPPV(G(I):#P-G(Z))
:2)-BAL:IF(S(PRIN):PRIN
+G(B)-BAL:IF(S(INT):#P×
RND(PMT:2)-PRIN-INT+L(Z
:0):PV+(1+BEG?×G(I)÷100
)×PMT×USPV(G(I):N)+FV×S
PPV(G(I):N))))))))
```

<u>Approximate Memory Required</u>:   35% to use, 9% to store.
<u>Required Knowns</u>:   RB%, #P.

Example: How long will it take to pay down a 30-year, $100,000 mortgage at 10%, (monthly payments, *in advance*) to 75% of the original balance? How about 50%? 25%? Also, find the payment amount and run an amortization on the first year of payments.

Solution: ③✕①②〓(ALG) *or* ③⓪〔INPUT〕①②✕(RPN) **N**
⓪ **I%YR** ①⓪⓪⓪⓪⓪ **PV** ⓪ **FV** , **MORE**
①② **P/YR** **BEG?** (toggle this until BEG?=1.00)

⑦⑤ **RB%** **YRS** .... Result: YRS=17.49
⑤⓪ **RB%** **YRS** .... Result: YRS=23.53
②⑤ **RB%** **YRS** .... Result: YRS=27.28
MORE **MORE** **PMT** .... Result: PMT=-870.32

Next, **MORE** **AMRT** (display: AMRT=0.00), to begin the amortization, then **MORE** and ①② **#P** to amortize 12 payments at once. Now, *in this order*, press:
NEXT to identify the payments in the group:
  NEXT=1,012.00 (that is, payments 1-12)
BAL BAL=98,622.26
PRIN PRIN=-1,377.74
INT INT=-9,066.10

Notice:
- PMT and YRS are independent as unknowns. Also, the value of P/YR defaults to 12 if you forget and leave it as 0.
- With any of these TVM formulas with AMRT capabilities, you can shorten them a lot by omitting those five IF(S... statements (AMRT, NEXT, BAL, INT and PRIN).

11. This formula works a lot like TVM except that I%YR must be a known value. Then you can find the constant principal amount (PRN) in each payment and, for any given period (PER), the total payment amount (PMT) :

```
▶TVM~CNSTPRN:0×(N+I%YR+
PV+PRN+FV+L(I:I%YR÷100÷
IF(P/YR=0:L(P/YR:12):P/
YR)))+IF(S(BEG?):ABS(G(
BEG?)-1)-BEG?:IF(S(PER)
 OR S(PMT):IF(PER=0:0:(
PV+PRN×(PER-1))×IF(PER=
BEG?:0:G(I))-PRN)+PMT:I
F(S(AMRT):L(BAL:RND(PV:
2))×L(NEXT:L(INT:L(PRIN
:0)))-AMRT:IF(S(NEXT):1
E3+#P+1001E3×FP(G(NEXT)
÷1E3)-NEXT-0×L(B:BAL):I
F(S(BAL):BAL-G(B)-RND(P
RN:2)×#P:IF(S(PRIN):#P×
RND(PRN:2)-PRIN:IF(S(IN
T):Σ(T:0:#P-1:1:RND((G(
B)+RND(PRN:2)×T)×G(I):2
))-IF(NEXT<2E3 AND BEG?
×SGN(#P)=1:RND(G(B)×G(I
):2):0)+INT:(PV+N×PRN)×
(1+BEG?×G(I))+FV))))))
```

Approximate Memory Required: 31% to use, 8% to store.
Required Knowns: I%YR, P/YR, #P.

Example: What is the amount of the first payment on a 30-year, $72,000 loan at 12% (monthly payments, in arrears), with constant payments to principal? How much is the last payment? Run an amortization on the first year of payments.

Solution: 3 0 $\times$ 1 2 $=$ (ALG) *or* 3 0 INPUT 1 2 $\times$ (RPN) **N**
1 2 **I%YR** 7 2 0 0 0 **PV** 0 **FV** , **MORE**
1 2 **P/YR** **BEG?** (toggle this until BEG?=0.00)

MORE **MORE** **PRN** .... Result: PRN=-200.00
(the constant principal portion of the payment)

MORE 1 **PER** **PMT** .... Result: PMT=-920.00
3 6 0 **PER** **PMT** .... Result: PMT=-202.00

AMRT (display: AMRT=0.00), to begin the amor-tization. And then **MORE** and 1 2 **#P** to amortize 12 payments at once. Now, *in this order*, press:
NEXT to identify the payments in the group:
NEXT=1,012.00 (that is, payments 1-12)
BAL .... Result: BAL=69,600.00
PRIN .... Result: PRIN=-2,400.00
INT .... Result: INT=-8,508.00

Notice:

- I%YR is a *required known* in this formula. Also, you must calculate PRN before calculating PMT.

- BEG? is a *toggle* mode key: press it once to change to BEG mode; again to switch back to END.

- P/YR and BEG? values default to 12 (monthly payments) and 0 (END mode), respectively—like the real TVM Menu.

12. This formula behaves like TVM, except that you can also specify a percentage change (%CH) or an amount change ($CH) in the beginning PMT. This change occurs periodically after a specified number of payments (GRUP):

```
▶PMT$CH%:0×(N+I%YR+PV+P
MT+FV+IF(P/YR=0:L(P/YR:
12):0))+IF(S(BEG?):ABS(
G(BEG?)-1)-BEG?:PV+FV×S
PPV(L(I:I%YR÷P/YR):N)+(
1+G(I)÷100×BEG?)×USPV(G
(I):GRUP)×(PMT×USFV(((1
+CH%÷100)÷(1+G(I)÷100)^
GRUP-1)×100:N÷GRUP)+$CH
×Σ(G:0:N÷GRUP-1:1:G×SPP
V(G(I):G×GRUP))))
```

<u>Approximate Memory Required</u>:   16% to use, 4% to store.
<u>Required Knowns</u>:   None.

<u>Example</u>:   What should you pay now to take over as lessor on a five-year office lease whose current monthly rent (due in advance) is $900, increased yearly by 5%, plus $50? Assume a discount rate of 8%. Then, for a yield of 12%, what should you sell the lease for in 3 years?

<u>Solution</u>:   ⑤✕①②〓 (ALG) *or* ⑤ INPUT ①②✕ (RPN) ■ N ■
⑧ I%YR ⑨⓪⓪ PMT ⓪ FV , MORE
①② P/YR BEG? (toggle this until BEG?=1.00)
①② GRUP ⑤ CH% ⑤⓪ $CH
MORE PV .... Result: PV=-53,567.52
③⑥ N ①② I%YR
■ FV ■ .... Result: FV=33,652.04

<u>Notice:</u>

- The formula uses only a whole number of groups (i.e. it uses the *integer portion* of N÷GRUP).

- As usual, I%YR compounds once per period (P/YR times per year); but %CH compounds once every GRUP periods.

- This formula obeys normal TVM sign conventions, *including the dollar amount specified in $CH.* Thus, if PMT is negative in the perspective you adopt, then to indicate an *increase* in the amount of the PMT, $CH must be negative also. That's *not* true for CH%, where a positive value always increases the PMT amount, and a negative percentage decreases it.

13. On this BOND Menu, you specify a TYPe *value*: 1 or 2 (annual or semiannual coupons)—*positive* for an actual calendar, *negative* for a 30/360 basis. Also, you specify capital gains and income tax rates and the sales commission (as a percentage of the PRICE). Interest is treated as taxable income, and any difference between price+commission and par or call is taken as capital gain (loss).

```
▶BND~T&C:0×(IF(TYP=0:L(
TYP:2):0)+L(E:.01×(FP(1
00×SETT)+IP(100×MAT)))+
L(Z:SGN(DDAYS(G(E):SETT
:1)))+IF(G(Z)=0:L(Z:1):
0)+L(F:IF(L(T:ABS(TYP))
=1:G(E)+1E-6×G(Z):G(E)-
G(Z)×(6-1E-6)))+IF(G(F)
>=13:L(F:G(F)-12+1E-6):
IF(G(F)<1:L(F:G(F)+12-1
E-6):0))+IF(G(Z)>0:L(D:
G(E))+L(E:G(F)):L(D:G(F
)))+L(P:IF(TYP<0:DDAYS(
SETT:G(D):3)÷360×TYP:DD
AYS(G(D):SETT:1)÷DDAYS(
G(D):G(E):1)))+L(N:1E4×
(FP(100×MAT)-FP(100×G(D
)))×G(T)-IF(G(Z)<0 AND
G(T)=2:1:0))+L(A:G(P)×C
PN%÷G(T))+IF(CALL=0:L(C
ALL:100):0)+L(I:CPN%÷G(
T)×(1-FP(G.I)))+CM%+L(Y
:YLD%÷100÷G(T))+L(C:CAL
L+IP(G.I)÷100×FP(G.I)×(
PRICE-CALL+CM%÷100)))+I
F(S(ACCRU):ACCRU-G(A):I
F(G(N)<2:(G(C)+G(I))÷(1
```

```
+(1-G(P))×G(Y)):G(C)÷(1
+G(Y))^(G(N)-G(P))+Σ(K:
1:G(N):1:G(I)÷(1+G(Y))^
(K-G(P))))-G(P)×G(I)-PR
ICE×(1+CM%÷100)+0×YLD%)
```

Approximate Memory Required: 44% to use, 11% to store.

Required Knowns: All *except* YLD%, PRICE and ACCRU.

Example: With all capital gains taxable at a tax bracket of 33%,
for a 10% after-tax yield-to-maturity, what price (and
accrued interest) can you pay on 7/28/90 for a 7% bond
(semiannual coupons, 30/360 basis) maturing on 9/9/
99? The commission is .15%. What's your yield-to-call
if the bond is callable at 88.125 on 3/9/95?

Solution: [2][+/-] **TYP**
[7][·][2][8][1][9][9][0] **SETT** [9][·][0][9][1][9][9][9] **MAT**
[7] **CPN%**
MORE [1][0][0][·][3][3] **G.I** [·][1][5] **CM%**
[1][0] **YLD% PRICE** ....   Result: PRICE=65.72
ACCRU ....   Result: ACCRU=2.70
MORE [8][8][·][1][2][5] **CALL** [3][·][0][9][1][9][9][5] **MAT**
MORE YLD% ....   Result: YLD%=11.02

Notice:

- TYPE defaults to a value of 2; CALL defaults to 100.

- The formula uses the bond equations in Appendix B of the
  Owner's Manual, but it works only for MM.DDYYYY date
  format and doesn't use "end-of-month" conventions. So, for
  an actual-basis bond maturing on the last day of the month
  (or on 8/29 or 8/30), move all dates forward by one day.

14. This formula works like TVM, except:

You enter the future value as a residual percentage, RES%, of the lease's Present Value (PV). *BEGIN mode is assumed.* Also, you can specify a number of *extra* payments, #ADV, to be made in advance (#ADV does *not* include the normal first payment, made at the same time). Use the SKP? toggle to indicate if the annual payment pattern includes skipped payments. If so, use a CFLO list named LP, to show that pattern (a year of $1 payments)—and in that case, N must be a whole number of years.

```
▶LEASE~TVM~SKP~ADV:0×(N
+I%YR+PV+PMT+RES%+IF(P/
YR=0:L(P/YR:12):0))+IF(
S(SKP?):ABS(G(SKP?)-1)-
SKP?:PV-ABS(RES%)÷100×P
V×SPPV(L(I:I%YR÷P/YR):N
)+(#ADV+IF(SKP?=0:(1+G(
I)÷100)×USPV(G(I):N-#AD
V):0×(L(A:#ADV)+L(C:1)+
L(S:0))+Σ(G:SIZEC(LP):0
:-1:Σ(F:#T(LP:G):1:-1:L
(D:SGN(ABS(FLOW(LP:G)))
×SPFV(G(I):G(C)))+0×IF(
G(D)>0 AND G(A)>0:L(S:G
(S)+G(D))+L(A:G(A)-1):0
)+0×L(C:G(C)+1)))×USPV(
((1+G(I)÷100)^P/YR-1)×1
00:IP(N÷P/YR))-G(S)×SPP
V(G(I):N)))×PMT)
```

Approximate Memory Required: 24% to use, 7% to store, not
                                including the list, LP.

Required Knowns: N, #ADV.

<u>Example</u>: Find the monthly payment for a 5-year lease with ir-
regular payments (annual schedule shown below) on
a $40,000 computer with a 10% residual buy-out. The
lessor wants 4 advance payments and an 18% yield.
What's the residual percentage for a $1400 payment?

Month	Payment?	Month	Payment?
1	yes	7	no
2	yes	8	no
3	yes	9	no
4	no	10	yes
5	no	11	yes
6	yes	12	yes

<u>Solution</u>: First, build the LP list:

■(MAIN) **CFLO** **GET** **%NEW** **NAME** (L)(P)(INPUT)
(1)(INPUT) (1)(INPUT)(2)(INPUT) (0)(INPUT)(2)(INPUT)
(1)(INPUT)(INPUT) (0)(INPUT)(3)(INPUT) (1)(INPUT)(3)(INPUT)

Now ■(MAIN)**SOLVE**, key in the formula and **CALC**.
Then(5)(×)(1)(2)(=)(ALG) *or*(5)(INPUT)(1)(2)(×)(RPN) **N**
(1)(8) **I%YR** (4)(0)(0)(0)(0) **PV** (1)(0) **RES%** , **MORE**
SKP? (toggle this until SKP?=1.00)
(4) **#ADV**

MORE **PMT** .... <u>Result</u>: PMT=-1,496.36
(1)(4)(0)(0)(+/-) **PMT**
RES% .... <u>Result</u>: RES%=25.09

<u>Notice</u>:

• The LP list is necessary only with skipped payments.

• P/YR defaults to 12, and the formula obeys the normal TVM
sign conventions—except for RES%, which needs no sign.

15. Which has a greater Net Present Value?

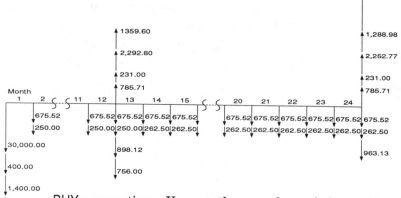

BUY assumptions: You own the asset for a whole number of years, depreciate it via straight-line, then sell it, taking a capital gain or loss on the difference between the sales price and the depreciated basis. Both the loan payment and maintenance are paid in arrears each month. Insurance premiums (in advance) and taxes (in arrears) are paid yearly.

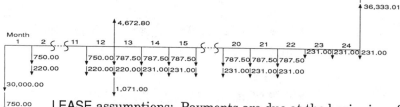

LEASE assumptions: Payments are due at the beginning of each month; the lessor may demand some more payments in advance. You may also pay property taxes. You do pay yearly income tax on the interest on your down-payment investment. *In both scenarios, insurance and maintenance (and your payment in the LEASE case) increase yearly by the inflation rate.* Property assessments increase yearly, in a compound growth pattern. All rates are annual but compound monthly.

```
▶B~LS:0×(L(P:($PR+0×(NY
+I%YR)-L(D:IP($D.PT)))÷
USPV(L(I:I%YR÷12):NY×12
))+$C.B+$SV.L+L(T:FP(G%
.IT))+B$IN+B$UM+PTX%+$L
P+L(A:IP(AD.IF))+L$IN+L
$UM)+IF(S(LTX?):ABS(G(L
TX?)-1)-LTX?:L(Z:SPPV(L
(C:(((((1+DSC%÷1200)^12-
1)×(1-G(T))+1)^(1÷12)-1
)×100):YRS×12))×($SL×(1
-FP($C.B))-IP(G%.IT)÷10
0×G(T)×($SL×(1-FP($C.B)
)-$PR+L(S:($PR-IP($SV.L
))÷FP($SV.L)÷100×YRS)-
($PR-G(D)-G(P)×USPV(G(I
):YRS×12))÷SPPV(G(I):YR
S×12))-Σ(K:12:YRS×12:12
:SPPV(G(C):K)×(IF(LTX?=
0:(1-G(T))×PTX%÷100×$PR
×($SL÷$PR)^(K÷12÷YRS):0
)-G(T)×(12×G(P)-(($PR-G
(D)-G(P)×USPV(G(I):K-12
))÷SPPV(G(I):K-12)-($PR
-G(D)-G(P)×USPV(G(I):K)
)÷SPPV(G(I):K))+G(S)+L(
F:FP($D.PT)×($PR-G(D)))
÷YRS+(12×(B$IN-L$IN+B$U
M-L$UM)-$LP×(12+IF(K=12
:G(A):IF(K=YRS×12:-G(A)
:0))))×SPFV(FP(AD.IF)×1
00÷12:K-12))))-G(P)×USP
V(G(C):YRS×12)-G(F)-IP(
$C.B)×(1-G(T)×SPPV(G(C)
:12))-(((B$UM-L$UM-$LP×
```

```
(1+G(C)÷100))×USPV(G(C)
:12)+12×(B$IN-L$IN))×US
FV((((1+FP(AD.IF)÷12)÷(
1+G(C)÷100))^12-1)×100:
YRS)+G(Z)×($LP×(1+FP(AD
.IF)÷12)^(12×(YRS-1))×(
1+G(C)÷100)×USFV(G(C):G
(A))+G(D)×SPFV((SPFV(IN
V%÷12:12)-1)×100×(1-G(T
)):YRS))-G(A)×$LP)-B~L)
```

Approximate Memory Required: 59% to use, 16% to store.

Required Knowns: NY, I%YR, $C.B, G%.IT, $D.PT, AD.IF, $SV.L

Example: A manufacturing firm needs an extra warehouse for
2 years. A suitable building is available for $100,000,
of which 75% is depreciable. The company has $30,000
in ready cash. The 20-year mortgage rate is 10%, and
inflation is 5%; cash funds earn 7%; stock funds earn
15%. To buy the building, closing costs are $400, and
the loan fee is 2%. Insurance will be $60/mo.; utilities/
maintenance, $250/mo. Property taxes are 1.25% per
year. The income tax bracket is 33%; capital gains are
100% taxable. A broker will charge 6% to resell the
building. Estimated re-sale price: $115,000.

Alternatively, to lease the building from the current
owner, rent would start at $750/mo. (including prop-
erty taxes), with 2 payments (in addition to the first
regular payment) due immediately, and with annual
adjustments for inflation. Insurance would be $85;
maintenance/utilities would be $220.

Should the company buy the building or lease it?

Solution: Key in the formula, and **CALC**. Then:

10000 **%PR** 20 **NY**

10 **I%YR** 30000·02 **%D.PT** (down. points)

400·06 **%C.B** (closing costs. broker's com%)

MORE

25000·315 **%SV.L** (salvage. depr. life)

100·33 **G%.IT** (CG taxability%. tax bracket)

60 **B%IN** 250 **B%UM** 1·25 **PTX%**

MORE 750 **%LP**

2·05 **AD.IF** (advance payments. inflation)

85 **L%IN** 220 **L%UM**

LTX? (toggle this until LTX?=0.00; lessee does
not pay property taxes in addition to lease payment)

MORE 7 **DSC%** 2 **YRS**

115000 **%SL** 15 **INV%**

B~L .... Answer: B~L=-1,225.12

Under the assumptions of the problem, the company
would do slightly better by *leasing* the warehouse.

Notice:

- B~L is the *difference* between the Net Present Value of the
  BUY scenario and that of the LEASE. Only if B~L is positive
  is it better to buy than to lease.

- The menu has been ordered so that the five variables you
  might be most likely to play "What-If?" with are all located
  on the last "page" of the menu.

16. This formula computes the value of an income property, using up to two different rental rates, floor areas and vacancy rates. For the capitalization rate, the formula averages the Summation Method (a Safe rate for liquid funds, plus increments for Risk, Illiquidity and Management) and the Band of Investment method (weighting current market expectations for mortgage and equity funds by the Loan-to-Value ratio on the property's mortgage).

```
▶IPVAL:0×(L(N:$RT1×SFT1
×(1-VAC%1÷100)+$RT2×SFT
2×(1-VAC%2÷100)-$PTX-$M
GT-$MNT-$INS)+L(C:(SAF%
+RSK%+ILQ%+MGT%+LTV%÷10
0×MRT%+EQR%×(1-LTV%÷100
))÷2))+IF(S($NOI):$NOI-
G(N):IF(S(CAP%):CAP%-G(
C):$VAL-G(N)÷G(C)×100))
```

<u>Approximate Memory Required</u>:   20% to use, 3% to store.
<u>Required Knowns</u>:   All *except* $NOI, CAP% and $VAL.

<u>Example</u>: Find the NOI, cap rate and value of this property:

	Office	Warehouse
Rent ($/ft^2/year)	7.80	4.07
Floor area (ft^2)	2,277	2,005
Vacancy rate (%)	0.5	1.0

Taxes: $3,647   Mngmt: $3,060   Maint.: $2,318

Insurance: $773   Loan-to-Value: 70%

Safe rate: 10.5%   Risk factor: 2.0%

Illiquidity factor: 0.5%   Management factor: 0.4%

Mortgage rate: 12.75%   Equity return rate: 14%

<u>Solution:</u> [7]•[8] %RT1 [2][2][7] SFT1 •[5] VAC%1
[4]•[0][7] %RT2 [2][0][0][5] SFT2 MORE [1] VAC%2

[3][6][4][7] %PT% [3][0][6][0] %MGT
[2][3][1][8] %MNT [7][7][3] %INS MORE

[1][0]•[5] SAF% [2] RSK% •[5] ILQ% •[4] MGT%
[7][0] LTV% MORE

[1][2]•[7][5] MRT% [1][4] EQR%

%NOI....	<u>Result:</u> $NOI=15,952.54
CAP%....	<u>Result:</u> CAP%=13.26
%VAL....	<u>Result:</u> $VAL=120,283.08

<u>Notice:</u>

- All rates are yearly but are compounded monthly. All dollar amounts are yearly.

- Besides being a property valuation tool, this formula is also handy for calculations of Net Operating Income ($NOI).

17. This formula allows up to two mortgages and a "wrap" loan. You specify when the second mortgage and the wraparound loan begin, via the variables M and W, respectively:

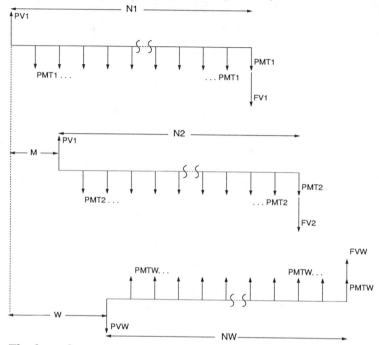

The formula can compute the payments (or any of the other usual loan parameters) on the first two mortgages, then the borrower's overall APR (including any points paid on the first two mortgages), and also any of the loan parameters on the wraparound mortgage.

Of course, the formula can also wrap a single mortgage, or find the APR on one or two conventional mortgages (no wraparound at all). But if there is a wraparound mortgage, it may start no earlier than the last mortgage.

```
▶WRAP~2ND:0×(N1+I%1+PV1
+PMT1+FV1+N2+I%2+PV2+PM
T2+FV2+PTS1+PTS2+L(W:IF
(M)=W:MAX(N1:M+N2):W))+
APR%+NW+Y%W+PVW+PMTW+FV
W)+IF(S(APR%):-(USPV(L(
A:APR%÷12):NW)×PMTW+FVW
×SPPV(G(A):NW)+PVW)×SPP
V(G(A):W)+PV1×(1-PTS1÷1
00)+PMT1×USPV(G(A):MIN(
N1:W))+IF(N1<=W:FV1×SPP
V(G(A):N1):0)+SPPV(G(A)
:M)×(PV2×(1-PTS2÷100)+P
MT2×USPV(G(A):MIN(W-M:N
2))+IF(N2+M<=W:FV2×SPPV
(G(A):N2):0)):IF(S(N1)
OR S(I%1) OR S(PV1) OR
S(PMT1) OR S(FV1):PV1+P
MT1×USPV(I%1÷12:N1)+FV1
×SPPV(I%1÷12:N1):IF(S(Y
%W) OR S(PVW) OR S(PMTW
) OR S(FVW):Y%W÷12-L(Y:
Y%W÷12)+PVW+PMTW×USPV(G
(Y):NW)+FVW×SPPV(G(Y):N
W)+IF(N1>W:FV1×SPPV(G(Y
):N1-W)+PMT1×USPV(G(Y):
N1-W):0)+IF(N2+M>W:FV2×
SPPV(G(Y):N2+M-W)+PMT2×
USPV(G(Y):N2+M-W):0):PV
2+PMT2×USPV(I%2÷12:N2)+
FV2×SPPV(I%2÷12:N2))))
```

<u>Approximate Memory Required</u>:   34% to use, 9% to store.
<u>Required Knowns</u>:   M, W, NW.

<u>Example:</u> A home currently has two mortgages: $100,000 at 10% for 30 years (no balloon); and $50,000 at 11.5% for 10 years, with a $10,000 balloon. The second mortgage began after the 15th year of the first. Now, after the 20th year, the owner wishes to consolidate loans and get financing for more remodelling. You offer to wrap his current mortgages, loaning $50,000 in new money, for 120 monthly payments and then a $25,000 balloon. What should the payment amount be to get you a 17% yield? What then is the borrower's overall APR%? He paid 1 point up front on the first mortgage, 2 points up front on the second.

<u>Solution:</u> [3][6][0] **NI** [1][0] **I%1**
[1][0][0][0][0][0] **PV1** [0] **FV1**
PMT1 ....   <u>Result:</u> PMT1=-877.57

MORE [1][2][0] **N2** [1][1]·[5] **I%2**
[5][0][0][0][0] **PV2** [1][0][0][0][0][+/−] **FV2**
PMT2 ....   <u>Result:</u> PMT2=-658.22

MORE [1][8][0] **M** [2][4][0] **W**

MORE [1][2][0] **NW** [1][7] **Y%W**
[5][0][0][0][0][+/−] **PVW** [2][5][0][0][0] **FVW**
PMTW ....   <u>Result:</u> PMTW=2,201.26

MORE **MORE** **MORE** [1] **PTS1** [2] **PTS2**
APR% ....   <u>Result:</u> APR%=10.51

<u>Notice:</u>

- *Important:* For cash-flow signs (+ or -), take the viewpoint of the *borrower* on the first two mortgages; take the *lender's* perspective on the wraparound loan.

- All payments are assumed to be monthly, in arrears.

- You must solve for the payments (and all other parameters) on the first two loans before computing the APR% or any parameters on the wraparound mortgage.

- The formula doesn't allow points for the wraparound mortgage; for PVW, use the *net* new money loaned.

- The formula can also be handy for determining whether it makes sense simply to refinance a single mortgage:

    - First, compute the APR% of the original mortgage (including any points and other fees charged), if you pay it off over its normal term.

    - Next, calculate its current balance. Use this number as the "balloon" on the "first" mortgage *and* as the "starting balance" on a "second," which starts now (at the same time you pay off the first). Be careful of the cash-flow signs!

    - If the overall APR% of this "back-to-back" pair of mortgages (including the lower interest rate and the refinance points/fees for the "second"), is *lower* than the first APR%, you save by refinancing.

18. This formula will analyze an income property for net cash-flows at purchase, annually during operation, and upon re-sale. It also computes investment measures for the first year of operations: GRM, cap rate, equity return rate, and cash return rates before and after taxes. It allows for two mortgages on the property, and can handle inflationary increases of rent, property assessment, insurance and maintenance. The investor holds the property for a whole number of years and sells at a price based upon a given cap rate and Net Operating Income in the year after the re-sale.

```
▶IPA:0×(L(D:$PR+0×$COA-
$M1+0×(N1+I1%+PTS1)-$M2
)+L(C:G(D)+($M1×PTS1+0×
(N2+I2%)+$M2×PTS2÷100+
$COA)+L(N:(IP($R.V)×(1-
FP($R.V))-$INS-$MNT+0×I
MP%-$PR×FP(F%.PT))×L(I:
1+IP(F%.PT)÷100)^(G(Y)-
1))+L(Z:IF(TYRS+0×(G%.I
T+B%.CP)<Y OR Y<1:0:1))
L+(P:$M1÷USPV(L(J:I1%÷1
2):12×N1))+L(Q:$M2÷MAX(
1E-99:USPV(L(K:I2%÷12):
12×N2)))+0×($NCF+GRM+CA
P%+EQ%+CC%+ATCC%)+L(E:(
$M1-P×USPV(J:12×(Y-1)))
÷SPPV(J:12×(Y-1)))+L(F:
($M1-P×USPV(J:12×Y))÷SP
PV(J:12×Y))+L(G:($M2-Q×
USPV(K:12×(Y-1)))÷SPPV(
K:12×(Y-1)))+L(H:($M2-Q
×USPV(K:12×Y))÷SPPV(K:1
2×Y))+L(A:N-12×(P+Q)-FP
(G%.IT)×(N+E+G-F-H-12×(
```

```
P+Q)-$PR×IMP%÷3150-(C-D
-$COA)÷TYRS-IF(Y=1:$COA
:0))))+IF(S($NCF):A×Z-I
F(Y=0:C:0)+IF(Y=TYRS:(1
-IP(B%.CP)÷100)×N×I÷FP(
B%.CP)×(1-L(T:IP(G%.IT)
÷100×FP(G%.IT)))-F-H-T×
$PR×(Y×IMP%÷3150-1):0)-
$NCF:IF(S(GRM):GRM-Z×$P
R÷IP($R.V):IF(S(CAP%):C
AP%÷100-Z×N÷$PR:IF(S(EQ
%):EQ%÷100-Z×($PR×(I-1)
+A+E-F+G-H)÷D:IF(S(CC%)
:CC%÷100-Z×(N-12×(P+Q))
÷C:ATCC%÷100-Z×A÷C)))))
```

Approximate Memory Required: 60% to use, 14% to store.

Required Knowns: All variables *except* \$NCF, GRM, CAP%,
EQ%, BTC%, and ATCC%.

Example: A certain office building is appraised at \$750,000, of
which 70% is improved). The proposal: Put \$250,000
down and secure two mortgages: \$350,000 at 10.5% (20
years, 1.5 pts.); and \$150,000 at 12% (10 years, 2 pts.).
Costs of closing/acquisition will be \$2,000. Maximum
gross rents are \$125,000 annually, with 6% vacancy/
loss. Insurance will be \$3,000; maintenance/manage-
ment will be \$12,000. Property taxes are 2.5%. Rents,
expenses and property value will follow inflation: 5%.
The income tax is 33%; capital gains are completely
taxable. In 5 years, the property will sell (through a
broker, for a 6% commission), at a cap rate of 11.5% on
the Net Operating Income expected for the 6th year.

Find the net after-tax cash-flows for the initial investment and for each year of operation. Also, for Year 1, find the GRM, cap rate, equity return rate, and cash return rates before and after taxes.

Solution: Key in the formula and **CALC**.

Then `7` `5` `0` `0` `0` `0` **$PR** `2` `0` `0` `0` **$COA**
`3` `5` `0` `0` `0` **$MI** `2` `0` **NI**
`1` `0` `.` `5` **I%** **MORE** `1` `.` `5` **PTS1**

`1` `5` `0` `0` `0` **$M2** `1` `0` **N2**
`1` `2` **I2%** `2` **PTS2**

MORE `1` `2` `5` `0` `0` `0` `.` `0` `6` **$R.V** `3` `0` `0` `0` **$INS**
`1` `2` `0` `0` `0` **$MNT** `7` `0` **IMP%**

`5` `.` `0` `2` `5` **F%.PT**
MORE `5` **TYRS**
`1` `0` `0` `.` `3` `3` **G%.IT** `6` `.` `1` `1` `5` **B%.CP**

`0` **Y** **$NCF**....	$NCF=-260,250.00
`1` **Y** **$NCF**....	$NCF=12,896.17
`2` **Y** **$NCF**....	$NCF=14,497.89
`3` **Y** **$NCF**....	$NCF=16,834.20
`4` **Y** **$NCF**....	$NCF=19,244.15
`5` **Y** **$NCF**....	$NCF=414,242.86

`1` **Y** **MORE**

GRM....	GRM=6.00
CAP%....	CAP%=11.17
EQ%....	EQ%=25.64
CC%....	CC%=6.15
ATCC%....	ATCC%=4.96

<u>Notice</u>:

- The formula will calculate values for the investment test values (GRM, CAP%, etc.) for any year within the scenario (and give zero values for years outside the scenario), but the investment tests are generally applied *only to Year 1*. So be sure that Y=1 when computing these test values.

- Tax relief from costs of acquisition is taken in Year 1. Tax relief from loan fees ("points") is prorated evenly over the term of the analysis.

- Mortgage terms may be for whole numbers of years only.

- Projected property appreciation in Year 1 (at the assumed rate of inflation) is included in the equity return rate.

- If an investment scenario has uneven income (expense) projections, you can account for such odd or special cash-flows with a simple extra calculation for any given year: Take the resulting $NCF and add (subtract) the *after-tax* portion of the extra income (expense). For example, if, in Year 3 in the example scenario, an extra expense of $1000 is projected, the true $NCF for that year would be:

  $$\$16,289.70 - 1000 \times (1 - .33) \quad \text{or} \quad \$15,619.00$$

- To conserve memory, the formula does not use G ⟨ ⟩ to keep intermediate variables off of the menu. These single-letter variables therefore appear in the last pages of the menu; they may be ignored.

- This formula and the next one (FMRR) can both fit into the machine at one time. Together they form a potent combination for analyzing commercial real estate investments.

19. This formula will analyze a CFLO list named $:

```
▶FMRR%~IRR%:0×(IF(G(P/Y
R)=0:L(P/YR:1):0)+L(Z:Σ
(G:1:SIZEC($):1:#T($:G)
))+L(N:L(F:L(M:L(W:0)))
)+Σ(G:SIZEC($):0:-1:Σ(T
:#T($:G):1:-1:L(M:G(M)+
FLOW($:G))+IF(G(M)<0:L(
M:G(M)×SPPV(SAFE%÷G(P/Y
R):MIN(G(Z)-G(N):1)))):L
(W:G(W)+G(M)×SPFV(RSK%÷
G(P/YR):G(N))+L(M:0)))+
L(F:G(F)+IF(G=0:0:FLOW(
$:G))×SPFV(G(IRR%)÷G(P/
YR):G(N)))+L(N:G(N)+1))
))+IF(S(FMR%) OR S(SAFE
%) OR S(RSK%):0×(SAFE%+
RSK%)+G(M)×SPFV(FMR%÷G(
P/YR):G(Z))+G(W):IF(S($
MIN):$MIN-G(M):IF(S($FW
) OR S(P/YR):$FW-G(W)+0
×P/YR:FLOW($:0)×SPFV(IR
R%÷P/YR:G(Z))+G(F))))
```

<u>Approximate Memory Required</u>:   28% to use, 8% to store, not
including the $ list.

<u>Required Knowns</u>:   The number of cash-flow periods per year
(P/YR), and a CFLO list named $.

<u>Example</u>: Find the FMRR for the following cash-flow scenario,
assuming that all cash is taken from—and returned
to—an account earning 6%. Compare the FMRR with
the IRR for the same situation.

Year	Cash-Flow
0	$ (75,000)
1	15,000
2	15,000
3	(60,000)
4	75,000
5	(35,000)
6	200,000

Solution: First, build the $ list (if it doesn't exist already):

■(MAIN) **FIN** **CFLO** **GET** ***NEW** **NAME** (S) (INPUT)
(7)(5)(0)(0)(0)(+/−)(INPUT) (1)(5)(0)(0)(0)(INPUT)(2)(INPUT)
(6)(0)(0)(0)(0)(+/−)(INPUT)(INPUT) (7)(5)(0)(0)(0)(INPUT)(INPUT)
(3)(5)(0)(0)(0)(+/−)(INPUT)(INPUT) (2)(0)(0)(0)(0)(0)(INPUT)(INPUT)

Now **■**(MAIN) **SOLVE**, key in the formula and **CALC**.
Then (6) **SAFE*** (6) **RSK***

FMR*	Answer: FMR%=16.70
*MIN	Answer: $MIN=−97,876.27
*FW	Answer: $FW=247,170.00
MORE **IRR***	Answer: IRR%=20.69

Notice:

- The P/YR defaults to a value of 1 (i.e. yearly cash-flows) if you neglect to give it a value.

- The
  ```
  IF(S(FMR%) OR S(SAFE
  %) OR S(RSK%)...
  ```
  lets you use the same portion of the IF(S structure to solve for each of several variables. Normally, you do this by leaving that portion for *last* in the structure, but you get a better menu by placing this "multiple" option earlier.

20. From an asset's basis and salvage values, class life and current year, this formula computes that year's best depreciation and Remaining Depreciable Value (RDV),* with these MACRS rules:

Property examples	Class	Allowed Depr. Method
tractors, racehorses	3 years	200% DB or SL
vehicles, office/lab equip.	5 years	200% DB or SL
furniture, fixtures, misc.	7 years	200% DB or SL
fruit/nut trees/vines	10 years	200% DB or SL
roads, shrubbery,	15 years	150% DB or SL
farm buildings,	20 years	150% DB or SL
residential rental prop.	27.5 years	SL
nonresidential real prop.	31.5 years	SL

```
▶$MACRS:0×(L(B:(BASIS-S
ALV)÷CLASS)+L(F:IF(CLAS
S<11:2:IF(CLASS<21:1.5:
0)))+L(C:1-G(F)÷CLASS)+
L(A:BASIS×G(F)÷CLASS)+L
(Y:IF(CLASS>20:0:IP(1+L
N((BASIS-SALV)÷BASIS÷G(
F))÷LN(G(C)))))+L(R:MAX
(BASIS-SALV-Σ(N:1:MIN(Y
R#-1:G(Y)):1:G(A)×G(C)^
(N-1))-MAX(0:YR#-1-G(Y)
)×G(B):0)))+IF(S(MACR):
MIN(G(R):MAX(G(A)×G(C)^
(YR#-1):G(B)))-MACR:RDV
-G(R)+MIN(G(R):MAX(G(A)
×G(C)^(YR#-1):G(B))))
```

<u>Approximate Memory Required</u>: 21% to use, 6% to store.

---

*Assume for this formula that an asset is placed into service at the beginning of the tax year.

<u>Required Knowns</u>: The asset's BASIS and SALVage values, and its CLASS life.

<u>Example</u>: You buy a small office building with an improvements value of $75,000. You also buy a $10,000 computer for the office, and you landscape the property with $5000 in shrubs. Estimate salvage values for these new assets: $15,000, $500 and $0, respectively. What depreciation can you take for each in tax years 3 and 4?

<u>Solution</u>: Key in the formula and press **CALC**. Then take the assets one-by-one, starting with the building:

⑦⑤⓪⓪⓪ **BASIS** ①⑤⓪⓪⓪ **SALV** ③①·⑤ **CLASS**
③ **YR#** **MACR**   <u>Answer</u>: MACR=1,904.76
                  RDV RDV=54,285.71
④ **YR#** **MACR**   <u>Answer</u>: MACR=1,904.76
                  RDV RDV=52,380.95

①⓪⓪⓪⓪ **BASIS** ⑤⓪⓪ **SALV** ⑤ **CLASS**
③ **YR#** **MACR**   <u>Answer</u>: MACR=1,900.00
                  RDV RDV=1,200.00
④ **YR#** **MACR**   <u>Answer</u>: MACR=1,200.00
                  RDV RDV=0.00

⑤⓪⓪⓪ **BASIS** ⓪ **SALV** ①⑤ **CLASS**
③ **YR#** **MACR**   <u>Answer</u>: MACR=405.00
                  RDV RDV=3,645.00
④ **YR#** **MACR**   <u>Answer</u>: MACR=364.50
                  RDV RDV=3,280.50

<u>Notice</u>: This is a modification of a built-in formula, so those equations (for Depreciation) in your Owner's Manual (Appendix B) are the starting point of this formula.

21. The strategy for a short formula is to create two SUM lists (V and C) containing the volumes and costs as bid by the manufacturer. Then you use the built-in forecasting tools (in the SUM Menu) to find the best-fitting curve type and its parameters (M and B), which you then key in as known values in the formula (for CTYPE, use these values: LIN=1; LOG=2; EXP=3; PWR=4):

```
▶INV:0×(TOTAL+HOLD%+BVO
L+VOL+$EA.+CTYPE+M+B)+I
F(S(BVOL):(M×BVOL×HOLD%
÷200÷TOTAL+IF(CTYPE>2:M
:0))×IF(MOD(CTYPE:2)=0:
1:BVOL)-IF(CTYPE=4:1:B-
IF(CTYPE=2:M×(1-LN(BVOL
)):0)):VOL×$EA.-B×IF(CT
YPE<3:1:IF(CTYPE=3:EXP(
M×VOL):VOL^M))-M×IF(CTY
PE>2:0:IF(CTYPE=1:VOL:L
N(VOL))))
```

Approximate Memory Required: 16% to use, 4% to store, not including the lists, V and C.

This version does the curve-fitting, too, from *one* SUM list, Q:

```
▶INV:0×(TOTAL+HOLD%+BVO
L+VOL+$EA.+T+M+B)+IF(S(
BVOL):0×(L(N:SIZES(Q))+
L(X:Σ(I:1:N-1:2:ITEM(Q:
I))÷N×2)+L(W:Σ(I:1:N-1:
2:LN(ITEM(Q:I)))÷N×2)+L
(Y:Σ(I:2:N:2:ITEM(Q:I))
÷N×2)+L(Z:Σ(I:2:N:2:LN(
ITEM(Q:I)))÷N×2)+L(S:Σ(
```

```
I:1:N-1:2:(ITEM(Q:I)-X)
^2))+L(L:Σ(I:1:N-1:2:(L
N(ITEM(Q:I))-W)^2))+L(U
:Σ(I:2:N:2:(ITEM(Q:I)-Y
)^2))+L(V:Σ(I:2:N:2:(LN
(ITEM(Q:I))-Z)^2))+L(C:
Σ(I:1:N-1:2:(ITEM(Q:I)-
X)×(ITEM(Q:I+1)-Y)))+L(
D:Σ(I:1:N-1:2:(LN(ITEM(
Q:I))-W)×(ITEM(Q:I+1)-Y
)))+L(E:Σ(I:1:N-1:2:(IT
EM(Q:I)-X)×(LN(ITEM(Q:I
+1))-Z)))+L(F:Σ(I:1:N-1
:2:(LN(ITEM(Q:I))-W)×(L
N(ITEM(Q:I+1))-Z)))+L(G
:C^2÷S÷U)+L(H:D^2÷L÷U)+
L(J:E^2÷S÷V)+L(K:F^2÷L÷
V)+L(T:IF(G>H AND G>J A
ND G>K:1+0×(L(M:C÷S)+L(
B:Y-M×X)):IF(H>J AND H>
K:2+0×(L(M:D÷L)+L(B:Y-M
×W)):IF(J>K:3+0×(L(M:E÷
S)+L(B:EXP(Z-M×X))):4+0
×(L(M:F÷L)+L(B:EXP(Z-M×
W)))))))))+(M×BVOL×HOLD%
÷200÷TOTAL+IF(T>2:M:0))
×IF(MOD(T:2)=0:1:BVOL)-
IF(T>3:1:B-IF(T=2:M×(1-
LN(BVOL)):0)):VOL×$EA.-
B×IF(T<3:1:IF(T=3:EXP(M
×VOL):VOL^M))-M×IF(T>2:
0:IF(T=1:VOL:LN(VOL))))
```

Approximate Memory Required: 56% to use, 14% to store, not
                              including the list, Q.

<u>Required Knowns</u>: The TOTAL sales volume estimated for an
item over a period of time; the added cost
(as a %) of holding it in inventory over that
time (HOLD%); SUM list(s), V and C or Q,
of order Volumes and their corresponding
Cost quotes (Q contains successive *pairs*
of values: volume, bid, volume, bid, etc.).

<u>Example</u>: A certain book will sell 75,000 copies over its life. It
will cost the publisher an additional 60% to sit in inventory over that time. To manufacture the book, a
printer bids as follows. Use the short formula to find
the publisher's optimum order volume, that unit cost,
and the unit cost of an order of 15,000 copies.

<u>Order volume</u>	<u>Manufacturer's bid</u>
2,500	$ 8,500
5,000	$ 14,000
10,000	$ 25,500
20,000	$ 44,000
40,000	$ 82,000

<u>Solution</u>: First, build the V and C (Volume and Cost) lists:

[MAIN] [SUM] [GET] [\#NEW] [NAME] [V] [INPUT]
[2][5][0][0] [INPUT] [5][0][0][0] [INPUT] [1][0][0][0][0] [INPUT]
[2][0][0][0][0] [INPUT] [4][0][0][0][0] [INPUT]
[GET] [\#NEW] [NAME] [C] [INPUT]
[8][5][0][0] [INPUT] [1][4][0][0][0] [INPUT] [2][5][5][0][0] [INPUT]
[4][4][0][0][0] [INPUT] [8][2][0][0][0] [INPUT]

Find the best-fitting curve: [DISP] [FIX] [6] [INPUT] (to see
small differences in "fit"), [CALC] [MORE] [FRCST] [V]

LIN **CORR**	(result: CORR=.999499)	
EXIT **LOG** **CORR**	(result: CORR=.942971)	
EXIT **EXP** **CORR**	(result: CORR=.942620)	
EXIT **PWR** **CORR**	(result: CORR=.999398)	

Thus, LIN is the best-fitting curve type. So EXIT **LIN**
and **M** (M=1.945430) STO 0;
B (B=4,645.833333) STO 1.

Now, to use the short formula, DISP **FIX** 2 INPUT, then
MAIN **SOLVE**, key in the formula, and **CALC**. Next,
MORE 1 **CTYPE** (1=LIN), RCL 0 **M** RCL 1 **B**.
Now **MORE** 7 5 0 0 0 **TOTAL** 6 0 **HOLD%**

BVOL....	Answer: BVOL=24,433.97
STO **VOL** **$EA.**	Answer: $EA.=2.14
1 5 0 0 0 **VOL** **$EA.**	Answer: $EA.=2.26

Notice:

- The longer formula would require only the last four lines of this solution—no curve fitting. That formula uses the same Forecasting equations as SUM (in Appendix B of the HP Owner's Manual). You could use it for any such SOLVE-formula curve-fitting solution. Note that for speed here, you must compute BVOL before doing VOL/$EA. calculations. And, because of memory limits, variables normally hidden by $G()$ appear harmlessly (later) on the menu.

- The formulas compute the order volume, v, that minimizes

  this total cost, T: $T(v) = \dfrac{TOTAL}{v}C(v) + \dfrac{C(v)}{2}\left(\dfrac{HOLD\%}{100}\right)$

  where $C(v)$ is the function (one of the four CTYPE's) that best describes the manufacturer's set of quotes.

22. You key in parameters for a scenario that looks like this:

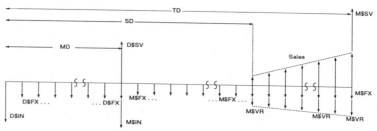

The formula:

```
▶MANF.ROI%:0×(I%YR+P/YR
+D$IN+D$FX+D$SV+M$IN+M$
FX+MD.SD+M$SV+$VAR+$PRC
+L(P:L(F:M$SV))+L(N:TD-
IP(100×FP(MD.SD))+1)+L(
V:G(#SLD)÷(G(N)÷2×(G(N)
+1)))+Σ(T:TD:1:-1:L(P:G
(P)+IF(T=IP(MD.SD):D$SV
-M$IN:0)-IF(T<=IP(MD.SD
):D$FX:M$FX)+IF(T<TD+1-
G(N):0:($PRC-$VAR)×G(V)
×(G(N)-TD+T)))+IF(G(P)>
0:L(F:G(F)+G(P)×SPFV(I%
YR÷P/YR:TD-T)+L(P:0)):L
(P:G(P)÷(1+I%YR÷P/YR)))
))+IF(S(R%YR) OR S($PRC
) OR S(#SLD) OR S(TD):(
1+R%YR÷P/YR÷100)^TD×(G(
P)-D$IN)+G(F)+0×$PRC+#S
LD-#SLD:$MIN+G(P)-D$IN)
```

<u>Approximate Memory Required:</u> 29% to use, 7% to store.

<u>Required Knowns:</u> All *except* $PRC, TDAT, R%YR, #SLD and $MIN.

<u>Example</u>: The capital equipment to develop a new product will cost $10,000, of which $2500 is salvageable afterwards. Development overhead is $25,000/mo. over 3 months. Then manufacturing will begin, requiring a capital expenditure of $150,000 (of which $30,000 is salvageable) and fixed monthly costs of $15,000 (continuing throughout the sales life). Sales will begin a month after manufacturing. If each unit costs $20 to make and sells for $99, how many must be sold within 2 years of first investment to break even (i.e. to return the cost of money, 11%)? What minimum cash must the company commit up front to fund this project?

<u>Solution</u>: [1][1] I%YR [1][2] P/YR [1][0][0][0][0] D%IN
[2][5][0][0][0] D%FX [2][5][0][0] D%SV

MORE [1][5][0][0][0][0] M%IN [1][5][0][0][0] M%FX
[3][.][0][4] MD.SD [3][0][0][0][0] M%SV [2][0] %VAR

MORE [9][9] %PRC [2][4] TD
[1][1] R%YR #SLD ....<u>Result</u>: #SLD=2618.79
%MIN....   <u>Result</u>: $MIN=56,381.72

<u>Notice</u>:

- The assumed sales pattern is *linear growth*—where the number of units sold each month increases by a set number.

- Each project checkpoint (Manufacturing Date, Sales Date, Target Date) is measured as the number of periods *since the start of the project*. Two of these points are formatted in one number, MD.SD ("Manufacturing Date. Sales Date").

- $MIN is an unknown entirely independent of R%YR.

23. This formula behaves like TVM, except that you also specify the yearly inflation rate (INF%) and income tax rate (TAX%):

```
►TAXES~INFL:0×(N+I%YR+P
V+PMT+FV+IF(P/YR=0:L(P/
YR:12):0))+IF(S(BEG?):A
BS(G(BEG?)-1)-BEG?-0×(T
AX%+INF%):IF(S(R%YR):((
(1+(SPFV(I%YR÷P/YR:P/YR
)-1)×(1-TAX%÷100))÷SPFV
(INF%÷P/YR:P/YR))^INV(P
/YR)-1)×100-R%YR÷P/YR:P
V+FV×SPPV(L(I:(((1+(SPF
V(I%YR÷P/YR:P/YR)-1)×(1
-TAX%÷100))÷SPFV(INF%÷P
/YR:P/YR))^INV(P/YR)-1)
×100):N)+(1+G(I)÷100×BE
G?)×USPV(G(I):N)×PMT))
```

<u>Approximate Memory Required</u>:   19% to use, 5% to store.
<u>Required Knowns</u>:   None.

<u>Example</u>:   Assuming a 5% annual inflation rate and an income tax rate of 28%, if you invest $166.66 of *buying power* each month (at the end of the month) into a mutual fund that earns 15% per year, what buying power will accumulate in this account over 30 years? What is the equivalent annual growth rate of this buying power? What if the account were tax-deferred —like an IRA?

Solution: ⌊3⌋⌊0⌋⌊×⌋⌊1⌋⌊2⌋⌊=⌋ (ALG) or ⌊3⌋⌊0⌋[INPUT]⌊1⌋⌊2⌋⌊×⌋ (RPN) **N**
⌊1⌋⌊5⌋ **I%YR** ⌊0⌋ **PV** ⌊1⌋⌊6⌋⌊6⌋⌊·⌋⌊6⌋⌊6⌋⌊+/−⌋ **PMT** , **MORE**
⌊1⌋⌊2⌋ **P/YR** **BEG?** (toggle this until BEG?=0.00)
⌊2⌋⌊8⌋ **TAX%** ⌊5⌋ **INF%**

R%YR....   Result: R%YR=5.98
MORE **FV** ....   Result: FV=166,687.52

MORE
⌊0⌋ **TAX%** **R%YR** ....   Result: R%YR=9.96
MORE **FV** ....   Result: FV=373,414.62

Notice:

- The formula assumes that interest is taxable once per year, but that the inflation, interest and growth rates compound once per period (that is, P/YR times per year). Keep in mind that the level, periodic PMT amount is in terms of *buying power* ("today's dollars"). In order for that buying power investment amount to remain steady, its *face value* would be increased every period—to keep pace with inflation.

- The money accruing in a tax-deferred account—such as an IRA—may be taxable upon withdrawal.

- The equivalent interest calculation (I) in the formula is done twice—in the IF(S(R%YR)... and the general TVM formula—to allow for independent unknowns. You could, of course, use G(I) for all but the first L(I: ... definition, but this would destroy the total independence of the unknowns. Alternatively, you could move the L(I: ... definition to the menu-ordering section, and use G(I) thereafter. But then I%YR, TAX% and INF% would be *required* knowns; you could never solve for them.

24. This formula is extremely useful and versatile for all sorts of retirement scenarios:

```
▶RETIRE:0×(WYRS+$GI+TBR
%+INF%+I%YR+%INV+$RET+R
YRS+R%YR+$RGI)+IF(S($RE
T):$RET×SPPV(L(I:(((1+(
SPFV(I%YR÷12:12)-1)×(1-
TBR%÷100))÷(1+INF%÷100)
)^INV(12)-1)×100):WYRS×
12)-USPV(G(I):WYRS×12)×
$GI×%INV÷100:USPV((((1+
(SPFV(R%YR÷12:12)-1)×(1
-TBR%÷100))÷(1+INF%÷100
))^INV(12)-1)×100:RYRS×
12)×$RGI-USPV(L(I:(((1+
(SPFV(I%YR÷12:12)-1)×(1
-TBR%÷100))÷(1+INF%÷100
))^INV(12)-1)×100):WYRS
×12)×$GI×%INV÷100÷SPPV(
G(I):WYRS×12))
```

<u>Approximate Memory Required</u>:   23% to use, 6% to store.
<u>Required Knowns</u>:   None.

<u>Example</u>:   Your monthly salary is $3333.20/month, with annual cost-of-living raises (5% a year). If, for 35 years, you invest 5% of each monthly paycheck into a growth-oriented mutual fund IRA (tax-deferred until withdrawal) averaging 15% growth per year, what gross income (today's dollars) could you draw for 30 years of retirement if you roll the account into a more secure bond fund at 10%? What is the rollover amount?

Repeat the problem for a taxable account (28% income tax bracket). What if, in addition to the 5% of income that you're putting away in that (taxable) account, you were also allowed to invest the 7.65% that now goes for Social Security and Medicare?

Solution: ③⑤ **WYRS** ③③③③·② **%GI**

⓪ **TBR%** (the IRA incurs no taxes until withdrawal)

⑤ **INF%** ①⑤ **I%YR** , **MORE**

⑤ **%INV** ③⓪ **RYRS** ①⓪ **R%YR**

%RGI.... <u>Result</u>: $RGI=3,494.37

%RET.... <u>Result</u>: $RET=644,295.72

MORE ②⑧ **TBR%**

MORE %RET .... <u>Result</u>: $RET=242,340.26

What a difference an IRA makes.

①②·⑥⑤ **%INV**

%RET.... <u>Result</u>: $RET=613,120.85

%RGI.... <u>Result</u>: $RGI=2,388.29

<u>Notice</u>:

- The formula assumes that interest is taxable once per year, that the inflation rate compounds annually, that interest rates compound monthly, and that salary and investment cash-flows occur at the end of the month.

- Since there are no required knowns, you can solve for any parameter by specifying all the others.

- The money accruing in a tax-deferred account—such as an IRA—may be taxable upon withdrawal.

25. This formula estimates the remaining balances of two IRA's and three other accounts after being drawn upon by a retired couple.

From the retirement date onward, the retiree(s) draw(s) a steady *after-tax* annual income, adjusted for inflation. No more contributions are made to any account; rather, they are drawn upon to provide the portion of income *not* covered by the Social Security benefits that each retiree receives, starting at a given age. These benefits are assumed to have yearly Cost-of-Living Adjustments to match inflation. Half of the benefits are assumed to be taxable.

The elder spouse is designated as spouse A. The three non-IRA accounts are depleted first (in direct proportion to their starting balances—so that they all exhaust at once), then IRA_A, then IRA_B. All withdrawals on the IRA accounts are assumed taxable (and a 10% penalty is applied to withdrawals from an IRA account of a spouse not yet 60 years old). Non-IRA accounts #1 and #2 earn taxable interest; account #3 earns tax-free interest.

The retirement ages given must be no later than when the first Social Security benefits are drawn, and both spouses must live at least until they are both drawing Social Security benefits. Upon the death of spouse A, the formula assumes that spouse B will then maintain the income level and tax bracket; inherit all accounts unencumbered; and draw the *greater* of the two Social Security benefits for the rest of his/her life.

```
▶RET~IRA~SS:0×(L(A:RND(
AGEA- IF(AGEB=0:L(AGEB:A
GEA):AGEB):0))+L(I:IP(I
%.T%)÷100)+L(T:1-FP(I%.
T%))+$SA+SAGA+$SB+SAGB+
L(E:IP($1.%)+IP($2.%)+I
```

```
P($3.%))+L(F:IP($A.%))+
L(Q:(1+FP($A.%))÷(1+G(I
)))+L(G:IP($B.%))+L(R:(
1+FP($B.%))÷(1+G(I)))+L
(J:IP($1.%)÷G(E))+L(K:I
P($2.%)÷G(E))+L(P:(1+(I
P($1.%)×FP($1.%)×G(T)+I
P($2.%)×FP($2.%)×G(T)+I
P($3.%)×FP($3.%)÷G(E))
÷(1+G(I)))+L(L:RND(100×
FP(AGB.L):0))+L(N:IP(AG
B.L))+$NYI+Σ(M:RND(AGEB
:0)+1:MIN(G(L):G(N)):1:
L(Y:$NYI-(1+G(T))÷2×(IF
(M+G(A)>=RND(SAGA:0) AN
D M+G(A)<=MIN(G(N)+G(A)
:G(L)):$SA:0)+IF(M)>=RND
(SAGB:0):$SB:0)+IF(M+G(
A)>G(L):MAX($SA-$SB:0):
0)))+L(E:G(E)×G(P)-G(Y)
)+L(F:G(F)×G(Q)+MIN(G(E
):0)÷L(Z:IF(M+G(A)<60:G
(T)-.1:G(T))))+L(G:G(G)
×G(R)+MIN(G(F):0)×G(Z)÷
IF(M<60:G(T)-.1:G(T)))+
L(E:MAX(G(E):0))+L(F:MA
X(G(F):0))))+0×$NYI+L($
B1:G(E)×G(J))+L($B2:G(E
)×G(K))+L($B3:G(E)×(1-G
(J)-G(K)))+L($BA:G(F))+
L($BB:G(G))=$TRB+0×($B1
+$B2+$B3+$BA+$BB)
```

Approximate Memory Required: 52% to use, 13% to store.

Required Knowns: *All* except $NYI, $TRB, and $B1-$BB

Example: The husband is 55; his wife is 46. Their income tax bracket is 33.4% (including state and local taxes) and inflation averages 5%. Both will begin to draw Social Security benefits at age 65. His yearly benefit will be $22,800; hers, $17,700. The couple has $60,000 in a bank account earning 6.5%; a taxable mutual fund of $34,330, earning 15%; and a tax-free fund of $57,000, earning 8.0%. The husband's IRA of $495,600 earns 7%. The wife's IRA of $200,000 earns 11.0%. Both expect to live to be 89. What after-tax income (today's dollars) can they expect for the rest of their lives? If they draw that amount for 3 years, how much buying power is left in each account? 10 years? 30 years?

Solution:

5 5 AGEA 4 6 AGEB 5 · 3 3 4 TX.T%
2 2 8 0 0 $SA 6 5 SAGA
MORE 1 7 7 0 0 $SB 6 5 SAGB
6 0 0 0 0 · 0 6 5 $1.%
3 4 3 3 0 · 1 5 $2.%
5 7 0 0 0 · 0 8 $3.%
MORE 4 9 5 6 0 0 · 0 7 $A.%
2 0 0 0 0 0 · 1 1 $B.%
8 9 · 8 9 AGB.L
0 $TRB $NYI ....Answer: $NYI=46,754.98
4 9 · 8 9 AGB.L $TRB $TRB=777,921.92
MORE RCL $B1 $B1=6,810.36
RCL $B2 $B2=3,896.66
RCL $B3 $B3=6,469.84
RCL $BA $BA=524,462.85
RCL $BB $BB=236,282.22

MORE **MORE** **MORE**	
5 6 · 8 9 **AGB.L** **♯TRB**	$TRB=475,998.27
MORE RCL **♯B1**	$B1=0.00
RCL **♯B2**	$B2=0.00
RCL **♯B3**	$B3=0.00
RCL **♯BA**	$BA=127,366.64
RCL **♯BB**	$BB=348,631.64
MORE **MORE** **MORE**	
7 6 · 8 9 **AGB.L** **♯TRB**	$TRB=298,050.79
MORE RCL **♯B1**	$B1=0.00
RCL **♯B2**	$B2=0.00
RCL **♯B3**	$B3=0.00
RCL **♯BA**	$BA=0.00
RCL **♯BB**	$BB=298,050.79

Notice:

- The couple retires at the same time, at the ages given. All rate compounding, incomes and taxes occur annually; all dollar amounts are buying power *at the time of retirement*.

- To save space, many variables in the formula represent two values—formatted on each side of the decimal point.

- You specify the term of the analysis by projecting that age for spouse B—the integer portion of the variable AGB.L.

- The calculation of $NYI is slow. To speed things up, key two "ballpark" values (one after another) into $NYI, and then *compute* $NYI. The machine will take these as suggested guesses and home in faster on the correct solution faster.

- To see the values of the individual remaining balances, you don't *solve* for them; you RCL them—*after* computing $TRB.

Where To Now?

Time to come down to Earth and check the road map again. Read the sign and choose your next destination....

Basic Arithmetic...............24

Using Menus.......................60

TVM.....................................94

The CFLO Menu...................202

SUM Lists............................258

TIME, Dates and Appts.....280

The SOLVE Menu................294

TEXT Lists..........................409

Appendix............................424

10. THE NOTES YOU MAKE:
TEXT Lists

Saving TEXT

With all that memory space in your calculator, you can certainly store a lot of solutions, as you've just seen.

But you can also store plain *text*—just simple notes to yourself, or lists of names and addresses, or to-do lists, etc. In fact, the HP 19BII is one of very few financial calculators that allows you to do this.

So try it...

Take a Memo: Make a note in a To Do list to "Remind Martha (x 8092) about Thursday conference."

Here's How: From the MAIN Menu, press **TEXT**.

Notice the little α (the "alphabetic annunciator") at the top of the display, indicating that the calculator will now be expecting you to enter alphabetic characters. So, use the left-hand keyboard to type in the note—including the parentheses and numerals. Here's how it should look:

Now press INPUT to finish the memo.

Notice that you've begun a new list. Once you type the first entry into a list, it then shows the characteristic dotted line—the TOP of the list:

Add Another: Remind yourself about your lunch appointment with George on Friday at 1:00.

Just Type: LUNCH WITH GEORGE (FRI. AT 1:00)

And press [INPUT].

Notice that once it's input, each note's display is abbreviated to one line (indicated by the ellipsis ...). And the list pointer always points to the *current* entry. As usual, press [↑] to move up the list; [↓] to move down.

Uh-Oh: Just now, you remember that tomorrow is your mother's birthday. How do you *insert* a note to remind yourself—in the middle of the list?

Easy: Move the pointer to the entry before the intended entry (So in this case, you move the pointer to REMIND MARTHA...). Then just type: FLOWERS FOR MOM and [INPUT].

And you can insert entries even at the very top of the list: **■⊞** will move you immediately to the **TOP** marker, where you can then type.

Question: As you've seen, each entry gets one line in the display, and **...** indicates if there's more than what's visible. So how do you get to see a whole message? What if you can't remember what you're supposed to remind Martha?

Do This: Move the pointer to **REMIND MARTHA**. Press **EDIT**. There's the whole message. And if a message needs more than *three* lines, use ⊞ to see the others. When you're finished, just press ⌈EXIT⌉ to return to the list view.

And, now that you've created a "To Do" list, how about giving it a name so that you can retrieve it later?

Do It: Press **NAME** **TO DO** ⌈INPUT⌉. It's just like naming any other kind of list. Now you can create other text lists without erasing your **TO DO** list....

Multiple-Entry Records

Your **TO DO** list is a *simple* list. That is, although some entries occupy more than one line, each note that you made was truly a separate entry. But you can also group entries together into *records*....

Example: Create a text list of these important clients:

```
Edward J. Davis
9032 SW 96th Pl.
Roisterburg, ID  88670
206-187-3492
```

```
Abraham L. President
16000 Pennsylvania Dr.
Gettysburg, PA  21199
717-TOP-HAT1
```
```
Lizbeth Regina
10 Buckingham Circle
Piccadilly, WA  98660
206-RED-HEAD
```

Solution: First, get and name a new list: **GET** **:NEW** **NAME** **CLIENT** (INPUT). Now just start typing:

> **EDWARD J. DAVIS** (INPUT)
> **9032 SW 96TH PL.** (INPUT)
> **ROISTERBURG, ID 88670** (INPUT)
> **208-187-3492** (INPUT) **MARK**

Each (INPUT) creates an *entry*. Then **MARK** groups into a *record* all entries since the previous mark (or since the TOP). Notice the dotted line marking the end-of-record.

Now enter the other two records similarly:

ABRAHAM L. PRESIDENT (INPUT)
16000 PENNSYLVANIA DR. (INPUT)
GETTYSBURG, PA 21199 (INPUT)
717-TOP-HAT1 (INPUT)
MARK

LIZBETH REGINA (INPUT)
10 BUCKINGHAM CIRCLE (INPUT)
PICCADILLY, WA 98660 (INPUT)
206-RED-HEAD (INPUT)
MARK

Of course, just as with your TO DO list, you can move through your CLIENT list entry-by-entry with ↑ and ↓. But when entries are grouped into records, you can also move *record-by-record*....

Try It: Use **MORE** to get the second page of the TEXT Menu. Then use **PREV** and **NEXT** to jump between consecutive records.

Notice how the HP 19BII treats the TOP marker as its own record.

Question: Can you insert a new client record between Ed and Abe?

Answer: Sure: Move the pointer to the record marker (the dotted line) between the Ed Davis and Abe President records. Then just type in the new record:

> GEORGE WILLIAMS `INPUT`
> 2643 LONGVIEW LANE `INPUT`
> FEASEL, WA 98702 `INPUT`
> 206-138-4990 `INPUT`

Now press **MORE** **MARK** to insert the record marker.

Problem: Delete Lizbeth's record from your **CLIENT** list.

Quickie: Press **MORE** **NEXT** to move to Ms. Regina's record. Then press **MORE** **DELET** to delete the first entry in the record. *Notice* that you delete only one *entry* at a time—not a whole record. So finish off the whole record by pressing **DELET** three more times. As you delete the last entry, you'll see the record marker go away, too.

Sorting TEXT Lists

The HP 19BII has just one kind of built-in sorting—alphabetizing.

Try It: Alphabetize your TO DO list (though you don't usually).

Like So: Get the TO DO list: **GET** **TO DO**. Then press **MORE** **SORT** **YES**. Move down the resulting list and notice how the entries are now alphabetized by their first characters.*

Easy, right? But how does this alphabetical sort work when the list is divided into records?

Find Out: Sort your CLIENT list.

Like This: Get the CLIENT list: Press **MORE** **GET** **CLIEN**. Then press **MORE** **SORT** **YES**.

Now move through the records using **NEXT**. Notice that the records are alphabetized by the first characters of their *first entries*.

Page 197 of your Owner's Manual lists the exact sorting order of all characters—especially useful when you have entries beginning with symbols (, &, #) or foreign characters (Å, Ç, Ñ)

Editing a Record

By now, it's probably bothering you:

Ahem: If the TEXT sorter alphabetizes only by the first character in a record, then how are you going to get your CLIENT list ordered by *last* name—as you'd normally use it?

Oh: You put the last name first in each record. Whatever you want to sort by *must* come first in the record.

Looks like you'll have to edit your records...

Edit: With the ▶ at ABRAHAM L. PRESIDENT, press **EDIT** and re-type: PRESIDENT, ABRAHAM L. [INPUT]

Now repeat this for the other records:
NEXT EDIT DAVIS, EDWARD J. [INPUT]
NEXT EDIT WILLIAMS, GEORGE [INPUT]

Re-Sort: Press **SORT YES** .... Now you've organized the records by the last names.

Moral Of The Story: You should carefully plan any lists you'll want to alphabetize *before* you enter the data. It will save a lot of editing.

Finding an Entry

Of course, making lists probably wouldn't be worthwhile in the first place if there weren't a quick way to search the list for a particular entry—the one you need *right now.*

Keeping the list alphabetized is one way to enhance its usefulness, but, the HP 19Bɪɪ also has a searching tool to help you find items quickly.

Example: Use **FIND** to locate clients who live in Pennsylvania.

Hmmm... With the ▶ at the TOP marker, press **FIND**.

You'll then be prompted to enter a sequence of characters—and you can request any sequence up to eight characters long—to locate in the list. So type PA (INPUT).

The pointer now points to the third entry in Abe's record. Sure enough, Abe lives in Pennsylvania.

Are there any other clients who live in PA? To find out, just press **FIND** (INPUT)....

Ah—the pointer returns to the TOP marker, meaning that the HP 19Bɪɪ didn't find any other matches. So Abe was the only client who lives in Pennsylvania.

Another: Now find all clients in the state of Washington.

Solution: Press **FIND** once again…. You'll see the PA still sitting there, waiting to be used again. So change this search sequence to WA, and press (INPUT)….

What's this? The ▶ stops at EDWARD J. DAVIS, who lives in Idaho, not Washington! What gives?

Nothing's wrong, actually. Your HP 19BII is being very reliable: Notice that EDWARD does indeed contain the sequence WA. So **FIND** found it.

OK, But: You really want to find the state abbreviation and not a part of some larger word, so change the search sequence so that it has a space before and after the WA. And remember to return to the TOP of the list before you try the **FIND** again….

Better: This time you get good results. George Williams is your Washingtonian client.

Moral Of This Story: Your HP 19BII will take you quite literally, so when searching for information in a list, make your search sequence as precise as you can (within the eight-character limit).

TEXT Quiz

A few things to review... and a few new twists to discover....

1. How would you delete an entire list?

2. What's the crucial difference between the ⬆ and ⬇ keys and the **PREV** and **NEXT** menu tools?

3. Suppose you wanted to organize your TO DO list by days of the week. How might you do this?

4. Suppose that you keep two name-address-telephone lists—one for CLIENTS and one for CONTACTS. How do you move a record from the CONTACTS to the CLIENTS list?

5. What happens if you perform a **FIND** without starting from the top of the list?

TEXT Quiz Solutions

1. To delete an entire list, you must first make it the current list, using **GET**. Then you press **CLEAR DATA** and confirm that you want to clear the list by pressing **YES**. Finally, you confirm that you want to clear the list name (if it has one) by pressing **YES** once again.

2. The ⬆ and ⬇ keys move through a list *entry by entry*—regardless whether the entries are grouped into records. The menu tools, **PREV** and **NEXT** move through a list *record by record*. They aren't very useful in lists of single entries—such as the TO DO list—where all entries are essentially in one big record.

3. One very straightforward approach is to divide the TO DO list into seven records whose first entry is numbered and contains the name of that day of the week. Watch:

    GET the TO DO list (it should now have three entries). Make each entry into its own record by adding record markers: Move the pointer to each entry and press **MARK**.

    Next, add the properly numbered day-of-the-week label to each record (assume that Martha's reminder comes on Wednesday, Mom's birthday on Thursday and lunch with George on Friday).

To do this, move the pointer to the **TOP** of the list and type:

```
4.  THURSDAY      (INPUT)(↓)(↓)
5.  FRIDAY        (INPUT)(↓)(↓)
3.  WEDNESDAY     (INPUT)
```

The numbers allow you to sort your day-records chronologically. Press **MORE** **SORT** **YES** to see this.

Of course, you can add records for other days of the week and insert "To-Do" notes wherever appropriate, giving each task the priority it deserves within that day's record. Then, as you finish a task, you would delete its entry, thus "clearing your calendar."

4.   Unfortunately, the HP 19Bᴨ has no "cut-and-paste" feature. You cannot move a record from one list to another; you must delete it from one list and retype it into the other.

5.   **FIND** searches the current TEXT list starting from the entry *below* the current entry (the one with the ►) and stopping at the bottom of the list (at which time the ► returns to the **TOP**). Thus, if you begin a search from anywhere except the **TOP** marker, **FIND** will have skipped one or more entries and so may not find what you're looking for—even though it is indeed in the list.

Therefore, *make it a habit* to move to the **TOP** marker (via ■(↑)) before using **FIND**.

What's Next?

This is the last chapter in the Course. Now you can go back and read or review any chapter you wish.....

Basic Arithmetic 24

Using Menus 60

TVM 94

The CFLO Menu 202

SUM Lists 258

TIME, Dates and Appts 280

The SOLVE Menu 294

TEXT Lists 409

Appendix 424

A. APPENDIX

Here are some Solver formulas and related explanations to help your calculations with Canadian mortgages. Be sure to read and digest Chapter 9, to familiarize yourself with the Solver, before trying to use these formulas:

Canadian Mortgage Interest Conversions

Use the following formula to compute the equivalent U.S. A.P.R. (that's the I%YR) for Canadian mortgages with *monthly* payments and *semi-annual* compounding interest (most Canadian mortgages carry these terms).

Formula: ▶C%~US%:((1+CI%YR÷200)^
(1÷6)-1)×1200=I%YR

<u>Approx. Memory Required</u>: 3% to use, 1% to store.
<u>Required Knowns</u>:   None.

Example: A Canadian mortgage with monthly payments is written at 12% A.P.R., compounded semi-annually. What is the equivalent U.S. A.P.R.?

Solution: Key in the above Solver formula (the ▶ will appear when you type the formula or review it via `EDIT`).

Then press `CALC` `1` `2` `CI%YR` `I%YR` ....

<u>Result</u>: I%YR=11.71

Use the following formula for Canadian mortgages with *monthly* payments and *annual* compounding of interest (not common).*

Formula: ▶C%~US%:((1+CI%YR÷100)^
(1÷12)-1)×1200=I%YR

Approx. Memory Required: 3% to use, 1% to store.
Required Knowns: None.

Example: A Canadian mortgage with monthly payments is written at 12% A.P.R., compounded annually. What is the equivalent U.S. A.P.R.?

Solution: Key in the above Solver formula (the ▶ will appear when you type the formula or review it via **EDIT**).

Then press **CALC** ①② **CI%YR** **I%YR** ....

Result: I%YR=11.39

*The rate specified on a Canadian mortgage document may compound no more than twice per year. Most such mortgages use semi-annual compounding (in which case you should use the formulas on pages 425 or 427); the only alternative is annual compounding, given here for completeness.

Use the following formula for Canadian mortgages *in general* (you specify the payment and compounding periods during calculation). Canadian rules allow no more than 2 compounding periods per year.

Formula: ▶C%~US%:(((1+CI%YR÷C/YR
÷100)^(C/YR÷P/YR))-1)×P
/YR×100=I%YR

<u>Approx. Memory Required</u>: 5% to use, 1% to store.
<u>Required Knowns</u>: None.

Example: A Canadian mortgage is written at 12% A.P.R.. Find the equivalent U.S. A.P.R. if:

a. compounding is semi-annual, payments monthly;
b. compounding is annual, payments monthly;
c. compounding is semi-annual, payments quarterly;
d. compounding is annual, payments annual;

Solution: Key in the above Solver formula. Then:

a. `1``2` `CI%YR` `2` `C/YR` `1``2` `P/YR` `I%YR` ....
<u>Result</u>: I%YR=11.71

b. `1` `C/YR` `I%YR` ....
<u>Result</u>: I%YR=11.39

c. `2` `C/YR` `4` `P/YR` `I%YR` ....
<u>Result</u>: I%YR=11.83

d. `1` `C/YR` `1` `P/YR` `I%YR` ....
<u>Result</u>: I%YR=12.00

Canadian TVM

Use the following formula to do any general TVM calculation (except AMRT) for Canadian mortgages.

Formula:
```
►CTVM:0×(N+CI%YR+PV+PMT
+FV+IF(P/YR=0:L(P/YR:12
):0))+IF(S(BEG):1+L(END
:0)-BEG:IF(S(END):1+L(B
EG:0)-END:PV+(1+BEG÷100
×L(I:((1+CI%YR÷100÷IF(C
/YR=0:L(C/YR:2):C/YR))^
(C/YR÷P/YR)-1)×100))×PM
T×USPV(G(I):N)+FV×SPPV(
G(I):N)))
```

Approx. Memory Required: 15% to use, 3% to store.
Required Knowns: None.

Example: A 30-year, $150,000 Canadian mortgage is written at 10.5%, compounded semi-annually.

   a. Find the monthly payment (in arrears).

   b. Find the balloon due in 10 years.

   c. Repeat **a** and **b** for a 20-year amortization.

Solution: Key in the above Solver formula. Then:

a. ③⓪☒①②= (for ALGebraic arithmetic); *or*
③⓪|INPUT|①②☒ (for RPN arithmetic)
N ①⓪•⑤**CI%YR**①⑤⓪⓪⓪ **PV** ⓪ **FV** ,
MORE ② **C/YR** ①② **P/YR** **END** (END=1.00).
MORE **PMT** .... Result: PMT=-1,347.21

b. Continuing from the previous solution:
①⓪☒①②= (for ALGebraic arithmetic); *or*
①⓪|INPUT|①②☒ (for RPN arithmetic)
N . Then **FV** ....
Result: FV=-136,984.93

c. Continuing from the previous solution:
②⓪☒①②= (for ALGebraic arithmetic); *or*
②⓪|INPUT|①②☒ (for RPN arithmetic)
N . Then ⓪ **FV** and **PMT** ....
Result: PMT=-1,475.21

d. Continuing from the previous solution:
①⓪☒①②= (for ALGebraic arithmetic); *or*
①⓪|INPUT|①②☒ (for RPN arithmetic)
N . Then **FV** ....
Result: FV=-110,344.15

As you can see, this substitute TVM formula can allow you to do the
same sorts of "What-If?" calculations as you could do with the built-in
TVM—but this one uses the compounding assumptions required for
Canadian mortgages.

Use the following formula to do any general TVM calculation *including* AMRT for Canadian mortgages. This works the same in all respects to the previous formula, plus it offers an AMRT capability similar to that built into the HP 19Bɪɪ. However, there are some keystroke differences to this version of AMRT, as illustrated here.

Formula:

```
▶CTVM~AMRT:0×(N+CI%YR+P
V+PMT+FV+IF(P/YR=0:L(P/
YR:12):0)+BEG+END+IF(C/
YR=0:L(C/YR:2):0)+AMRT+
#P)+IF(S(BEG):1+L(END:0
)-BEG:IF(S(END):1+L(BEG
:0)-END:IF(S(AMRT):L(Z:
BEG)×L(BAL:RND(PV:2))×L
(NEXT:L(INT:L(PRIN:0)))
-AMRT:IF(S(NEXT):NEXT-1
E3-#P-1001E3×FP(G(NEXT)
÷1E3)+0×L(B:BAL):IF(S(B
AL):RND((RND(PMT:2)×USP
V(G(I):#P-G(Z))+G(B)+G(
Z)×RND(PMT:2))÷SPPV(G(I
):#P-G(Z)):2)-BAL:IF(S(
PRIN):PRIN+G(B)-BAL:IF(
S(INT):#P×RND(PMT:2)-PR
IN-INT+L(Z:0):PV+(1+BEG
÷100×L(I:((1+CI%YR÷100÷
C/YR)^(C/YR÷P/YR)-1)×10
0))×PMT×USPV(G(I):N)+FV
×SPPV(G(I):N))))))))
```

<u>Memory Required:</u>   32% to use, 8% to store.

<u>Required Knowns:</u>   As with the built-in AMRT, you must solve for the PMT first.

Example: A 30-year, $150,000 Canadian mortgage is written at 10.5%, compounded semi-annually. Find the balance, interest and principal paid in each of the first two years.

Solution: Key in the above Solver formula (the ▶ will appear when you review the formula via **EDIT**).

First, find the payment: ③ ⓪ ✕ ① ② ▢ (ALG) *or*
③ ⓪ INPUT ① ② ✕ (RPN)

N ① ⓪ · ⑤ **CI:YR** ① ⑤ ⓪ ⓪ ⓪ ⓪ **PV** ⓪ **FV** ,**MORE**
② **C/YR** ① ② **P/YR** **END** (END=1.00) **MORE** **MORE**
PMT .... Result: PMT=-1,347.21

Press **MORE** **AMRT** (display: AMRT=0.00) to start the amortization. Then **MORE** to go to the next menu page. Press ① ② **#P** to amortize 12 payments at once.

Now, *in this order*, press:
NEXT to identify the payments in the group. You'll see:
   NEXT=1,012.00 (that is, payments 1-12)
BAL to see the new balance: BAL=149,213.23
PRIN to see the principal paid: PRIN=-786.77
INT to see the interest paid: INT=-15,379.75

NEXT   NEXT=13,024.00   (payments 13-24)
BAL   BAL=148,341.68
PRIN   PRIN=-871.55
INT   INT=-15,294.97

As with the built-in AMRT, you may change #P between groups or use **AMRT** to start over completely.

Discussion

Here's a little more detail about the calculations in these formulas.

A mortgage rate, as used in the U.S., is the nominal annualized rate that you must divide by the number of payments per year (PMTS/YR) to get the actual Defined Interest Rate (D.I.R.). Thus, a U.S. mortgage rate and the HP 19Bɪɪ's I%YR are directly equivalent.

Not so for Canada. On most* Canadian mortgages, the rate _actually used_ (the D.I.R.) is the rate which, when compounded over a year's worth of payment periods (D.I.P.'s), produces the same _effective_ yield as the rate appearing on the mortgage document would produce when compounded _not more than twice per year_.

That calls for a little thought....

As you saw in the interest conversion (ICONV) discussion on pages 138-139, an effective yield is higher than a nominal annualized rate whenever the interest compounds more often than once per year. And the more often it compounds, the bigger this difference becomes.

But when competing for borrowers, a lender wants to put his rates in the best possible light. So, for example, if he's allowed to quote a 10.5% nominal rate alongside the effective yield of 11.02%, he'll probably want to emphasize the nominal rate. The lower number is simply more attractive to the loan shopper.

---

*If the mortgage payments are for interest only or if the mortgage is placed outside of Canadian territory, a Canadian lender may not be required to use the Canadian convention.

Well, the Canadian law simply puts a limit on how "approximate" the quoted nominal rate can be. The rule says that the quoted rate may not be converted into an effective yield by compounding any more than twice a year. Thus, for a 10.5% quoted nominal rate, the *effective* rate may not be any higher than 10.78%—*no matter how often the actual D.I.R. is compounded.* 10.78% is the limit on the effective yield.

But the HP 19Bᴜ needs a *nominal* rate (I%YR) to work with, since it then converts this to a D.I.R. according to U.S. assumptions. So the idea is to translate the known effective yield limit of the Canadian mortgage back into its nominal-rate equivalent under the U.S. convention. That's what these formulas do with the value of CI%YR—and you can do it "manually" with the ICONV Menu:

Canadian rate = **NOM%**

Key in ① or ②* —> **P**

Solve for **EFF%**

Key in payments/year in actual loan —> **P**

NOM% = U.S. rate (I%YR for TVM)

And remember that this works both ways: You can also start at the bottom—with a known U.S. mortgage rate (I%YR)—and work back up to the top to find the comparable rate for Canada.

*Most Canadian mortgage documents will specify semi-annual compounding for computing the effective yield, in which case the value to use here is 2. But if a Canadian mortgage happens to use annual compounding, you would use 1 for this value.

Index

SYMBOL

#P 147
#TIMES 206-207
%CHG 68
>HMS 66
>HR 51
>RAD 51
%NEW 262
-HR 290
-SEC 283
+HR 283, 290
∡ 51
12/24 282
360 152
360D 285
365D 285
Σ (summation) 344-345
▶ 206

A

α annunciator 298, 300, 409
A.P.R. 209, 212, 324
A/PM 76, 282
ACCRU 153
ACRS 159
ACRS2 159
ADJST 283, 290
Adjustable Rate Mrtg. (ARM) 165, 185, 362
adjusting the time 283
ALG 32
ALGebraic mode 38, 305
ALL 31
Alphabetizing TEXT 415
Amortization 126, 134, 149, 181
    table 145-147, 182-183

AMRT 145-146
Analysis term 221
Analyzing lists 267
Angle conversions 50
Annualized yield 227
Annunciators 21-22
    alpha 298, 300, 409
    radian 50
    shift 20, 22
Annuity
    advance 121, 222, 229
    arrears 121
    increasing 233
Appointments 286
    acknowledge 286, 288
    clear all 289, 291
    clear one 289, 291
    come due 288
        without beeping 289
    date and time 286
    message 286
    past due 286
    pending 286
    repeat interval 286, 288, 289, 291
Appraisal formula 378
APPT 286, 291
AREA 91
Arithmetic 25
    ALGebraic 32-34, 49
    evaluation order 305
    RPN 32, 40–45, 49
ARM (Adjustable Rate Mrtg.) 362
Asset 390
Average, moving 266

B

Balance investments and returns 211, 214
Balloon payment 126, 130, 132, 148, 225, 238
Band of Investment method 166, 378
BASIS 155
BEEP 292
BEEPER 292
BEG 122
BEGIN mode 121
BOND 74, 150
Bonds 151
    accrued interest 153
    after-tax price/yield formula 370
    call date 153
    call value 166
        vs. mat. value 153
    coupon rate 151, 153
    maturity date 151
    settlement date 152
Break-even
    direct mail 342
    manufacturing 397
BUS 68
Buying power 168, 197-198, 399, 405

C

C X,Y 52
C.RCL 83
C.STO 83
CALC 62, 299
CALC Menu (CFLO) 213, 216

Calculations
  amortization 163-165,
    182-183, 190
  bonds 151, 166, 188
  buying power 197-199
  cap rate 166, 189, 196
  cash ret. rates 167, 196
  comm. investment 224
  compare investments
    161-163, 171, 174,
    181, 190, 199-200
  currency 80, 82, 87-92
  dates 284
  depreciation 166, 188,
    191
  double mortgage 239
  editing 27
  equity ret. rate 167, 196
  FMRR 251
  future value 118, 130,
    161-162, 175, 180
  Gross Rent Multiplier
    (GRM) 167, 196
  inflation 161, 168, 199
  interest 97-98, 163,
    171, 178-179
  investment 199-200
  lease vs. buy 243
  leases 163, 240
  lists 267
  loan amount 222
  monthly payment 125,
    161, 164, 184
  mortgages 120, 125,
    164-165, 185
  Net Operating Income
    (NOI) 166, 189
  NFV 208
  NPV 208, 212, 222
  NUS 208
  percentages 37, 54, 68,
    70-75
  personal finance 227
  points 163, 179

Calculations (cont.)
  principal 163
  probability 52, 55
  qualifying a
    buyer 165, 186
  refinancing 223, 238
  rent vs. buy 223
  res. real estate 164
  savings plans 161
  side 150
  solving for unknown
    variable 69
  taxes 161, 168, 192,
    197-198
  term, loan 161, 164, 172
  Time Value of Money
    (TVM) 94, 162, 170
  trigonometric 55
    arc length 51
  unit conversions
    87, 90-91
Calendar
  alternatives 285
  basis of a bond 152
  functions 343
  using 281
  CALL 152
Call value, bond 152, 370
Canadian mrtg. int.
    conversions 425-426
Canadian mortgage rate
  effective limits 432-433
Canadian TVM
  formula w/AMRT 430
  formula 428
Cap rate 166, 378, 386
Capital gains 223, 225,
    234, 241, 356, 370,
    374
Cash-flows 104
  $1 stream of 240
  calculation of 192
  combining 211
  diagrams 106, 114

Cash-flows (cont.)
  discounting 109-10, 210
  equivalent 209
  even 231
  flip-flop 218
  groups 204, 205
  increasing 233
  initial 205-207
  irregular 113, 151
  negative 206
    in FMRR 248
  positive
    in FMRR 248
  random intervals 203
  sliding 210
  T-bars 104
  uneven 203-205, 231
  unknown 228-230, 240
  zero 203, 211
Cash return rate 386
CDATE 343
CFLO 204
CFLO 202, 203, 216
  CALCulations
    Menu 208, 213
    A.P.R. to D.I.R. 212
    discount rates 217
  list 204, 206
  Menu 206, 212
Changing
  annuity mode 122, 128
  degrees to radians 50
  display format 30
  formula menu 323
  menus 74
  payments per year 115
  radians to degrees 50
  sign of number 36, 42
  value of variable 141
  values by rounding 49
Character sequence to
    find TEXT entries 417
Clearing 17
  calculator line 26-27

Clearing (*cont.*)
  data from lists   274
  display   26
Clock   281, 283
Closing costs   167, 223
Combinations   52
Combining formulas   309
  311, 313-315, 325, 327
Commercial invest.   224
Commission
  bond purchase   370
  home sale 223, 234, 356
  sale of building   225
Comparing
  interest rates   140, 178
  investments 163, 174,
    181, 190, 199-200
  IRA's   227
Compounding interest
  daily   138
  monthly   222
Constant payment to
  principal formula 366
CONV   51
Conversions
  currency   82
Converting
  A.P.R. to D.I.R.   212
  interest rates   138
  decimal degrees   51, 55
  units   86, 89
Coordinates of plot   272
Copying
  list   273-274
  values   260
CORR   276
Correlation   269
  best type   277
  exponential   276
  linear   276
  logarithmic   276
  non-linear   273
  power   276
COST   70

Cost-of-Living Adjust-
  ments   402
CPN%   152
Create formulas 299, 312
Crosshairs
  curve-fitting   272
CURR   275
CURR2   84
Currency   80
  conversion rates   82-83
  exchanges   80
  names   81
  store/recall menu 83, 89
Current date format   284
CURR%   81
Curve fitting   272, 276
Curve models   272

D

D.I.P.   123, 432
D.I.R.   124, 432-433
  from A.P.R.   212
D/R   50
Data frequencies   267
DATE   343
Date
  current format   284
  setting   281
DATE   76, 282
DATE1   284, 290
DATE2   284, 290
Dates
  calculations   284
  formats   153
Daylight Savings   283
DAYS   284, 290
days between dates   284
DB   157
DDAYS   343
Debt, long-term   165
Debt service   191
Degrees   50-51

DELET   266
Deleting
  TEXT list   420
  formulas   312, 315
  item from list   266
  variables 312, 315, 317
  records   414
DEPRC   64, 150
Depreciable value   225
Depreciated basis   374
Depreciation 154-159
  Accel. Cost Recovery
    System (ACRS)   159
  basis value   154
  declining bal.   156-157
  lifetime of asset   154
  Remaining Depreciable
    Value (RDV)   156
  salvage value   154
  Straight Line (SL) 155,
    241, 374
  Sum-Of-the-Years'-
    Digits (SOYD)   158
  total deprec. value 154
  tax relief from   242
  MACRS formula   390
Diagram, cash-flow   206
Direct-mail formula   342
Discount
  cash-flows 109-110,
    210-14
  in FMRR   248
  rate 212-218, 220, 237
    annualizing   217
    less tax   243
Discounted mortgage 224
Display   17, 21-22
  adjusting contrast   17
  amortizations   149
  characters   19
  clearing   26
  dec. places   28-31, 49
  full precision   49
  menu lines   18

Display (*cont.*)
  messages 17
  number lines 18
  previous results 38, 44
  rounding numbers 29
Division 305
OM 83
Dotted line, TEXT list 410
Double mrtg. 224, 239
Down payment 135, 223, 235, 241

E

EDIT 411
Editing
  calculator line 27
  lists 265
  TEXT lists 411, 416
EFF% 139, 230
Effective yield 138, 140
END 122
END mode 121
End-of-record 413
Entering cash flows 112
Equation
  as formula 309
  combined structure 311
Equity return rate 386
Equiv. cash-flows 209
  even vs. increasing 222
  even vs. uneven 222
  NUS vs. uneven 232
EXP 48, 276
Exponential curve 272
Exponentiation 305

F

FACT% 157
Federal income tax 346
FIN 64, 204

Fin. Management Rate of Return (FMRR) 246
Fin. transactions 104
  combining 105, 108
FIND 417
Finding TEXT entries 417
  order of search 421
First entries 415
First mortgage 224
FIX 30
FLOW( ) 206-207
FMRR (Financial Mngmt. Rate of Return) 226, 246-247, 253
  formula 388
  vs. IRR% 226, 252
Forecasting 269, 272
  rental income 271
Format, date 284
Formula
  accel. paydown 336
  addition/subtract. 305
  amort. table 336-337
  AMRT features 365
  area of slab 303
  ARM 336
  bond, after-tax 338, 370
  built-in 319
  buying power 341
  Canadian mortgage int. conversions 425-427
  Canadian TVM 428-430
  cash-flow analysis 339
  combined 309-315, 325
  constant payment to principal 337, 366
  conv. loan 336, 352
  creating 299
  decreasing annuity 368
  deleting 312, 315
  direct mail 334, 342
  equations 309
  exponentiation 305
  FHA loan 336, 352

Formula (*cont.*)
  FMRR 339, 388
  FNMA loan 336, 352
  functions in 305
  Future Wealth 339
  GNMA loan 336, 352
  inc. prop. analysis 384
  inc. prop. valuation 378
  increasing annuity 368
  inflation 337
  invntry. mngt. 340, 392
  known values 309
  lease vs. buy 338, 374
  lease values 338, 372
  list 295, 308
  liters to gallons 301
  MACRS 340, 390
  manuf. Return On Investment 340, 396
  memory 317, 330, 333
  menus built from 309
  menu convenience 342
  mileage reimb. 334, 344
  minimum investment mode keys 349
  mult./division 305
  naming 316–317
  obstet. dates 334, 343
  operation priorities 305
  parentheses 305-306
  payroll 334-335, 346
  percent. paydown 337
  property valuation 338
  qualifying 336, 352
  rent vs. buy 336, 356
  ret. plan. 341, 400, 402
  rewriting with =0 310
  rounding up in 307
  second mortgages 380
  sharing variables 310
  slab volume 303
  solving order 310
  tax on gross pay 350
  taxes/inflation 398

Formula (*cont.*)
  units 303-304
  unknowns 309
  VA loan 336, 352
  variables (*see Variables*)
  verifying 299, 333
  wrap-around mrtg. 380
FRCST 277
FRED 209, 218
Fred 209, 213-214, 217
Functions 305
  exponential 48, 55
  rounding 49
  trigonometric 50
Future Value (FV) 112,
    114, 126
  sign of 118
FV 112

G

G() 329-330
GAL 90
Gas mileage formula 299
GET 262
GET 268
GLOBL 275
GRM (Gross Rent
  Multiplier) 386
Group, cash-flow 204-206
Guesses for speed 405

H

Help 76
HELP 76, 282
HIST 267
Histogram, list data 267

I

I% 214
I% 208, 212, 215
I%YR 432
I%YR 112
ICONV 139
ICONV 230
ICONV Menu 433
IF(S... functions
  nested 313, 327-328
Inc. prop. analysis 384
Income tax 346, 370
  on interest 234, 237
Indep. unknowns 331
Individual Ret. Account
  (IRA) 168, 198
Inflation 161, 168, 223,
    225, 234, 356, 402
Init. cash-flow 205, 207
INITIAL FLOW 206
Insert into TEXT list 414
Integer Portion (IP) 307
Interest 96, 209
  accrued 153
  Annual Percent. Rate
    (A.P.R.) 101, 123-124
  annualize 101, 112, 115
  comparing 140, 142
  compound 97-98, 177
  convert 138-142
    Canadian mrtg. 425
  Defined Interest Period
    (D.I.P.) 101-102, 112
  Defined Interest Rate
    (D.I.R.) 101-102, 124
  effective 101
  partial periods 102
  nominal 101, 138
  simple 97
  taxes on 356, 374
  Internal Rate of Return
    (IRR%) 216
  Internat'l Date Line 289

INTI 81
Investment 206
  /return pairs 119, 220
  balance w/NPV 211,
    214
  compare 163, 215, 222
  constraints, risks 246
  conventional 218
  Future Value 112, 114
  IRR% balances 216
  opportunity 209
  Present Value 112, 114
  term vs. analysis 221
IP (Integer Portion) 307
IRA compared 227, 254
IRR% 217
IRR% (Internal Rate of
  Return) 216, 218
  confirm with TVM 219
  multiple 218, 245
  nearest solution 245
  nonexistent 218
  re-invest. assumed 220
  starting guess 245
  vs. FMRR 226, 252
  yield 218-219
ITEM() 345

K

Keyboards 19
Keys
  [↑] key 204, 265, 410
  [↓] key 204, 207, 265
  [ENTER] key 40-41
  [%] key 43
  [+] key 34
  [−] key 36
  [=] key 32, 35
  [+/−] key 36, 42
  [◄] 300
  [►] 300
  [◆] key 17, 27, 34

Keys (*cont.*)
 CLEAR key 27
 DEL 300
 DISP **ALL** key 217
 DISP key 30
 E 47
 EXIT key 49, 63, 66
 ENTER key 32
 INS 300
 INPUT key 40, 44, 207
  with a list 264-265
 MODES key 32
 ON key 15
 RCL key 69, 260
 STO key 141, 260
 STO MODES 292
 key 20
 ↑ key 204, 207, 265
 ↓ key 204, 265
 x≷y key 38, 44
 R↓ key 38, 44
 ^ key 57
 √x key 57
 MEM 302
 INS key 56
 CLEAR key 34
 MAIN key 63
 SHOW key 49, 90
 MATH key 48
 x² key 57
 arrow 38, 44, 272
 "Caps Lock" 20
 review current vals. 69
 shift 19
 toggles 15, 20-22, 36, 42
 typing 19
 KM 90
 Knowns in formulas 309

L

LABEL 275
Labels, list items 273
LB 86
Leap year 290
Lease 163, 224, 240, 372
Lease vs. buy 225, 374
LENG 90
L{ } 326-330
LIFE 155
LIN 272, 276
Linear curve model 272
List 261
 analyzing 267
 check with TOTAL 265
 data cells 267
 data frequencies 267
 deleting 273
 deleting item from 266
 editing 265
 floor areas 269, 270
 items, numbered 264
 of formulas 295, 308
 of rent income 261, 270
 pointer 263, 266
 reviewing 265
 sub-ranges 267
 SUM 258
 TEXT
  TOP 410
 TOTAL 264
 using INPUT with 264
Lists 259
 clearing data
  from 274
 copying 274
 correlating for forecasting 269
 forecasting with 269
 GET 268
 item labels 273
 labels, global 275
 labels, individual 275

Lists (*cont.*)
 making copies of 273
 moving averages 266
 naming 262, 268
 predicting with 269
LITER 90
Loan calculations
 accel. paydn. 164, 183
 amount 135, 222
 balloon 132, 148, 163
 checklist 127
 const. pmts to princ.
  164, 184
 down payment 135
 loan fees (points) 136,
  163. 223, 322
 monthly payment 164
 term 134, 179
Loan-to-value ratio 378
LOG 276
Logarithmic curve 272
LOGS 48
Long-term debt 352

M

M/D 282
M%C 70
M%P 70
MACRS formula 390
MAIN Menu 204, 262
Maint. 223, 225, 234
Manuf. ROI formula 396
MARK 413
MASS 86
MAT 152
MAX 267
MEAN 267
Medicare 346
MEDN 267
Memory 295-296
 formulas 317, 330, 333
 percent. available 302

Menu 18, 61
  formula 309, 342
  accessing variables 67
  AMRT 145
  BOND 74, 152
  built-in 320
  BUS 70, 86
  CFLO 150, 202-203
    CALC 216
  CONVert 52
  CURRency EXch. 89
  curr. st./recall menu 83
  DEPRC 155
  FIN 65
  FoReCaSTing 272
  GET 268
  keys 118
  Line 61
  lines 18, 22
  MAIN 18, 61, 63, 204
  MATH 48, 50
  pages 64
  MODES 50
  moving around 61, 74
  navigating 259
  OTHER 128
  playing "what-if" 67
  return to previous 66
  selecting 49
  SOLVE 294, 332
  SUM 262
  TIME 62
  toggle key 355
  triangle 51
  TRIG 51
  TVM 112, 212
  UNITS 90
  variables order 323
Messages 17, 21, 22
MILE 90
Mile. reimb. formula 344
MIN 267
Mode keys, formulas 349
Models, curve-fit. 272

Modes
  annuity 127, 319
  BEGIN 122, 127
  degrees 50
  END 122, 127
  radians 50
  MORE 32, 64
Mortgage 120, 125, 127
  accel. pay-down 164,
    360, 364
  Adjustable Rate Mort-
    gage (ARM) 165, 185
  balloon payment 225
  Canadian interest
    conversion 425
  discounted 224
  double 224
  first 224
  points 225
  rate 225
    US vs. Canadian 432
  refinancing 223, 383
  second 224, 380
  wraparound 225, 380
Move records between
  TEXT lists 421
Move in TEXT 413, 420
Moving average 266
MSG 287, 291
MUXC 70
MUXP 70
Multiple IRR% 218
Mult.-entry records 412
Multiplication 305

N

N 112
NAME 208
Name
  CFLO list 208
  formulas 316–317
  length for menu 268

Name (cont.)
  lists 262-268
  TEXT lists 411
  variables 304, 320, 342
Negative cash-flow 206
Negative numbers 36,
  42
Net Operating Income
  (NOI) 166, 379
Net Present Value (NPV)
  214
  buy vs. lease 377
  buy vs. rent 359
Net Uniform Series
  (NUS) 232
NEW 68
NEXT 147, 413
NFV 208, 253-254
NOI (Net Operating
  Income) 379
NOM% 139, 230
Nominal rate 138
Non-linear correlat. 273
NONE 291
Nonexistent IRR% 218
NPV 212, 214
NPV 208-213, 22
  advisory number 215
  balance against initial
    cash-flow 228
  confirm with TVM 229
  incomplete 228
  invest./ret. pairs 220
  negative 215, 228
  positive 215, 228
  ratios between 240
  zero 215-216
Number of periods 114
Numbered registers 260,
  273, 296
Numbers
  changing sign 36, 42
  finding reciprocal 56
  lists of 261

Numbers (*cont.*)
  raising to a power 57
  rounding 49
  scientific notation 47
  square root 57
  squaring 57
NUS 208, 232

O

Obstet. dates formula 343
OLD 68
Operation priorities 305
Optimal formula 318-323
OTHER 115
Overall rate of return 255
Overtime pay factor 348
Owner's Manual formu-
    las 371, 391, 395
02 86

P

P 139, 230
P R.Y 52
P/YR 212
P/YR 115
Par value, bond 370
Parentheses
  ALGebraic mode 35, 37
  in formulas 305-306
  RPN mode 41
Paydown of mortgage 364
Payments 112
  advance (lease) 372
  annuity mode 120-121
  balloon 126
  lease 240
  lump-sum 126
  per year 115-116
  skipped (lease) 372
  uneven 203

Payroll formula 346
Penalty, IRA 402
PER 139
Percentages
  ALGebraic mode 37
  RPN mode 43
Periods
  compounding vs. pmt
    123, 139, 142
  half-month approx. 255
  irregular 151
  number of 112, 114
Permutations 52
Personal fin. calc. 227
PI 50
PITI (Princ., Interest,
    Taxes, Ins.) 165, 352
PLOT 272
Plot of curve-fit 272
PMT 112, 113
PMT amount
  smooth 203-204
Pocketed returns 221
Pointer (▶) 204, 275, 300
  in TEXT list 410
  list 263, 266
Points up front 136, 321
Power curve model 272
Precision of numbers 28,
    50, 148
Predicting with lists 269
Present Value (PV)
  investment 112, 114
  sign of 118
  single-pmt (SPPV) 319
  unifrm-str. (USPV) 319
PREV 413
PRICE 70, 152
PRIN 147
Principal 147
Print AMRT tables 147
Priority, operations 305
PROB 52
Probability 52

Problem solving 95
  cash-flow diagrams 106
  drawing a picture 104
Proceeds of re-sale
  after taxes 236, 242
  before taxes 236, 242
Profit, direct mail 342
Property
  taxes 223, 225, 234,
    236, 242, 356, 374
  value growth 223, 356
PV 112
PWR 276

Q

Qualifying, home loans
  conv. 165, 186, 355
  FHA 165, 186, 187, 355
  FNMA 165, 186, 187, 355
  GNMA 165, 186, 187, 355
  VA 355

R

RANG 267
RATE 82
Rate, investment
  overall 255
  risk 249
  safe 249
RDV (Remaining Depre-
    ciable Value) 390
Real estate
  commercial 166-167
  residential 164
Recalling
  curr. conv. rates 83
  variables 69, 129, 132
Records
  TEXT lists 412
Refinancing 223, 238

Registers 73, 129, 259
  built-in 296
  numbers 260
  storage 181
  variable 296
Remaining Depreciable
    Value (RDV) 390
Renaming 300
Rent vs. buy 223, 234,
    356
Residential real estate
    problems 223
Retire. formula 400, 402
Returns, pocketed 221
Rewriting formulas with
    =Ø 310
Risk rate 215, 226, 249
Rounding 29, 307
RPN 32, 49
RPN ENTER key 32
RPT 287, 291
Running total 263

S

Safe rate 226, 249
SALV 155
Saving
  curr. exch. rates 83
  intermediate results 41
  numbers 259
Scientific notation 47, 54
Search sequence
  TEXT lists 417-418
Second mortgage 224
Security deposit
    223, 234, 356
SELCT 81
SELECT A MODEL
    272, 276
SELECT X VARI-
    ABLE 271
SET 66, 76, 282-283

SETT 152
Set
  date 74
  time 74, 282
  variable value 326-327
Settlement date 152
Shared variable 301, 306
Sign conventions 369
Similar investment 214
SIN 50
SIZES() 345
SL 155
Slide cash-flows 210
Social Security 346, 402
SOLVE 298
SOLVE
  calendar functions 343
  Menu 294, 332
  summation (Σ) 344-345
  using SUM lists in 344
Solving for unknown 118
SORT 415
Sorting
  TEXT lists 415
SOYD 158
Special characters 50
SPPV 319
SQ.FT 91
SQ.IN 91
SQ.M 91
Stack 274
  changing menus 74
  History 38, 90
  keeping results in 259
  reversing 273
  rolling 38, 44
  RPN stack 44, 90
  swapping in 38, 44
START 273, 275
State income tax 346
STDEV 267
Storing a variable 141
Straight-Line (SL) depre-
    ciation 374

SUBT 273, 275
Subtract percentages 37
Subtraction 305
SUM 262
SUM
  Menu 262
  list in SOLVE 344
  lists 258
Summation (Σ)
  in SOLVE 344, 345
Summation Method
  for cap rate 378

T

T-bars 104, 206
TABLE 147
Tax bracket 223, 225,
    234
Tax on gross pay, for-
    mula 350
Tax on interest 356, 374
Tax rate 370
Tax relief
  costs of acquisition 387
  depreciation 242
  expenses 241
  interest 234, 356
  mortgage points 236
  property taxes 234
Tax-deferred account 400
Tax-free account 402
Term
  of analysis 221
  of loan 134
TEXT 409
TEXT list
  deleting 414, 420
  dotted line 410
  editing 411, 416
  finding entries 417
  inserting 410, 414
  movement 413, 420

TEXT list (*cont.*)
  moving records between lists 421
  mult.-entry records 412
  naming 411
  order of searching 421
  search sequence 418
  sorting 415
  storing 409
  TOP 410
TIME 62, 281, 282
TIME
  adjusting 283
  setting 281-282
Time Value of Money (TVM) 94, 109, 128, 154, 175, 181, 209
TODAY 62, 285
Toggle key, formula 355
TOP of TEXT list 410
TOTAL 213, 267
TOTAL
  check list values 265
  of a list 263-264
TRIG 50
TVM 112, 204
TVM 96, 113
  Canadian formulas 428-430
  confirm IRR% 219
  confirm NPV 229
  Menu 212
  simulation 318-328
  variables 117, 204, 319

U

UK£ 88
Uneven
  cash-flows 204-205
  payments 203
Units 303-304
  converting 86, 304

UNITS 86
Unknown
  cash-flow 228, 230, 240
  values in formulas 309
US$ 81
US:YE 92
USPV 319
Utilities 223, 225, 234

V

Variables
  composite val. 343, 358
  deleting 312, 315, 317
  dependent 271
  hidden 348-351, 363
  independent 271, 365
  intermediate 387
  known 310, 367
  memory 395
  name 300, 304, 320
  temporary 345
  registers 73
  review values 69
  set value in passing 326-327
  shared 296, 301 306, 310, 320
  solving order 310, 331
  TVM 204
  toggles 355, 367
  unknown 310, 349, 399
Verifying formulas 299
Viewing angle 17
VOL 90

W

W4 allowances 348
What-If analysis
  BOND Menu 153
  TVM 119, 128, 132

Withholding allowances (W4) 348
Wraparound mrtg. 225
  IRR% 244

X

X variable selection 271
X-value 272
XCORD 51
XLIST 272, 276

Y

Y-value 272
YCORD 51
YES 206
YLIST 272, 276
Yield 226
  bond 152
  double mortgage 239
  effective 138, 140
  IRR% 218-219
  overall 227
  term 221
  wraparound mrtg. 225
YLD% 152
YR# 155

Z

Zero
  cash-flow 203, 211
  discount rate 213
  trailing 31, 34, 40
  TVM value 126

"The Book Stops Here"

That's about it—the end of the Easy Course.

Of course, it doesn't mean you've seen it all. As we said at the start, this Course doesn't even pretend to cover all of the many possible uses of your machine. But now that you know the basics, learning new uses should be fairly straightforward. So explore and enjoy: get the most out of your HP 19Bɪɪ!

So, how did you like this book? Do you find yourself wishing we had covered other things? More of the same things? Or did you find any mistakes, typos, or other little mysteries we ought to know about (we usually have a few innocent-looking little errors—did any leap out and grab you by the lapels)?

Please let us know. Your comments are our only way of knowing if these books help or not. Besides, we like to receive mail, so drop us a note (and there's also room for comments on the back of the order forms—see the following pages):

Grapevine Publications, Inc.
P.O. Box 2449
Corvallis, Oregon   97339-0118   U.S.A.

Anyway, thanks for going along for the ride. When all is said and done, we hope this book has said and done a lot for you, helping you and your HP 19Bɪɪ to become good business partners—and good friends.

By the way, if you liked this book, we have others that you or someone you know might enjoy:

The HP 19B Pocket Guide: Just In Case

For the Easy Course graduate, here's the perfect "carry-on" companion. Take this handy little book wherever you go. It's a ready reminder of keystrokes for common financial calculations—fast reference and convenient reminders whenever and wherever you need them. Just check the index on its back cover and flip right to the help you need *now*.

An Easy Course in Using Lotus 1-2-3

If you liked this Easy Course for your HP 19BII calculator, we have a computer book to suit you, too! It's a clear, "plain-English" course in all facets of the powerful Lotus 1-2-3, including version 2.3. The book offers Grapevine's same example-rich, conversational format and unique readability. Don't miss this great opportunity—the best instruction book of its kind!

You can use the order forms on the following pages.

Or, you can contact us for further information on the books and where you can buy them locally:

Grapevine Publications, Inc.
P.O. Box 2449
Corvallis, Oregon 97339-2449 U.S.A.
Phone: 1-800-338-4331 (Fax: 503-754-6508)

Item #	Book Title	Price
	Personal Computer Books	
34	An Easy Course in Using **Lotus 1-2-3**	$ 18
28	Lotus Be Brief	9
30	An Easy Course in Using **DOS**	18
29	A Little **DOS** Will Do You	9
N/A	An Easy Course in Using **WordPerfect**	18
32	Concise and **WordPerfect**	9
N/A	An Easy Course in Using **dBASE IV**	18
	Hewlett-Packard Calculator Books	
19	An Easy Course in Using the **HP-19BII**	$ 22
22	The **HP-19B Pocket Guide:** Just In Case	6
20	An Easy Course in Using the **HP-17B**	22
23	The **HP-17B Pocket Guide:** Just In Case	6
05	An Easy Course in Using the **HP-12C**	22
12	The **HP-12C Pocket Guide:** Just In Case	6
31	An Easy Course in Using the **HP 48**	22
33	**HP 48** Graphics	20
18	An Easy Course in Using the **HP-28S**	22
25	**HP-28S** Software Power Tools: **Electrical Circuits**	18
27	**HP-28S** Software Power Tools: **Utilities**	20
26	An Easy Course in Using the **HP-42S**	22
24	An Easy Course in Using the **HP-22S**	22
21	An Easy Course in Using the **HP-27S**	22
	Curriculum Books	
14	Problem-Solving Situations: A Teacher's Resource Book	$ 15

(Prices are subject to change without notice)

Grapevine Publications, Inc.

626 N.W. 4th Street   P.O. Box 2449

Corvallis OR, 97339-2449

For Orders and Order Information Call:

1-800-338-4331 (or 503-754-0583)

Fax: 503-754-6508